Published By: Tamika INK

Library of Congress Cataloging – in- Publication Data has been applied for.

PRINTED IN THE UNITED STATES OF AMERICA.

# Table of Contents

FOREWORD By Sheila Farr........................................................... 1

BO$$ Words From The Visionary Dawn Lieck................................. 7

Learn From Your Mistakes By Eric Willoughby ............................ 14

Being the BO$$ Costs By Ketrice Keys.....................................22

The Bo$$ Who Finds Themselves Finds Their Lane
By Dr. Shadaria Allison ... .....................................................31

Are You Prepared to Bo$$ Up?: By Kearn Crockett Cherry...........37

Sales Swagger 3 Secrets All Sales Superstars Use to Have Influence
and Impact By Che Brown .....................................................45

Rising Boss By Jonathan Haynes.........................................55

Your Business Foundation: By Kathy White .........................62

Take Accountability You Train People How to Treat You & Your
Business By Stephanie Brauchle..........................................77

Small Business Certifications/Tools for Business Growth
By Robin Hughes ..............................................................87

Self-Investment is the Best Investment By Dr. Pamela Henkel. 107

Success Strategies for Bossing Up in Business
By Nadia Francois ......................................................... 118

Proficient Use of Behavior and Experience Exudes Excellence
By Kristin Brooke........................................................... 128

Worldwide Wealth Digital Currency Conversations

Crypto "BIG BAG" Karmen ................................................ 138

Quick Guide to Turning Your Vision Into a Nonfit Organization

By Daphine Priscilla Brown-Jack........................................ 159

Quid Pro Quo By Angela Singletary ................................... 170

Creating Cakers By Becky Barton ...................................... 180

Passion into A Paycheck through Network Marketing

By Latoya Griggs ................................................................ 192

Don't Put the Cart Before the Horse By Chandra Nicole........... 200

BO$$ YOUR LANE THE SPIRITUALITY OF BUSINESS

By Irma Matos.................................................................... 216

BEFORE AND AFTER THE LEAP By Eseverere............................ 227

Bought Sense By Misty Stevenson...................................... 240

To Change From Within By Joanna Kleier............................ 246

The Time is Now!! By EL'Nadeana Patterson........................ 260

THE CEO MINDSET By Sher Graham ................................... 267

You Are What You Think; It's All About Mindset
by Sharm Ieshie McInnis.....................................................279

v

# FOREWORD

## By Sheila Farr

'Ve always had a love for digging in and learning to understand more about the attributes and skills that make leaders outstanding. In my 30+ years in the workforce, I've been blessed to have seen many great leaders at work and have received mentorship from some true business geniuses. For that reason, when Dawn told me about "Bo$$ Your Lane," I was extremely intrigued. I mean, who wouldn't love to be a novice entrepreneur and have the expert advice of 27 seasoned entrepreneurs showered down on them, sowing into their business? This book is one of the best ideas for a literary collaboration that has come along in a long, long time!

Of course, it comes as no surprise that a force such as visionary author Dawn Lieck took the lead on this venture. For years, she's counseled, advised, instructed, coached, and lead hundreds of people into new and explosive projects and careers. She's brought beauty from ashes, successes from failures, and freedom from the chains of bondage for so many people. She has demonstrated true leadership in so many facets of her life and she truly is the best of the best!

When it comes to being the best in business, I firmly believe that just saying you're the best doesn't really make you the best. *Being* the best makes you the best, which Dawn truly is, and that is why I am so excited about "Bo$$ Your Lane!" It challenges leaders to look beyond "business as usual" and use innovative strategies that will propel them forward. I know many of the leaders in this book, and they aren't just business leaders; they are thought leaders. Thought leaders are those who provide direction and guidance to businesses, governmental and non-governmental organizations, laypersons, readers, and just about anyone who is interested in understanding future trends, present events, and lessons learned from past events. In other words, thought leaders are those who by virtue of their intellect and intelligence and due to their unique insights into work and life function parley their knowledge and skills to comment about the past, present, and the future and its impact on new and emerging businesses. It is these types of leaders who can truly make a difference for the "up and coming" leaders of tomorrow!

Every day I see people doing great things in the world. What do they have in common? Aside from being leaders in thought, they also possess the courage to go after their dreams and make a positive impact in their community and in the world. This anthology shows how that message of determination can support you in running your life and your business. In all my years in the workforce, one thing I've truly learned is that good mentorship can be the biggest catalyst for enriching career development. Receiving mentorship from courageous leaders of thought and business such as these in this book can help grow new business owners in ways that are unimaginable! Mentors not only teach about their real-life lessons and share skills with their mentees, but they also open doors to professional networks, facilitating connections to other professionals who can help shape career success. I've spent my career working to sow into others and grow new leaders. I know that to do this, we must be accessible, authentic, objective, have solid core values, and always continue learning. You'll see this demonstrated time and time again through each chapter here in this incredible anthology.

So, while you may think you're simply leafing through the pages of the newest leadership book, what you're really digging into are stories of how some of the greatest leaders in their fields have overcome their struggles to become true successes. Bosses. The absolute *best* at what they do...and the good news is, you're about to gain a huge benefit from the trails they've blazed and the lessons they've learned.

Congratulations to Dawn, all the Bo$$e$ who contributed to this incredible book, and especially to you - - the reader – for having the good sense to seek out valuable and practical advice that can definitely put you in a position to Bo$$ YOUR Lane!

# About
# Sheila Farr

In a generation filled with driven professionals, it is the integrity of those called to pioneer that will show many, *the way*. Sheila Farr is a fundamental leader. Having over three decades of applied experience in the realms of business strategy and development, she is no stranger to executing with profound excellence. Sheila Farr is a 12-time best-selling author, business strategist, and teacher; with a reputation for serving others with pure enthusiasm.

The object of her profession is to help individuals and small businesses turn their stumbling blocks into success stories by developing solid business plans that work.

As the proud CEO of **Gulf Coast Training & Education Services, LLC**, in Biloxi, Mississippi, she does just that.

Sheila is an eternal optimist who serves her community as a Board member for Lighthouse Business and Professional Women, Mississippi Heroes, and the Gulf Coast Human Resource Association, where she serves as the Director of Workforce Readiness. She's a cheerleader for others, inspires and motivates people through her blog, "Thankful and Blessed 365," and is the founder of "Biloxi Reads!" a literacy initiative along the Mississippi Gulf Coast.

When she is not out showing businesses how to be their absolute best, she is serving her best energy to the world, *with a smile*.

Sheila loves to connect with others through her company's website at: www.gulfcoasttraining.org or email at: trainthegulfcoast@gmail.com.

# BO$$ Words From The Visionary

## By Dawn Lieck

For so many, it seems that the new "American dream" is to work for ourselves, have freedom, financial security and be our own BO$$.

It's one fabulous dream that can definitely become your reality, but not always as easy as some may think!

There are many variables to becoming an entrepreneur. Let me share some of my experiences with you.

Contrary to popular belief, it doesn't just "happen". There's some hard work and a few hard knocks involved in this American dream!"

1. You must have a plan with a timeline. Success will evade you if you don't have a written plan on how you're going to accomplish living your dream. Notice I said, "Written Plan". If it's just an idea or plan in your head when things become hard or uncomfortable your mind will let you change up your plan. If it's written, you have your original plan to look at and remember what you really wanted to accomplish when you started out! Now

understand, I'm not saying your plan can't be tweaked, but don't change your overall goal.

2. The old saying is true. You have to spend money to make money. I've tried to make my way around it, however, all it got me was stuck. I came to a point where my knowledge could take me no further in my business. I had to invest in myself and my business to go to the next level. One of the reasons I felt the calling to put this book together is this; When investing in products or services to help you in your business, do your homework. Research whatever it is and confirm that it is something that will help you at your current place. Sometimes we take other's advice or think we need to have things that we aren't even going to utilize until later in our entrepreneurial journey. An example may be a fancy website when we really have no need for it yet. A landing page may suit your purpose just as well, and at a fraction of the cost. You don't have to invest in everything others have to start or even within the first year. We know that comparison is the thief of joy. Don't compare your day 1 to someone else's day 365!

In all investments you make, calculate your return on investments (ROI). How long will it take to make your money back or how will this investment change the trajectory of your business? If you can't come up with an answer to one of those two questions, you may want to reconsider that investment. I learned this quite early on. I was investing in things that everyone else was doing. Things I saw on social media that I thought would jump-start my business through visibility. Well, not so much!

I was out thousands, but I sure had cute social media posts! No clients, no gigs, no return on my investment. I now access every single dollar I spend on my business with plans of my calculated return

3. Collaboration is king in entrepreneurship. The relationships you build can directly correlate with the success of your business. When you work with other leaders, you put yourself in front of their audience as well as your own. The more collaboration, the more opportunities for bigger success and profitability. Again, I say, do your homework and research. All potential collaborations may not fit your vision, standards, or business morals. Check for integrity and work ethics that match your own.

There's so much advice that can be given to you as an entrepreneur, I could write an entire book on lessons learned, good and bad. It's all about trial and error!

This I know to be true for myself. I stay coached up! At different times during your journey, you will find that you truly need some one-on-one help and direction. It may not always be the same coach throughout your journey. Invest in a coach that can help you where you're at. Once you progress to a new level, you may need a new coach for that specific level.

It's fine to switch up whenever you feel the need. Your success depends solely on you. Don't be afraid to seek out exactly what you need, when you need it.

In this thing called entrepreneurship, putting in the work with 100% commitment to yourself and your vision is the path to success. It may not always go the way you expect, but that's ok, it'll go exactly as it should. No giving up, just a do-over from time to time if needed!

When I'm feeling like I want to give up, I say this quote to myself; If it is to be, it starts with me!

It all starts with you, keep going! You've got this!

# About
# Dawn Lieck

Dawn Lieck is a world-class business professional with remarkable expertise in the areas of wellness and multidimensional coaching. A *mirrored portrait* of what it means to be a *"Renaissance Woman"*, Dawn's abilities have earned her professional respect amongst generational influencers.

Setting the standard in her field, Dawn is an International Speaker, best-selling author, and the CEO of both Finally Free, LLC, and Dawn Lieck Enterprise. Affectionately known as the "Transformation Life Coach", Dawn helps successful professionals harness their true potential by putting them in touch with themselves on an intrinsic level. Having an unyielding passion for personal development, Dawn motivates clients to renew their perspective, conquer fear, and to create life balance using a system of pragmatic strategies.

**Dawn's mantra is simple; "DO IT SCARED."**

The result has been phenomenal, as Dawn has enjoyed wide-ranging success and is in high demand, from both domestic and international audiences. Dawn has held a three-year consecutive election, as one of the Top 100 Women to Know on the Gulf Coast, where she was also featured as a Woman of Achievement Entrepreneur Finalist.

Though her talents lead her reputation, her heart for service leads her path, as Dawn is involved in many organizations on the Gulf Coast including the Gulfport

Chamber of Commerce Board, Back Bay Mission Advisory Council, Leadership Gulf Coast Graduate, VP Membership Chair for Lighthouse Business and Professional Women, Chair for Success Women's Conference and a team lead for women at Habitat for Humanity.

Email; Dawn@dawnlieckenterprise.com

Facebook; Dawn Lieck

# Learn From Your Mistakes

## By Eric Willoughby

Hello, my name is Eric Willoughby, and today I want to talk to you about the importance of customer service. It is a well-known fact that great customer service leads to the success of a business. Customer service is not always a skill that is just there, you must learn it, master it, and excel at it. Now there are going to be those who are natural-born customer service specialists, but for many, it takes time and years of experience to get to where we need to be.

I, myself have had many times where my own customer service has gone wrong. Today I am going to be telling you about what happens when customer service can fall short and why it's important to master the skill as well as learn from the failures.

Several years ago, while dealing in a retail environment, I had what you could imagine, could be a routine experience in today's world. I was in a management position, and of course, when anything goes wrong, the customer would like to speak to the manager. I was the person that the upset customer was going to be talking to this particular day.

Thinking back on the beginning of my time becoming management, there wasn't much training on what real-life situational interactions would be like. We know people will get mad, upset, and frustrated, especially in a retail environment. We always hear the phrase, "The Customer is always right.", but what does that really mean? Should we be willing to give away the farm to make things right for the customer? As a brand-new manager or business owner the first thing that comes to mind when someone has a complaint, is what can I give them to make them happy. Making the customer happy is a good thing, but so is not giving away all profits that keep us in business.

So going back to that day, several years ago, I was called up to the service desk to speak to an upset customer. I wanted to be prepared for what I was about to encounter, so I talked with the associate that had helped the customer, while I was on my way to speak with them. I needed to know how bad the situation was going to be. While speaking with the associate, I find out that a return was being denied. I find out why the associate is denying the return and what I will be able to do when I get to the customer.

The time has come, I have reached the customer. At this point, I already had a solution in my mind. I was going to take the side of my associate no matter what the customer was going to say. My associate knew what they were doing, so why wouldn't I go along with what they had said, but at that point I only listened to one side of the story. There is also a saying, "There are 3 sides to a story, my side, your side, and the truth." At this point, I had only heard one side before deciding what I was going to do. So, when I reach the customer, all I hear is screaming and yelling. I can already tell this is not going to go well. What is the first thing I say to the customer? "You need to calm down and talk to me like an adult!" You can probably take a guess as to how this helped the situation right? It didn't help at all! This is when the customer is screaming at me directly now and telling me what I can do and where I can go. So being a new manager, I start to take things personally. I mean at this point who wouldn't right? So, I start to elevate my voice to match the tone they are giving me. This is the only decision I can make in my current elevated state.

This experience did not end well for me or the customer. The customer did not get taken care of with the level of customer service they were accustomed to, and I was not being a good role model to my associates as well as the surrounding customers. This specific encounter was a real learning experience for me. When I reflect on this situation it makes me think of a couple of best practices that can help lead to exceptional customer service.

## 1. Listen to understand, not to respond.

When you think about this step, you should be actively listening to what the other person has to say. Don't start thinking about possible solutions while the other person is talking, as this could cause you to miss half of the conversation. Wait until they are done speaking and ask questions and summarize what was said, so that you can show that you were listening and that you understand what they were saying.

## 2. Remain calm with an open mind.

Encounters with upset customers can be rough. You must lead the conversation with your tone to help drive on the road and not fall off the cliff. If they start to raise their voice or escalate the situation, you can deescalate it by remaining calm. Remember, the customer is already upset at this point, and you want to make things better not worse.

## 3. Show empathy and do what you can to help.

Like I touched on earlier, you can do things to help make a situation right with an upset customer, but it doesn't have to break the bank. If a customer has a bad experience with us and we don't handle it properly, they are likely not to return, but if we handle things in a way that pleases them without breaking the bank, everyone can be happy! An example of this is, as a new manager, if a customer is upset the first step may be to give out a gift card. This may be fine but was it the necessary step. We will incur the total cost of a gift card. That can eat into our profit, but what about instead, we offer to buy the family dinner on us. This could be a couple of frozen pizzas and a soda. This will cost us a lot less and still be sufficient to help make things right for the customer.

## **4. Make decisions and learn from your mistakes.**

It is ok to make tough decisions. As a manager, it is your duty but sometimes, they may be the wrong decision. It is ok to make the wrong decision if you can use it to your advantage by realizing it was a wrong decision and learn from it to do better next time the opportunity comes around. Making mistakes and learning from them is an excellent learning tool when it comes to learning, mastering, and excelling at customer service.

Sometimes when dealing with an upset customer, all the customers may want is to vent and make us aware of what is going on. Then you may not have to give away anything at all. That is why it is so important that we follow the 4 steps that I have taken away from many years of experience learning from mistakes, whether they are my own or others.

There are many things that can make or break your business. Sales, expenses, location, and many more, but customer service is key in most of them. I know sometimes it can be difficult when you make a mistake, but just like in life, you have to be humble, acknowledge the mistakes, and learn from them.

# About
# Eric Willoughby

Eric Willoughby is a servant leader, diversity advocate, a master facilitator for a fortune 500 Company, as well as a Best-Selling Author and CEO of A Man's Perspective. In his professional vocation, he is known for his outstanding reliability and commitment to the development of people. Using his keen insight as a conduit, Eric allows his pupils to embrace change, Corporate Core Values, and become Compliance Champions. As one adding quintessential value to any professional setting, he empowers leaders; as well as future leaders, with the tools and strategies needed for them to provide reliable leadership to their teams.

Contact Eric:

Email: amansperspectivellc@gmail.com

Facebook: A Man's Perspective

# Being the BO$$ Costs

## By Ketrice Keys

Oftentimes, new business owners fail to do the number one thing that they seek others to do. What? I'm glad you asked. INVEST IN THEMSELVES! You cannot expect anyone to invest in your business if you are not willing to first do so yourself. And please do not ask your customers to spend what you have never spent or have been unwilling to spend. Now that we have that out of the way.

It is essential to have a good deal of knowledge when it comes to running your business. It is important to make sure that those that are providing you with the necessary information are doing so without taking all your money just so that you can spend more.

For example, some of the most common mistakes the entrepreneurs that are just starting make are that they just keep purchasing information. This is especially true of those that are starting a business online.

There is no doubt that you do need to have a good amount of knowledge to make something happen. You need to know how to get started, you need to know what steps to take, and you need to know just where to do all of this. But there is a limit.

One thing that you should take into consideration is your ability to make decisions. Once you have purchased the latest tell-all kit, realize that you will need to make some decisions.

If you purchase one kit or program and see another that seems to offer some additional benefits, you may be tempted to purchase that one too. After all, it cannot hurt to have some more information, can it?

It doesn't hurt to have a good amount of information, except for the pocketbook, of course. Yet, that is not the problem.

The problem is what you do with it.

## A Principle

Remember this principle. If you find yourself purchasing one product after another product, you are not thinking about your next productive move, but rather holding yourself up.

If you purchase a product to benefit your business, it is essential for you to use it and get the most out of it prior to moving on to the next purchase.

## Making It Count

You need to manage your money wisely. You must realize that an investment in any asset or tool to benefit your business needs to be used fully for it to be a wise investment.

No matter what business you are in, if you do not take the time to invest in a business product wisely, you are literally throwing your profit out.

If you fall victim to all those ploys to purchase this great kit/program or that sure-fire method of making a million dollars, you sure are helping someone else to make those million dollars and bankrupting yourself.

Now, that is not to say that you shouldn't purchase any of them. Instead, select the one that provides the best resources for you, invest in it wisely, and then use it completely, incorporating all that needs to be incorporated into the plan.

When you do this, your investment is beneficial to your business. If you just move on to the next thing, you find yourself facing pitfalls and an empty wallet to go with it.

## Making Wise Choices.

How do you make decisions? Do you make spur-of-the-moment choices because that is the way that you feel that day? Do you work hard at finding the right solution, so much so that by the time you make the decision it is too late?

If you do these things, you are not benefiting your business, but rather letting the chips fall where they may. This is a huge problem for most new entrepreneurs.

Making wise decisions is not easy, but it must be done, nevertheless.

Once you realize the way that you are currently deciding, you can begin to correct it. To help you to make the right choices, follow these steps and tips to securing the right decisions without letting them get past you.

**Decision Making Tips**

Deciding is hard work. Here are some tips to help you.

1. Invest time in learning about the possible product or problem that you are considering. If you are trying to decide on whether to purchase a product, consider what it will do to enhance your business's performance. What can it do for you?

2. Spend some time researching possible solutions. What can it do for your problem? What is the lowest cost you can find? What are the potential pitfalls of this item?

3. After this is done, determine if the investment is worth it to your own wellbeing or to your business's. Waiting until after you learn more about the product will allow a decision to form as a conclusion to the research you have done.

4. If you cannot decide within a few days, then perhaps you are too leery of this product, to determine if it is right for your business. Let it go and forget it. Or find another option. Do not dwell on it.

Making the right decisions also means that you need to realize your current situation.

If your business is not pulling in profits because it does not have the necessary tools, it is time to invest in some new tools otherwise your business will not be there long enough for you to worry about it.

If your business is doing okay and there is no hangup, then do not invest in something that does not have a direct return on your profit margin. Most entrepreneurs have tons of people coming to them offering them a wide range of different benefits, products, and services because, like you, they are looking to make their business work.

Don't fall for these lures and savvy businessmen that think they can solve your problems.

Although it may seem difficult to make good decisions in relation to the business that you have, it is imperative that you learn to trust yourself. If you do not trust your decisions, you cannot run a business.

In conclusion, you must do your due diligence, by having a game plan. Do not go out looking for products, etc., without knowing what it is that you need as well as what you can spend and still make a profit, after utilizing what it is that you have learned. Also, if you have invested in a particular product, course, etc. and it doesn't seem right for you, don't just ditch it. Shelve it for later use. I can attest to having purchased a course and just could not seem to get it. Well after a few months of being in business, that course came in handy.

Being an entrepreneur is ever-changing. You must be able to adapt and always ready to learn. And remember, BEING THE BO$$ COSTS.

# About
# Ketrice Keys

Today's *coaching culture* offers a buffet of enthusiastic professionals, energized in taking individuals to high levels of material success; often remiss, of their vital need for spiritual enlightenment, clarity, and introspection. Gifted with the innate ability in enhancing all three; is the compassionate life guru, Ketrice Keys.

Ketrice Keys is a **6x #1 International best-selling author**, international empowerment speaker, certified Christian life coach, licensed evangelist, and CEO and founder of **Ketrice Keys Enterprises, KMajestic Kouture (online clothing boutique), and the 'Spitting Fire with Ketrice' Podcast.** Though she is often noted for harnessing an undeniable vernacular for serial entrepreneurship, Ketrice has a true gift for servant leadership, far beyond an ability for multi-dimensional enterprising. Ketrice is an award-winning nursing professional, having over 20 years of expertise, in serving the world at large. Respected for her innovative contributions to her field, including the acquisition of "the CEO award", for achieving a successful implementation of electronic health records, and a certification as a Workforce Redesign Specialist; Ketrice has displayed a prolific history of a consistent relationship, with excellence. Though she led an impressive career in nursing, it was her sincere heart for women and business, that propelled her into the world of full-time entrepreneurship.

**Ketrice's Mantra is simple: she is adamant about equipping women with the keys to turn off the power of the enemy in their lives and activate the power of God.**

That activation has presented itself in a myriad of forms, highlighting Ketrice as a heart-felt chieftain; the world will not soon forget. Keys is the visionary author of the anthology, "Forged by Fire: Built God Tough"; an all-female testament, unveiling the power of God, in the face of virtually unconquerable circumstances.

Through her coaching platform, Keys specializes in helping women discover their God-given purpose, by uncovering limiting beliefs, changing fixed mindsets, and developing action plans to implement strategies to help them maintain the learned principles. As an entrepreneurial strategist, she specializes in helping women to establish their businesses and to develop credible action plans, in order to maintain their life goals. Ketrice is committed to inspiring women to uncover their purpose; in order to pursue their passions; reminding them often that though we all have a story, it does not just belong to us; but to the world. She empowers women to share their stories, thereby freeing themselves, and others as well.

When Ketrice is not out coaching the world at large, she is the loving wife of Curtis Keys, a mother of three beautiful children, and grandmother of twin boys; a native of Tylertown, MS., and now resides in Bassfield, MS.

**Ketrice Keys. Leader. Enterpriser. Philanthropist**.

Website: http://www.ketricekeys.com

http://www.kmajestickouture.com

Email: ketrice@ketricekeys.com

Facebook: http://www.facebook.com/ketricekeys.keys

IG:http://www.instagram.com/ketricekeys2000

# The Bo$$ Who Finds Themselves...

# Finds Their Lane

## By Dr. Shadaria Allison

When I was 14 years old, I sat in a pre-law class sketching plus size attire for Moschino, Versace, and several other mainstream fashion enterprises, who had not yet yielded to the idea that the world wasn't a size 2. I believe that was the moment I got bit by the *entrepreneurial bug*.

Though many definitions are competing for the best clarity of what it truly means to be an entrepreneur. However, I'd like to define entrepreneurship as a lucrative response to life's various deficits. Though entrepreneurship is often appreciated for its hand in inherent wealth creation, the real value of what it brings can be found in the solutions it creates, for the world.

## Entrepreneurship is Call and Response

I can remember listening to a millionaire orate his personal journey to wealth acquisition through the entrepreneurial vocation of trading foreign currency. He looked amazing!

Hair slicked back, tailored suit, Armani cologne, and a watch with enough bling to reintroduce a blind person, to their full sight. As he spoke with utter enthusiasm, dissertating the many paths to his inheritance, I looked on, in complete boredom. Though impressed with his ability to earn wealth, I found no true relation to his story outside of a common need for money. I watched on as artists, actors, pharmaceutical salesman, and blue-collar employees'; looked along and signed their life away; not toward fruitful entrepreneurship, but to money.

Not long after, I watched Million-dollar Motivational Speaker, Lisa Nichols do a tearful YouTube interview on her inspirational journey, towards wealth. Once a homeless mother, Lisa Nichols faced many adversities, and through acculturating perseverance, and a natural gift of exhortation, she found her life's calling, through the field of motivational speaking and helping others; this, in turn, led her into her wealthy place.

So, who won me over? Was it the fancily dressed foreign currency trader, or the enlivening motivational speaker?

Both entrepreneurs were self-made millionaires. Both seemingly enjoyed their careers, and both inspired many people. However, only one of them offered the intangible benefit of purpose through pain. While the trader applied a *foot in the door* approach to wealth and entrepreneurship acquisition, Lisa found her wealth and entrepreneurship, through purpose and obstacles of life.

***Monetary enthused entrepreneurship offers us an answer to lack; however, purpose-filled entrepreneurship offers solutions to the soul of humanity; an ethic that meets a continuous need provokes a continuous response; ignites the fabric of genuine entrepreneurship, from within.***

The entrepreneurial journey may be geared toward making money, but purpose must fuel its cause; or else it becomes a job. I imagine that those who signed up to trade foreign currency, though stimulated by the pay, seldom remained in the field because the wealth accumulation wasn't tied to *purpose.* Alternatively, those who like Lisa, are inspired by a career in motivating others, may sign up for a lifetime because the wealth tied to the money, is also tied to a *purpose.*

## Formula for Future Bosses'

If you find yourself wanting to start a purpose-based business (which I believe is the best kind) here is the best formula:

1. Ask yourself what problem will your business be solving?
2. Who is your audience?
3. What are 3 to 4 other businesses that can be born from this one business?
4. What is your 1, 5, 10-year plan of execution?
5. Who are your entrepreneur heroes/role models?
6. What are your immediate and future goals for your business?

Answering these questions will help you find your niche and achieve your financial goals in entrepreneurship.

**Remember: *Monetary enthused entrepreneurship offers us an answer to lack; however, purpose-filled entrepreneurship offers solutions to the soul of humanity; an ethic that meets a continuous need, provokes a continuous response; ignites the fabric of genuine entrepreneurship, from within*.**

# About
# Dr. Shadaria Allison

Dr. Shadaria Allison is a 5-time International best-selling author, speaker, wordsmith, and consultant. Her portfolio reflects a millennial entrepreneur of epic proportions; stewarding a myriad of professional and creative vernaculars; ranging from beauty, modeling, and PR-consulting; to social media management, freelance writing services, music, and content design. Affectionately known as "Dr. Allison The Beauty Practitioner" ™, Shadaria merges seamless creativity, with a huge heart for people; a trait she refuses to compromise. Shadaria Allison has over 16 years in the industry with a solid reputation for amazing results. She has served hundreds of commercial, celebrity, and business clients, with a signature that sets her apart from other curators. Whether it is beauty, branding, or business, Dr. Allison the Beauty Practitioner is guaranteed to deliver results so pristine, the world will know you have been to the Dr.

Personal Website: Drallison911.com

Email: **Info@Drallison911.com**

Instagram: Shadaria_Allison

Facebook: Shadaria Allison

Linked In: Shadaria Allison

# Are You Prepared to Bo$$ Up?

## By Kearn Crockett Cherry

As a business owner for 25 years, I definitely have learned many things over the years. I didn't start out planning to own my own business. At some point, I realized a job will not allow you to operate your gifts or talents. Many people have jobs that do not allow them to operate in what they are naturally good at. Becoming an entrepreneur allows you to do just that.

Along the way, I have been able to pick up a few things and improve my ability to be a successful entrepreneur. I also realize many things would have made the whole experience much easier. So, I am going to share with you some things that entrepreneurs can do or implement that would make your time as a business owner smoother.

Being an entrepreneur is definitely not an easy journey. Many individuals believe that if you are an entrepreneur that you have no boss. That is true in the sense of controlling the end results, but if you have clients or customers, they are also your boss. Now, it is how you handle those relationships that allow you to "Boss Your Lane." This is a critical area of business because it is much easier to nurture your current customer relationships and maintain them as customers. It is easier to sell to people who already know your product or services versus acquiring new customers.

In marriage, it is often said that money is the #1 thing that divides a couple. Well in business money can make or break. As an entrepreneur, you definitely want to have a plan and be flexible. Many years ago, I heard someone say you need to have multiple streams of income. Initially, an individual may think that this refers to having several businesses, but that is not necessarily true. As a business, you need to have more than one source of income. It may be a large contract, insurance reimbursements, clients who pay cash, and so on. It also can be another business that brings in another source of income as well. The key thing to remember here is "CASH IS KING". You must make sure that you have enough cash coming in order to be a viable business. That's dollars in the bank that you can actually retrieve easily.

As business owners, you must maintain a viable marketing business. If you are not spending part of your budget on marketing, you probably will not be able to survive. Many companies spend up to twenty percent of their budget on marketing. Now that many businesses are going digital you will need to work even harder to stand out from the rest. Being the best-kept secret in your industry will eventually destroy your business. If you don't have a large budget, then there are other things you can do in order to increase your company's presence in the marketplace. I highly recommend networking and collaborating with other businesses.

Networking is known to increase your Net Worth. Your ability to create new connections will increase your visibility. There's no need to be the best-kept secret in your industry. As a business owner, you need to be out front and present at as many events, meetings, and conferences as possible. Then your goal should be to leverage the relationships that you develop into possible collaborations or partnerships. Forming collaborations allows you to do more while spending less time, resources, and money. Just imagine deciding to partner with someone else on creating an event. Both will bring their own team, resources, and money. Each person will be able to contribute skills and talents as well. In the end, it will cost you less money.

One of the things that I realized during the world pandemic is that business owners must always be willing to pivot. As a business owner, you have to be willing to take risks and adapt to change. Successful businesses are constantly evolving. In some cases, it is because you are being required to adapt. COVID is a strong example of being forced to change. It also helps many to realize that you do have time to create your own business and you can balance it with raising a family.

As a business owner, you must take time to balance your personal life and business. There are many times we do not think there is enough time in the day, but most of the time we just need to create a better plan to achieve our goals. Your time with your family has to be interwoven with the time you spend on your business. This will also help you from reaching burnout. Spending time with your kids and/or spouse is necessary. It is definitely better if you can incorporate them into your business as well. Family support is powerful and can help you be more secure in your decision-making. Also, you should form a small support group of individuals who are not family that can advise you. Having great support teams can help you push past fear and procrastination. Both can be the death of a business. You never want to become complacent.

Finally, always be willing to listen and learn. You never want to surround yourself with people with just individuals who know less than you. Great leaders surround themselves with individuals who are at another level. People they can learn from. As a business owner, you want to be consistently learning and improving yourself and your business. Until you take your last breath you should always be looking to learn.

Best Wishes and Success in your business journey!

# About
# Kearn Crockett Cherry

Speaker, 10 x #1 best-selling author, and award-winning businesswoman, Kearn Crockett Cherry, is a female tycoon with a "leg-up" in successful entrepreneurship. Laying to rest any stigma surrounding the stagnancy of female leadership in the Deep South, Kearn has enjoyed more than two decades of excellence, as the CEO of a thriving health care business on the Gulf Coast of Mississippi.

Kearn hosts a portfolio holding countless awards, acknowledging her abilities; locally, nationally, and internationally. She is a recognized figure in both business and communal leadership, holding membership and chair positions on diverse councils and local organizations.

The Success Women's Conference is an award winning-business leadership conference attracting an annual audience of over 17,000 attendees worldwide. Les Brown, Dr. Iyanla Vanzant, Lisa Nichols, Robin Roberts, and Forbes Riley are some of the few "powerhouses" to take center stage; leaving Kearn Cherry and her contributing partners with a reputation for revolutionizing the way women interpret both public speaking and business, on a global scale.

Proving to be an unshakable force for over 25 years in her home care business, PRN Home Care, Kearn Cherry has been blessed with an ability to integrate the outstanding professional ethics she acquired throughout her generation, and seamlessly translate its importance, to *rising* millennial audiences. In 2020, Kearn facilitated her very own business-networking platform KKonnections.

In 2001, Kearn Cherry effortlessly graced the pages of one of the most popular publications in the world, **Essence Magazine.** Featured in both their local, and international publications; Kearn was recognized as the "**Comeback Queen**", confirming her commitment to exemplify dynamic business agility. Today, Kearn is a familiar face on several Magazine covers, all testifying to the *entrepreneurial giant,* she truly is. Out of many publications highlighting her expertise; **Black Enterprise Magazine, VIP Magazine, Speakers Magazine, Sheen Magazine, Courageous Woman Magazine and her very own, Power-Up Speakers Edition Magazine**; are amongst her favorites.

Giving birth to Amazon #1 best-selling book; **<u>Trailblazers Who Lead: Unsung</u> <u>Heroes</u>**, a manuscript comprising 29 stories featuring several well-respected female entrepreneurs, moguls, and business professionals. In the midst of its release, Kearn also facilitated two innovative web-conferences: the "**Level-Up Virtual Summit**" and the "**Power Up Summit**". Both by which, featured the best of multi-generational entrepreneurs, influencers, authors, and business professionals; all offering top-tier advice, recommendations, and business exhortation to professionals, entrepreneurial hopefuls, and those facing the unforeseen challenge in maintaining a successful business during a global crisis.

Enthusiastic about the future, Kearn remains diligent in helping entrepreneurs reach their destined potential. Recently She and 30 authors of "Make It Happen", a manuscript dedicated to those with an unyielding resilience to succeed; *a quality Kearn Cherry embodies all too well. The authors recently* garner #1 International Bestselling Anthology. She will follow up this with "Trailblazers Who Lead II".

Kearn Crockett Cherry

www.kearncherry.com

kearn@prnhomecareservices.com

# Sales Swagger

# 3 Secrets All Sales Superstars Use to Have Influence and Impact

### By Che Brown

What inspired me to do this work? Wish I had a different story but let me share. There I was, sitting in my director's office. I was there because he had called me into the office, and we had been having layoffs. It's corporate America, folks get laid off. I'd been on the other side, and I'm thinking to myself, "I've got to go back to my team and tell them that somebody doesn't have a job."

And then he looks right at me and says, "Che, I'm sorry to tell you this, but we got to let you go."

"What? Let me go? How can you let me go?" I'd received great reviews, I was a rising star, but because of budget restraints, because of products that weren't selling, I was being laid off. Now, not only was I being laid off, but I was being followed back to my desk so I could pack my stuff in a box. And if you have ever been laid off, it's a bad feeling.

I'm driving home, I'm feeling down wondering "What am I going to do now?"

I was blessed because I had almost a year severance, but I had no clue what to do, and remembered my homies who had their own companies. So, I told myself, "What? You have your own company? I'm going to start a company."

That night I went down to Kinko's had some business cards made up and the very next day I was in business. I hung my shingle out the door, and I called myself, "Coach Che." I got started in this industry to serve other folks. I got started in what's now known as the self-education industry to help other people do more, be more, and have more.

Here's what inspired me – no one was hiring me, and I ran out of money. I know it's not everyone's situation, but I burned through my 401(k), I know that might not be your situation. My wife left me, and I found myself going through a divorce. My sons moved in with me, and I didn't know what I was going to do. As you're reading this, have you ever found yourself in a situation where you're like, "Whoa, how did I find myself here? I'm at the bottom."

It was at that moment that I made a decision to learn how not only to sell but how to serve other folks so I could stay in business because I didn't want to get a job. So, what inspired me is that I hated sales, but I needed the money. What inspired me is that I didn't know how to sell, but I figured I could learn, because I wasn't born this way, I wasn't wired this way. And here's my point, here's my message that inspired me that I tell everyone else. You can put this in your notes if you're taking notes as you're reading this, **selling is a learned skill.**

You can learn how to sell, and selling is the auction to any great business. So, if you were reading this and saying, "Okay, Che, tell me, you're a stickler for the term, systems beat goals every single my time. I appreciate you sharing that story with me, but you always talk about systems beat goals every single time. Why is that?"

Well, I would share with you one of my 12 rules for life. The reason I say systems beat goals every single time, and you as an entrepreneur, you as a small business owner, you as someone that wants to be in business, systems beat goals because systems are duplicatable, systems are repeatable, and systems are something that you can pass the work on to other folks. Here's the problem, goals are in the future, and the future by definition doesn't exist. We're always using our existing system to get to the goals. Our mind only operates in three quadrants that I'm aware of, the past, which no longer exists, the present, which we're always in, and the future, which we're never at. We're always in the present moment. There's a moment, there's a moment, there's a moment.

So, what's my point to you? My point to you is to take a look at the systems you have in your life. You can look at the personal side, my systems for having great health. What type of systems do you need? What type of system do you need to do more of? My systems and my finances, spending less than I make, what do I need to do to generate more revenue? What do I need to grow the revenue I already have? And what do I need to do to leave a legacy? Your systems got you to where you are, let's apply that in business. There are three key systems you need in any business. You as the aspiring entrepreneur, you as the person listening, there are only three systems you need. Jot these three things in your notes, I want to share them with you.

1.  **Lead generation system**. You need a way to get in front of those who have a problem. I get asked, "Che, what should I be doing with my time?" Your number one job is to get up every single day and find someone with a problem and share how you solve it. Now, if you're not talking to someone who has a

problem, that's through a video, through social media, through a blog, on the phone, or face to face. If you're not talking to someone, you should be having systems in place to find people who have an interest in one or a desired system. Number one system, lead generation. Why? Because leads represent hope. No leads as an entrepreneur you ain't got no hope.

2. **Appointment Setting System**. When someone goes to your website, and they read your website, that's an appointment. You've got to connect with leads, that's where they get a connection or an engagement with your company.

3. **Closing System**. You have to have a way to move people to action. Now, I didn't say persuade, I didn't say convince. I didn't say to try to be armed twisted and manipulative. I was talking to someone recently and they said, "Che, I'm an entrepreneur, a financial planner, but I don't do sales." I said, "Imagine that – an entrepreneur not in sales."

Selling equals service. If I can serve, if I can make a difference, if I can have more meaning in the world, if I can have more impact, the income will come. So, selling equals service at its highest level when we serve, we are able to sell and we're able to make a difference.

Now, this is really important. As you're reading this right now, I want to offer you an opportunity for a free gift. And if I could wave a magic wand and solve one principle that there would forever take a headache away from me as an entrepreneur, I would say you want the Evergreen Revenue Playbook Business Model. As you're reading this, just go to www.evergreenrevenueplaybook.com.

Now once you get to the site, there is a playbook on the seven proven systems that you need in order to generate your own revenue. An evergreen revenue model is how do I do something one time and my labor's no longer involved. I said before, the system beat goals every single time. And so, I want you to have a system to generate revenue so you can purchase the resources that are necessary to execute that big, big, big, big, big vision you have for the people you were called to serve. I believe that you're already a winner as you're reading this. You're already a champion as you're reading this. You've already got greatness inside you. I know as you're reading this that you have three visions.

I believe, first, you have a vision for yourself. There's a certain way you want to live, there are clothes you want to wear, there's the food you want to eat, and it takes revenue. That means it takes some resources to make that happen. You need revenue to purchase those. The second vision you have is you have a vision for your loved ones. The people you care the most about. Some of you have children you want to send to a school of your choice. Some of you have some of your aunts and uncles, and you want to write a check for your nieces and nephews. Some of you want to write a check for just someone's course that you truly believe in right now. It takes revenue to purchase those resources. And the third vision you have, and this is the most important. This is why I believe you became an entrepreneur. And congratulations, welcome to this industry street. You became an entrepreneur because you have a vision for the people you were called to serve.

There's someone out there right now that is dependent on you. You are the answer. You are the TYLENOL to someone's headache. And I want to acknowledge you. Take your right hand as your read this if you are right-handed, take your left hand as your read this if you're left-handed, and just pat yourself on the back right now, and silently acknowledge yourself for the champion that you are. I want you to know this, and this is why I say this, it's a mindset that *today is my January 1st*. I always like to share this message.

*Today is my January 1st*. Write that down, *today is my January 1st*. It's one of our core philosophies.

*Today is my January 1st* represents that today is a fresh start, it's a do-over, that my past no longer equals my future. *Today is my January 1st* means you can make a decision today that you're going to learn lead generation systems. You can make a decision today that you're going to learn how to run appointment setting systems. You can make a decision today that you're going to learn how to close by just asking for the sale. My mentor taught me that the best time to plant a tree was 10 years ago. The next best time to plant a tree is when? *Now*. So, it's *now* clock time for you. You're an entrepreneur, the world is waiting on you. You've got to make a difference; you've got what it takes. *Today is your January 1st* you're going to crack the code.

Welcome to entrepreneurship, the fastest way for some of you to build your wealth. I'm proud of you. Thanks a lot for tuning in and just reading this one chapter. Thanks for being here. Make sure you connect over at www.evergreenrevenueplaybook.com. On social media, go to Instagram, find me at @iamchebrown. With that being said, I want you to make it a great day, and we're going to make some good things when we connect again next time. God bless, and I wish you success. Peace.

# About
# Che Brown

Che Brown is a globally renowned giant in the sales world. He has cracked the once elusive code of entrepreneurial success with a game-changing model that unlocks unlimited financial potential, power, and wealth. In just six short years, he has dominated the sales space, coaching thousands of rising business leaders to achieve exponential growth and success in their industries, to the tune of over $400 million and counting. His acclaimed 7-Figure Sales Team concept has forever erased the outdated notion that generating revenue in business is a sole-source game – instead illustrating it is indeed a team sport. Che lives, breathes, and sleeps his craft. He has his fingers on the pulse of profit generation and an instinctual insight into why the heart of a flailing business has stopped. Most importantly, he can resuscitate the flow of revenue in any company with just a whiteboard and a conversation. Che Brown is the Creator of Sales Team Guru ([www.SalesTeamGuru.com](www.SalesTeamGuru.com)), host of the #1 Business Development and Late Night Show In The Country: The Happy Entrepreneur Show ([www.HappyEntrepreneurShow.com](www.HappyEntrepreneurShow.com)), and Founder of Comeback Champion ([www.ComebackChampionSummit.com](www.ComebackChampionSummit.com))

Main site: [www.SalesTeamGuru.com](www.SalesTeamGuru.com)

Free Gift - [www.EvergreenRevenuePlaybook.com](www.EvergreenRevenuePlaybook.com)

Connect on:

Facebook: [https://www.facebook.com/groups/ComebackChampionNation/](https://www.facebook.com/groups/ComebackChampionNation/)

Instagram: [https://www.instagram.com/iamchebrown](https://www.instagram.com/iamchebrown)

LinkedIN: [https://www.linkedin.com/in/chebrown/](https://www.linkedin.com/in/chebrown/)

YouTube: [https://www.youtube.com/channel/UCzGOThly2z5KxPA2kI3hwVQ?view_as=subscriber](https://www.youtube.com/channel/UCzGOThly2z5KxPA2kI3hwVQ?view_as=subscriber)

Twitter: [https://twitter.com/CheBrownSales](https://twitter.com/CheBrownSales)

# Rising Boss

## By Jonathan Haynes

A re you ready to be a successful entrepreneur? Are you ready to be able to financially support your family and business without any hesitation? Are you ready to prove the doubters wrong who said you cannot make it and you can't get started because you don't have what it takes? Well, I am about to give you some key things on how to become a successful entrepreneur and how to start your business with the very things that helped me be who I am today and proved every doubter I had wrong. First thing, you must be passionate about what you're trying to achieve. That means you're willing to sacrifice a large part of your waking hours to the idea you've come up with. Your passion will ignite the same intensity in the others who join you as you build a team. And with passion, both your team and your customers are more likely to truly believe in what you are trying to do. Great entrepreneurs focus intensely on an opportunity where others see nothing. This focus and intensity help to eliminate wasted effort and distractions. Most companies die from indigestion rather than starvation. Companies suffer from doing too many things at the same time rather than doing too few things very well. Stay focused on the mission. Success only comes from hard work. There is no such thing as overnight success; behind every "overnight success" lies years of hard work and sweat. People with luck will tell you there's no easy way to achieve success-and that luck comes to those who work hard. Focus on things you can control; stay focused on your efforts and let the results be what they will be. The road to success is going to be long, so remember to enjoy the journey. Everyone will teach you to focus on goals, but successful people focus on the journey and celebrate the milestones along the way. Is it worth spending a large part of your life trying to reach the destination if you didn't enjoy the journey? Won't your team also enjoy the journey more as well? Wouldn't it be better for all of you to have the time of your lives during the journey, even if the destination is never reached?

There are too many variables in the real world that you simply can't put into a spreadsheet. Spreadsheets spit out results from your inexact assumptions and give you a false sense of security. In most cases, your heart and gut are still your best guide. We've all had experiences in a business where our heart told us something was wrong while our brain was still trying to use logic to figure it all out. Sometimes a faint voice based on instinct is far more reliable than overpowering logic. Every entrepreneur has to be agile, continually learning and adapting as new information becomes available. At the same time, you have to remain devoted to the cause and mission of your enterprise. That's where that faint voice becomes so important, especially when it is giving you early warning signals that things are off-track. Successful entrepreneurs find the balance between listening to that voice and staying persistent in driving for success because sometimes success is waiting right across from the transitional bump that's disguised as failure. It's a simple fact: no individual can be good at everything. Everyone needs people around them who have complementary skill sets. It takes a lot of soul-searching to find your core skills and strengths. After that, find the smartest people you can who complement your strengths. It's tempting to gravitate toward people who are like you; the trick is to find people who are not like you but who are good at what they do and what you can't do. Unless you are the smartest person on earth, many others have likely thought about doing the same thing you're trying to do. Success doesn't necessarily come from breakthrough innovation but from flawless execution.

A great strategy alone won't win a game or a battle; the win comes from basic blocking and tackling. No matter how much time you spend perfecting your business plan, you still have to adapt according to the ground realities. You're going to learn a lot more useful information from taking action rather than hypothesizing. I can't imagine anyone ever achieving long-term success without having honesty and integrity. These two qualities need to be at the core of everything we do. These two qualities need to be at the core of everything we do. Everybody has a conscience-but too many people stop listening to it. There is always that faint voice that warns you when you are not being completely honest or even slightly off track from the path of integrity. Be sure to listen to that voice. Success is much more rewarding if you give back. By the time become successful, lots of people will have helped you along the way. You'll learn, as I have, that you rarely get a chance to help the people who helped you because in most cases, you don't even know who they were. The only way to pay back the debts we owe is to help people we can help-and hope they will go on to help more people. It's our responsibility to do "good" with the resources we have available. So, no matter what you face through this journey keep your mind focused on your goals and your purpose and remember that God is with you always and just to keep your focus on the bigger picture, and that is remembering why you wanted to start your very own business and prove those doubters wrong because God will always make your enemies your footstool. Always keep the reason why you wanted to start your business at the forefront of your mind so when things come up against you and your business remember the reason why you wanted to be your own Boss. Now it's time for you to BOSS YOUR LANE!!!

# About

# Jonathan Haynes

Jonathan Haynes is an award-winning recording artist from Gulfport, MS, who has a passion to drive music as far as his mission reaches. He has shared the stage with some of the biggest names in the Gospel Industry. He is a #1 International best-selling author, talk show host, serial entrepreneur, life coach, business strategist & motivational speaker who exudes his anointing through his sound and passion to sing with a deep revelation of how God has been his source.

Contact Info

Phone: 228-314-0722

Email: sbirdproductions56@gmail.com

Website: jonathanlhaynes.com

# Your Business Foundation

## By Kathy White

Your business requires a strong foundation. Yet, sometimes, as entrepreneurs, we dive into our dream without creating the stability of a company. This chapter will explain why it's essential and what you need to do to get the foundation started.

Remember, we are not looking for a thermometer jump from 1 to 1,000 in a day. Instead, you want to get better every day by 1 to 2 micro notches on the thermometer. Soon, the micro-notch increases will compound into more than 1,000 times of improvement and success.

People tend to live on hopium (hope and prayer) that their business will succeed. But perhaps your business might succeed without the correct foundation. Rare, but it might.

**Your Big "WHY"**

Before we get into the foundation, what is your why? Your WHY Has to make you cry. But, as cliché as this sounds, you have to know your why. What gives you purpose and meaning in life? If your why is big enough, then your motive for action comes big enough.

Being an entrepreneur is fun yet challenging. Unfortunately, a lot of people don't have the discipline to do this on their own. When you ask yourself about your why, can you feel the emotion? Is your why big enough to take daily action?

Some people say their why is money. Although this can be part of a why I can almost guarantee you it is not your entire why. Look at the story behind the money. What can you do with that money? Maybe that money can change your family's financial blueprint. One of my "why's" is to build a school for the Jabez Orphanage in Kenya.

When your WHY is big enough, what you must do and what you must endure; becomes easier. Either your why will be big enough, or your excuses of nonaction will be. Your why will drive you more than your reasons will guide you for nonaction.

One exercise to help figure out your why is to write out your obituary, write down how you would live if you only had six months left, and write down how you would live if you had 500 years in good health left to live.

Once you have your why, you need to have clarity, vision, and goals. To succeed in business, you have to have a clear vision, a powerful mission, and core values to hire and live by. Then you must set clear financial and non-financial goals to achieve them.

## VISION

After you know your WHY, you need to have a clear VISION. Your vision/mission statement gives the company direction for its future state. It's the "tomorrow" for your business. If you don't know where you are going, how do you know when you get there? For example, if you started going on a road trip and didn't have a destination in mind, how do you know when you have arrived? You can tell someone you are going on a trip, but what do you reply when they ask where you are going? All you can say is west. You need a destination in mind for a trip just like you do with your business.

What is the purpose of your business? Do you want to give back to a charity? What do you see your business doing in the next five years? If I could wave a magic wand right now and gave you anything you asked for, what would your business look like? What would you tell me that you were doing with your business, family, charity, etc.?

A vision statement is a sentence or short paragraph that briefly describes a company's long-term goals, what you are trying to build, and serves as a guide for your future actions. The vision statement should define, in general, a company's planned future based on its core ideals. In addition, it should be inspiring and exciting to the world.

A vision statement doesn't tell you how you're going to get there; it does set the direction for a business plan. Poor planning is one of the reasons small businesses fail. Being able to craft and articulate a vision is one of the hallmarks of a strong business leader.

The vision statement answers the question, "where are we going?"

Here is a template that you can use to start crafting your vision statement: I am so happy and grateful that we (fill in what your company will have done in five years - how many people you have helped), we generate (how much $ in profit do you want) and donate (how much $ do you want to give away).

## MISSION STATEMENT

A mission statement is a brief description of an entity's fundamental purpose. It answers the question, "Why does our business exist?" It articulates the company's purpose external and internal.

Mission statements get at the heart of why a company exists rather than how it exists. A mission statement focuses on a company's present state, while a vision statement focuses on a company's future.

When crafting a mission statement, it needs to be robust and powerful.

A mission statement answers the question, "who are we?"

## CORE VALUES

Core values are the fundamental beliefs of a person or organization. Core values are the deeply ingrained principles that guide all of a company's actions. You hire, live by, and fire for core values. They serve as its cultural cornerstones. These guiding principles dictate behavior and can help people understand the difference between right and wrong.

When choosing your company's core values, select the ones that reflect you. Your business is a reflection of you. One of the companies I worked for had these as their core values: Innovative, Quality, Hard Working, Care, and Integrity.

When picking out your business's core values, my advice is to limit them to four or five. But, of course, these aren't set in stone and can be changed.

## GOALS

As you determine your vision and mission statement, you need to set goals to achieve them. The plans need to be clear and concise. I recommend having a three-year, five-year, and ten-year goal. Within each goal, there will be micro-goals within the big goal. Do not focus on goals that you think you can achieve, as there is no growth attached to these goals. Instead, focus on goals that are challenging and something you have no idea how to do. Then, as you look at your goals, reverse engineer how to get there.

John Assaraf states, "Awareness gives me a choice. Choice gives me freedom."

Think thoughtfully about these questions:

1. I have the beliefs and habits to achieve my revenue and business goals.
2. My business model is proven and solid.
3. My marketing message is complete.
4. My website is fantastic.

5. My sales process (from banner to the buyer) is complete.

6. My revenue plan is comprehensive.

7. I have the right team to achieve my vision.

8. I have my business set up in the proper structure. LLC, Sole Proprietor, etc.

9. Do I need a trademark or copyright?

10. I have a business plan.

11. Do I need to raise capital?

Many entrepreneurs feel defeated if they don't achieve every single goal set out in front of them for the year. Instead, choose your top five goals and say to yourself, "If I achieve those five goals, this will be a great year." Can you achieve these goals by yourself? Do you need a team? If you can't afford to pay someone, have you looked at hiring interns?

These are some examples of excellent goals: Revenue Goal, Profit Goal, Donation Goal.

## HABITS & PLAN OF ACTION

Successful days makes a successful life.

Your Power Hour, per Jack Canfield, is 5 am. To get the day started right, follow these habits daily. Meditate for 20 minutes. Study for 20 minutes. Exercise for 20 minutes. Write down ten things that you are grateful for every single day.

Remember, we are in the Information Implementation business, not the information overload business. Right now, we have so much information that is easy to consume that we get stuck thinking we need to know more details before we get started. What are you doing to guard your time?

Take daily actions. Write down on paper the six action steps you will take the following day, the night before. Keep that piece of paper in your pocket and cross things off as you get them done. If you don't get them done, add these tasks to the next day.

## ACCOUNTABILITY

It's easy to get stuck, trapped, and lose sight of your goals if you don't have an Accountability structure. Accountability for entrepreneurs provides a clear framework for greater productivity and higher performance. When you are accountable, you make better decisions and actions.

Find both an Accountability Partner/Group and a Master Mind Group. There are both free and paid groups. Be very selective with these groups. If one doesn't feel right, find a new group or partner. If there is a financial commitment, people tend to take these groups more seriously.

The primary purpose of an accountability group/partner is to help members reach a goal or complete a project, basically about getting things done. Whereas a Mastermind group involves a strong portion of brainstorming, problem-solving, decision-making, sharing of ideas/solutions, and resources. But, of course, your group can be both a Master Mind Group and Accountability Group.

Qualities to look for in an Accountability Partner/Group:

1. Do they care about your progress?
2. Are they trustworthy?
3. Do they give positive reinforcement?
4. Are they nonjudgmental?
5. Do they give good advice?
6. Are they dependable?
7. Do they celebrate your wins?
8. Do they support you through your failures?


Qualities to look for in a Master Mind Group:

1. Similar Success and Experience Levels.
2. Varied Skills.
3. Balanced sharing.

4. Members are Givers, not hoarders.
5. Effective Group Leader.
6. Commitment.

## HAVE A REST DAY

It is essential to have a rest day. As a budding entrepreneur, your business relies 100 percent on you. Therefore, your body needs to be in top form. If you don't take a day for yourself, your body will take it for you. As entrepreneurs, we tend to be constantly on the go. So, one day a week, turn off the phone and turn off the computer. It is okay to take one day a week to rest your mind and body.

## LAUGH AGAIN!

Human beings love to laugh as it feels good. Yet adults only laugh up to 17 times a day, if that. Laughter draws people together in ways that trigger healthy physical and emotional changes in the body. It strengthens your immune system, boosts mood, diminishes pain, and protects you from stress. Laughter makes us healthier and happier. It truly is the best medicine.

## CONCLUSION

Often, when we don't see the results we want, we quit too soon. Ninety percent of entrepreneurs quit because they lose hope. Don't give up. Success is on the other side of the mountain. Having a business gives you freedom of time, the ability to call the shots, and provides the ability to make an impact. More than anything, having a business allows you to leave a legacy.

# About
# Kathy White

Business structures flourish best when innovative leadership intersects with solicitous intention. Uniquely embodying this ethic is the compassionate professional, Kathy White.

Kathy White is an author, facilitator, and the CEO and founder of **Star Changers**, a personal development coaching business, and **VR Waffles, LLC**, a company specializing in telepresence team building for the benefit of welcoming human connection back into the remote workforce. Having spent several years of reputable leadership as a managerial and accounting professional, Kathy brings dynamic and methodical reliability to the growing world of entrepreneurial hopefuls. Leaving behind a role as the Accounts Payable Manager at Ultradent from 2014 to 2021, she is living proof that success is not linear- with calculated and assessed risk-taking, entrepreneurs can expect to transform their world *and stars.*

**Her Mantra is clear: "If you believe enough, you can change your stars."**

Kathy combines a successful career with high regard for education, achievement, and community service. She holds a Bachelor of Science in Accounting from the University of Utah and an Associate of Science in Business from Salt Lake Community College. As a profound believer in the power of philanthropic volunteerism, Kathy has participated in several service-based efforts, such as "The Dirty Dash" and TEDxSLC. Though her sincere heart for excellence has afforded her many accolades, including featured photography published in Ultradent's calendar in 2013 and 2016, Kathy is often sobered by her tenacity in overcoming life's various obstacles. She has had to navigate most of her victories while being a divorced single mom, battling a jaw tumor and breast cancer, each diagnosed within two weeks of each other in 2014.

Standing as one inclined to succeed against all odds, Kathy understands the power of determination when belief and commitment are applied to one's dream. She often pulls on this internal resource while coaching others on their path.

When Kathy is not out changing the world through the fabric of innovative entrepreneurship, she enjoys traveling, adventure, and watching the beauty of the mountainous outdoors.

**Kathy White. Leader. Innovator. Humanitarian.**

Business Email: kathy@vrwaffles.com

Website: https://www.vrwaffles.com/

Social Media:

FB Profile: https://www.facebook.com/kat.roe2/

FB Groups:

Star Changers:

https://www.facebook.com/groups/3670457359635226

VR Waffles:

https://www.facebook.com/groups/2857867437798880

Hiking:

https://www.facebook.com/groups/270912318204244

FB Page: https://www.facebook.com/starchangers

IG: https://www.instagram.com/coachkathywhite/

LinkedIn Personal: https://www.linkedin.com/in/kathy-white-5a121897/

LinkedIn Business:

https://www.linkedin.com/company/wafflesvr/?viewAsMember=true

TikTok: https://www.tiktok.com/@coachkathywhite?lang=en

# Take Accountability:
# You Train People How to Treat
# You & Your Business

## By Stephanie Brauchle

I f you are the type of person or business owner that takes accountability for how others treat you and your business, I applaud you. You are on the right track to mind-blowing success. On the contrary, if you do not see the value in taking accountability, you may feel resistance while reading this chapter. Try to be receptive because this concept can also be the paradigm shift needed for growth.

You train people how to treat you, take accountability for it. This idea may be new to you. As a business owner, it is best to be open to new ideas and adaptable to change. Some tend to wince at the word train. Try to remove the negative connotation associated with "to train someone." Otherwise, this concept may be hard to accept.

People also tend to have an issue with taking accountability for how others behave and interact, thinking it's entirely out of our control. You can't control others; however, you can create boundaries. What is *always* in *your* control is the way *you* react. The way you evaluate a conversation and how you set expectations. You train people how to treat you by deciding what you will and will not accept and making it known. You are constantly training the people who interact with you. This concept can apply to every interpersonal relationship in your life! Whether it be a child, spouse, friend, or especially in the business world. You train your employees, vendors, and clients on how to treat you.

As a Small Business Co-Pilot, I have worked with many business owners. I noticed the most successful business owners had a common denominator: they took accountability and understood the concept. A business owner should assume accountability for everything that happens in their business. Technically speaking, your business is your responsibility. The success of the company relies on you. Entrepreneurs have to work with numerous individuals to run a business. Even if you are not directly involved in an issue, it is best to find a way to hold yourself accountable as the owner to resolve or prevent the problem. For instance, if your employee makes a mistake, perhaps the process needs to be adapted, maybe they weren't trained well enough, or perchance you hired the wrong candidate in the first place. It could even be an underlying issue coming from the top down that needs to be improved in your leadership abilities. The most successful business owners *own* the mistake and use accountability as the advantage to find a solution.

To train, you don't have to voice demands to employees. You teach through actions, through leadership, and through creating the example—model how you'd like to be treated. When you show respect, you earn respect in return. You train others by how you respond. In conversation, you train with which parts you entertain and which topics you choose to ignore completely. You can teach people not to gossip in your presence simply by stating, "what we're not going to do is gossip about a client to me." You can do this in a stern but professional way to set an expectation. If an employee brings an issue to your attention, you don't encourage the venting of emotions or blaming others. As a manager, you guide the individual towards a solution-oriented conversation. Respond by saying, how can I help solve this? What could be changed to prevent this? If someone comes to you with a solution, you offer praise, then encourage the conversation to implement and execute the solution.

You train people on how to view your business with your brand. A business owner coaches the public's perspective by building expectations in a branding strategy. Your brand signifies the personality and reputation of your company, what target demographic you want to reach, and more. The brand concept derives from the emotion of how your customer feels when interacting with your business. This means you also have to train people how to feel about your business, so be intentional with your choices of slogans, colors, and marketing avenues. In a nutshell, branding defines the identity which evokes an emotion to match. With a solid brand, you can set expectations early on and train others how to view and feel about your business.

Take accountability for your schedule and time management. Ask yourself these questions honestly. Was your day productive? Did you complete your to-do list? Are you finding it challenging to stay on track with distractions? Do you value your timeline? First, you must learn to value your time by holding yourself accountable to complete your scheduled tasks. Be more aware of how you spend your time throughout the day. Find ways to delegate the minor assignments and prioritize money-making activities. Once you grasp and achieve time management for yourself, you can then train others how to value your time. This can be done by confirming a scheduled presentation and following up on the morning of the appointment. Being early and starting on time for your meeting is also a great way to train by example.

Take accountability for your daily schedule and explore ways to save time or use time more efficiently in your business. For example, lengthy meetings are not necessary. Every meeting should have a purpose, a plan, and a timeline expectation. Using brevity on a conference call shows that you value the caller's time and respect your schedule. If a topic needs more attention, schedule a follow-up conversation for the next conference call. Prepare meetings with a problem-solution goal in mind and train your team to be solution-oriented thinkers. Most employees focus too much on the problem and their emotions surrounding it. You don't want to hear elaborately complex matters; instead, you want to be presented with the solution then brief me on the problem. Time wasted is money wasted; value your time, train employees on time management, and respect the time of others!

If financial problems occur, take accountability. Perhaps you need to reevaluate your cost structure. Costs may need to be researched again to find more affordable vendors. You train your vendors how to treat you by how you respond to their price changes. Do you call your vendor and ask if you can be a long-term partner? Do you communicate with them about buying in bulk or signing a contract to keep the cost low? Assessing costs will help identify priorities and uncover which costs are unnecessary.

Once business costs are under control, then evaluate sales and retention. If retention rates are low, take accountability. Perhaps a new sales strategy is in order. Track the productivity of sales and migrate towards the most efficient methods. Provide detailed training for your sales team. Evaluate the marketing plan and advertising choices you have in place. Use data to analyze performance and results. Then allocate more dollars towards the avenues that bring the most profit.

Take accountability for training people when to pay you? Payment expectations are created at the beginning of working with a client. You can do this by having specific dates of payment in your packages, by setting deadlines, or by when you send your invoice. If you are late on sending your invoice, vendors and clients may also pay you late. Invoicing can be time-consuming but is a crucial component of showing others that you value payments on time.

When it comes to providing a service, how much do you think you're worth? Whether consulting, business coaching, or creating a graphic design, you are committing your time, energy, and knowledge. Ask yourself how you value your time hourly, by project, or per month? You can research pricing strategies and create a competitive analysis to choose what to charge. It is a contemplative task to value your worth, especially if you love your work. But don't give away your passion for free. Create expectations for your worth. You can start with entry-level prices because there is always room for growth.

If you dream of starting your own company, don't allow others to deflate your confidence or dilute your dreams! You not only train people how to treat you and your goals, but you also choose who you allow in your social circle. Surround yourself with a circle of friends & colleagues that have similar values and goals. Spend time with mentors you want to emulate—ones who lift your confidence and become a cheerleader who encourages your dreams.

I encourage you to start your dream business; it is never too late to bring more meaning or income to your life. You can begin while you have a job in place. It's even better to have more than one source of income and dabble in mini side hustles or projects. Find stability while also fulfilling your passion. A full-time career offers a stable environment while you write or create your business. Do what is necessary while giving to your craft. Most companies have formed from a side hustle that becomes so profitable that it replaces a full-time career. Soon enough, *your* side hustle could become your next company.

Train the world on how to treat you by brightening and focusing your energy. Gain a clear vision, write it down, or create a vision board. Choose the medium that you fancy the most and have fun with it. You can visualize and manifest your wildest dreams. Take accountability for your dream, train the world how to treat you and your business, and be relentless until that vision comes to fruition.

# About
# Stephanie Brauchle

With passion and persistence, Stephanie rebounded from the aftermath of the tourism & events industry crash by starting her own marketing business called Small Business Co-Pilot, helping Small Businesses along the Gulf Coast and abroad. As the rebirth of the hospitality industry emerges from the ashes, Brauchle has hit the ground running in her full-time hospitality sales career and running her company on the side. Small Business Co-Pilot services include business plans, marketing plans, graphic design, social media, blog writing, advertising content, phone script creation, recruitment, and project management. Now serving over a dozen small business clients from Chicago to San Diego, her business has shown proven methods of success for owners.

Brauchle's background consists of a USM Undergraduate degree in Business Administration with an emphasis in Marketing Management. Also, in progress pursuing an LSU Master's of Business in Human Resources. She has 10 years of experience working for boutique hotels such as Bourbon Orleans, Oak Crest Mansion, and White House Hotel, specializing in weddings & large events that culminated with crowning achievements of the 2018 and 2019 People's Choice Award while serving as Sales Manager.

Stephanie Brauchle

Owner/ Curator

Small Business Co-Pilot

Smallbzcopilot@gmail.com

& Sales Director in Nashville, TN

# Small Business Certifications/ Tools for Business Growth

## By Robin Hughes

A re you leaving money on the table that is designated for small business owners? Small business certification can be a gold mine for your business revenues. I started an HR & Business Consulting international firm and decided to get certified as a Minority Business Enterprise (MBE). It opened the door to the construction industry for me. I had never thought about doing business in the construction industry. If you do not offer construction services, you probably have not either. The MBE certification has increased my revenues and I have gained access to 6 figure contracts for my business. As a Diversity Director, one must identify minority and women-owned businesses that can perform work on projects/contracts. I had a concrete construction company that went through the certification process. As a result of successfully securing the MBE designation, he was awarded a $1.5 million contract. I helped a DBE secure a $3.5 million contract. The General Contractors (GCs), corporate buyers, and federally funded contractors are obligated to reach a participation goal on their projects for small businesses with certification credentials. When these entities successfully achieve their goals more owners of projects and contracts seek them out as well. A staffing company was awarded a contract with one of the largest hospitals in the city because she was certified as an MBE. That was 15 years ago, and she is still doing business with the hospital today. I assisted an MBE in getting their book included as part of the curriculum for a charter school. I have met so many corporate buyers at the networking meetings that have resulted in many contracts for my services over the years. Relationships and your network play a vital role in securing contracts too. I recently received a referral from the U.S. Virgin Islands as a result of networking. R Hughes & Associates offers business development services to assist you with growing your network and potential clients. Many consulting firms and coaches can benefit from certification and get in front of corporations to secure contracts. Remember, these buyers know other people that might benefit from your services too.

In a nutshell, small business certification gives you exclusive access to grow your revenues. Business owners are in business to make money. The certification designation gives you access to the certifying agencies corporate members, federal, state, and local government agencies. If you are not certified, you are leaving money on the table.

There are mixed reactions to small business certifications. Some people have heard about certification and attempted to go through the process. This might be the first time you and/or others are hearing about it. You cannot afford not to know about small business certifications. It gives you that competitive edge. The process can be very intimidating, but R Hughes & Associates has an extensive background in assisting small businesses successfully navigate the process to obtain their credentials.

## What are the Benefits of Certification?

The benefits of certification boil down to one word: **ACCESS.** Certification gives certified small businesses exclusive access to top prime corporate purchasing agents, premium networking events, searchable supplier databases, affordable consulting services, technology programs, and vital introductions to nationally known corporations. Certification gives you that competitive advantage that sets minority and women-owned companies apart from their competitors.

Corporate supplier diversity programs have committed to do business with minority and women-owned companies.

Many corporations use certification as a way to identify minority and women-owned businesses that are bidding on contracts. The certification process helps ensure that the contracts are awarded to minority and women-owned businesses.

Let's talk about the numbers, details, and what to do after you are certified.

## Minority Business Enterprises the Numbers

Demographics in the United States are continuously evolving. Minorities will represent more than 50% of the population by the year 2045. Minority Business Enterprises (MBEs) generated more than $400 billion in economic output that resulted in the creation and or preservation of 2.2 million jobs. According to the Minority Business Development Agency (MBDA) minorities own approximately 8 million firms and sole proprietorship that account for approximately $1.4 trillion in revenues. The National Minority Supplier Development Council (NMSDC), Economic Impact Report https://www.nmsdc.org/wp-content/uploads/Economic Impact Report FINAL.pdf (final report).

## What is a small business?

The Office of Advocacy generally defines a small business as an independent business having fewer than 500 employees. For industry-level small business size standards used in government programs and contracting, see

https://www.sba.gov/document/support--table-sizestandards.

**Minority Business Enterprise (MBE)**

**What does Minority Business Enterprise mean?**

Minority businesses must be at least 51% minority-owned operated and controlled. For NMSDC's program, a minority group member is an individual who is at least 25% Asian, Black, Hispanic, or Native American. Minority eligibility is established via a combination of screenings, interviews, and site visits.

**Women Business Enterprise (WBE)**

**Women Business Enterprises and Women Business Owners the Numbers**

According to the Woman Business Enterprise National Council (WBENC), there are 13 million women-owned businesses in the U.S. According to the National Association of Women Business Owners (NAWBO), women-owned businesses generate $1.7 trillion in sales and employ nearly 9 million people.

## What is a women's business enterprise (WBE)?

A Women's Business Enterprise, commonly referred to as a WBE, is an independent business that is at least 51% owned and controlled by one or more women who are U.S. citizens or Legal Resident Aliens; whose business formation and principal place of business are in the U.S. or its territories.

## Who qualifies as a Woman Business Enterprise (WBE)?

To qualify as a women's business enterprise, your business must meet the following requirements: the company must be 51 percent owned by women who are U.S. citizens. Women must manage the business operations daily and make long-term decisions for the company.

## Women-Owned Small Business (WBENC/SBA WOSB)

## What is a Woman Business Enterprise National Council/SBA Woman-Owned Small Business?

Women's Business Enterprise National Council (pronounced WE-BANK) is a certifying agency that certifies WBEs in the U.S. and U.S. territories. This is a national certification.

Women-Owned Businesses must be at least 51% owned, controlled, and operated by one or more women who are U.S. citizens or Legal Resident Aliens; whose business formation and principal place of business are in the U.S. or its territories.

## Who qualifies as a woman-owned small business (WBENC/SBA WOSB)?

Eligibility requirements for the Women-Owned Small Business (WOSB), states that your business must meet the following requirements: must be 51% owned by women who are U.S. citizens; women must manage the operations on a daily basis, and women must make long-term decisions for the company. The company must have a DUN's number and be registered in SAM (System for Award Management).

## Disadvantage Business Enterprise (DBE)

## What does Disadvantaged Business Enterprise mean?

DBEs are for-profit small businesses that are socially and economically disadvantaged. Individuals own at least a 51% interest and control management and daily business operations.

## What is Disadvantaged Business Enterprise program?

The USDOT Disadvantaged Business Enterprise (DBE) Program aims to increase the participation of minority and women-owned businesses in state and local transportation projects that are funded by the Department through the Federal Aviation Administration (FAA), the Federal Highway Administration (FHWA).

## Who qualifies as a DBE?

Eligibility requirements for the DBE program consists of the person(s) must own 51% or more of a "small business," and establish that they are socially and economically disadvantaged with a personal net worth of $750K or less, adjusted gross income of $350K or less and $6M or less in assets.

## HUBZone Program

## What is HuBZone Certification?

The HUBZone program limits competition for contracts to businesses in historically underutilized business zones. They get a 10% price evaluation preference in full and open contract competitions.

## Who qualifies for HUBZone Certification?

Eligibility requirements for the HUBZone program state the business must be small, 51% owned controlled by U.S. citizens, a Community Development Corporation, an agricultural cooperative an Alaska Native corporation, a Native Hawaiian organization, or an Indian tribe. The principal office must be in the HUBZone and at least 35% of its employee must live in the HUBZone area.

## What is SBA 8(a) Certification?

The Small Business Administration 8(a) business development program has committed to awarding at least 5% of all federal contracting dollars to small, disadvantaged businesses each year. The SBAs Mentor-Protégé Program (MPP) provides valuable business development to assist the 8(a) certified business in areas such as internal business management systems, accounting, marketing, manufacturing, and strategic planning. Financial assistance with loans and bonding. They also assist with federal contract bidding and the procurement process.

## Who qualifies for SBA 8(a) Certification?

Eligibility requirements for the 8(a) program consists of the person(s) must own 51% or more of a "small business," and establish that they are socially and economically disadvantaged with a personal net worth of $750K or less, adjusted gross income of $350K or less and $6M or less in assets.

Remember, these are not the only certifications. There are other certifications for veterans and small business owners.

## How to Become Certified

The process is very intense, but R Hughes & Associates can get you over the finish line. First, identify the certification to meet your business needs. Many times, more than one certification is necessary for you to have access to the right audiences. Then, the certifying bodies must be identified. The certifying bodies will depend on the certification you are seeking (i.e., MBE, WBE, DBE, etc.). Your target customer/client and projects will have bearing on the type of certification you should seek. If you do not have the long form of your birth certificate order it today. The certificate reflects the ethnicity of your parents which is relevant to certification. The majority of states have this version available at the state's capital and it can take up to 65 days to receive it. One of the biggest obstacles is gathering the necessary documentation to complete the application. The checklist is extensive but does not let that deter you. When all of the documentation has been gathered the application should be completed. Then the entire package must be submitted to the certifying agency for review. Another obstacle is responding to the request to edit. Commonly, additional information is requested in the process so do not be alarmed. After responding to the request and all of the documentation has been reviewed, a site visit is scheduled at the company headquarters. The owner will be interviewed and other parties (i.e., partners, etc.), if applicable. The investigator will gather information and return to the office to complete the investigation. It may take up to 90 days to get a response on the status of your application. Be patient. Do not get discouraged.

## I'm Certified...What's Next

Congratulations!! The certification process has been completed and your company has the credentials to gain exclusive access to prime corporate buyers and contracts designated for certified small businesses. The DBE designation gives you access to federally funded contracts with transit authorities, airports, utility companies, the Department of Transportation (DOT), etc. Now, it is time to get to work.

The corporate members of the certifying body will host monthly network meetings. These meetings give you access to their top prime procurement team to sell your goods and services. If you are personally unavailable to attend the meetings have one of your team members attend on your behalf. Introduce yourself to as many people as possible, including the other certified small businesses.

The supplier diversity programs have a procurement registration process. It can be time-consuming but complete the process for every corporate member. It is beneficial for the certified companies to complete the procurement registration. Think of this as a marketing tool for your business. Registration will match the certified companies with bid opportunities. This helps the certified company identify bid opportunities easily and it helps the buyers identify the certified companies to do business with.

Make sure you are on the distribution list for upcoming bid opportunities. Many opportunities require that you submit a Request for Proposal (RFP). There may be opportunities for Joint Ventures if you are too small to bid on a project alone. A Joint Venture is two more businesses that form a single enterprise to bid on a project where both parties share the risk. This allows small businesses to bid on projects they might not be able to bid on otherwise because they are too small.

## Return-On-Investment (ROI)

A return on investment (ROI) is a profitability metric that investors evaluate to determine how well an investment has performed. Businesses want to make a profit and have a good return on investment. Generally, a reasonable return on investment is approximately 7%. Return on investment is referred to as return on costs (ROC). For example, a business owner pays $3,000 for certification. The certification will help the business generate revenues. The credentials will give the business owner exclusive access to top prime corporate buyers and federal contracts. The business owner attends monthly networking events, collaborates with other business owners, and identifies bidding opportunities. This year the business is awarded a contract for $100,000. Based on an investment length of 1 year the ROI is 3,233.33% with a gain of $97,000.

The basic formula for ROI is:

$$ROI = \frac{\text{Gain from Investment} - \text{Cost of Investment}}{\text{Cost of Investment}}$$

In the scenario, the credentials have been utilized and yielded a great return on investment. It provides opportunities for joint ventures with other certified companies and general contractors. The contracts awarded will vary. The credentials give businesses access to buyers that might not have access to otherwise.

**Invest in yourself – Invest in your business!**

**Certifying Agencies**

**Local, State, and Counties Certifying Agencies**

There are local, state and county certifying agencies to obtain small business certifications. The number of corporate members will vary for each state.

# National Minority Supplier Development Council (NMSDC)

The NMSDC has a network of 23 Regional Councils throughout the country and 1,750 corporate members. The Regional Council tout that they certify and match over 12,000 minority-owned businesses with their corporate members.

United States Small Business Administration (SBA)

The SBA has several contracting programs that provide access to federal contracts in the U.S. They provide guidance to small business to assist in competing for federal contracts.

Let's stop leaving money on the table that is designated for minority and women-owned businesses. R Hughes &

Associates takes a lot of the frustration out of the small business certification process for you. We have conducted the investigations and signed off the cases to certify small businesses. Get the assistance you need to gain access to revenues dedicated to your company to increase your bottom line.

**Contact R Hughes & Associates to start the certification process today!**

Robin Hughes, CEO

robin@rhughesandassociates.com

www.rhughesandassociates.com

Phone: 469.554.9366

References

National Association of Women Business Owners (n.d.). https://www.nawbo.org/.

National Minority Supplier Development Council (n.d.). https://nmsdc.org/.

Small Business Administration (n.d.).

https://www.sba.gov/federal-contracting/contracting-assistance-programs/8a-business-development-program.

Women Business Enterprise National Council (n.d.). https://www.wbenc.org/.

# About
# Robin Hughes

R Hughes & Associates has over 20-years of experience in HR, Business & Legal arenas. Robin was a Certification Specialist (3 years) and acted in the capacity of Interim Director (8 months) of Certification for a certifying body. She conducted the investigations to ensure the small businesses were certifiable. As the Interim Director, she signed off the cases to approve the eligibility of certification and trained the incoming attorney. She also went through the process personally as a certified Minority Business Enterprise (MBE). Robin has assisted certified small businesses obtain millions on multi-million-dollar constructions projects, corporate buyer's procurement programs, and federally funded contracts. Some of the projects include the FedExForum (Grizzlies Arena - $257M), TN Air National Guard 164th Airlift Wing C-5 Hangars ($80M), Le Bonheur Children's Medical Center ($327M). She has assisted companies in securing local, state, government, and federally funded contracts in construction, education, banking, transportation, and many other areas. She has served as Chief Human Resource Officer, Corporate HR Director, and Director Labor Relations (1st Chair for collective bargaining agreements with the unions) throughout the U.S. and Canada. She has an extensive legal background in contract negotiations and arbitration.

The business world is shaped by the credibility of outstanding professionals displaying vetted expertise, in facilitation, administrative acumen, and a sincere tenacity, to serve humanity. Meeting today's culture with an overwhelming presence of these ethics; is the compassionate professional, Robin Hughes.

Robin Hughes is an Author, Human Resource *bravura*, business strategist, managerial specialist, and CEO and Founder of **R Hughes & Associates: Business & HR Consulting;** a multidimensional practice, providing quintessential management, authentication, and administration to both, established and growing businesses. Harnessing an extensive background in HR, Business, and Legal arenas, Robin brings over 20 years in the corporate workforce and consulting, to a diverse clientele. Recognized for having an incredible relationship with results and prioritizing others, Robin has become one of the most awarded professionals in her field.

**Her mantra is simple: She believes in treating people better than she treats herself, and she treats herself, *damn good.***

Robin's prodigious work ethic is joined by a sincere regard for higher learning, achievement, and servitude. Displaying an uncanny mastery in education, she holds degrees in Applied Science and Paralegal Studies, a Bachelors in Business Administration and Management, with a minor concentration in Leadership; by which she achieved, Cum Laude. Robin also holds a Master of Science in Human Resource Management and graduated from the program aligned with Society for Human Resource Management, Summa Cum Laude, with a 4.0 GPA. She is currently earning a Ph.D., in Industrial-Organizational Psychology.

Stewarding a professional portfolio that knows no boundaries, Robin is the proud member of several business and communal organizations, including The National Notary Association, by which she is a Certified Notary Signing Agent; an Endorsed LEAD Candidate for North Texas Leaders & Executives Advocating for Diversity, the Society for Industrial-Organizational Psychology, SIOP Government Relations Advocacy Team (GREAT), the American Psychological Association, and many more. Her meritorious skill sets have been recognized by corporate giants, non-profits, and firms in the public and private sectors, such as MidSouth Minority Business, where Robin was presented with the Creative Visionary Award, for her development of the FedExForum, used as a model for the City of Memphis, Shelby County, and Mortenson. As well as McGraw-Hill South Central Construction Magazine, for surpassing goals for the minority participation and community outreach program, on the FedExForum.

Robin's appreciated vernacular has offered excellence in a myriad of fields, requiring high levels of professional discernment and analytical proficiency. She served as a Certified Arbitrator for the National Council of Better Business Bureaus for 8 years and trained newly appointed arbitrators on complex cases. Robin also coordinated a Pre-Law Program under Judge Rita Stotts, for Cecil C. Humphreys School of Law. As well as served as a Special Licensed Counsel; representing indigent clients in the Memphis Area Legal Clinic, for her paralegal internship, and was the third paralegal to be appointed a law clerking position.

When Robin is not out making business easier for the modern professional, she is an asset to her local communal body and a loving member of her family and friendship circles. In all she does, Robin expects the validity that is promised by excellence, working in silence, so that success makes all the noise.

**Robin Hughes. Leader. Organizer. Humanitarian.**

# Self-Investment is the Best Investment.

## By Dr. Pamela Henkel

God's gift to you is "your life."

Your gift to God is, "What you do with your life."

You are here on purpose with a Purpose by Design, not by default. The way you secure your purpose is found in and through **self-investment**.

I want you to think about your dreams and goals. To fulfill them, two questions need to be answered.

1. Am I willing to do whatever it takes?
2. Am I able to do what is required? This part is an ongoing process. It takes time, energy, education, and dedication. It takes Self Investment.

Doing the work makes sense but investing in ourselves can be a hard pill to swallow. All our lives we are told self-investment is selfish. We are trained to put ourselves last on the list of education, mentoring, or even self-care.

This is a lesson I learned the hard way. For years, I worked hard for everyone else. Self-investment was not anywhere on my radar. Then in 2016, I fell backward, landing on the corner of a staircase. Injuring my back in such a way that it took me over a year to recover. I had to use a walker for months to get around. I felt helpless and angry. I could not cook, play with my kids, go out with my husband, travel, minister, coach or do much of anything. In desperation, I phoned my mentor hoping for an earth-shaking prayer or at least some sympathy. Instead, I received, "Pamela, you will have to walk this one out by faith, learn how to rest and how to delegate. It is time to invest in yourself spiritually, emotionally, physically, and trust the process."

Initially, I was upset. I wanted sympathy and compassion. Through reflection, I realized my mentor was right. I had to become my own advocate and learn how to invest in myself. My self-investment journey began with YouTube videos by Pastor Keith Moore, Mr. Les Brown, Dr. Billye Brim, Terry Seville Foy, and Bob Proctor. During these videos, I took lots of notes. I read those notes over and over again.

It is important to note that self-Investment always starts within and grows. My favorite book says, "a strong spirit sustains a man". (Proverbs 18:14). You cannot be sustained when you are empty and weak. Self-Investment will build a strong spirit, and it is the strong spirit that will sustain a person.

"Pamela, call things that are not as though they were. Live as If you are already there", my spiritual father told me. I began to journal my dreams and goals. What would I do when I was up and around? I would close my eyes and imagine I was there. Next, I began to say "Yes" when people wanted to help me. Instead of feeling guilty, I felt gratitude. Gratitude will change your attitude. Once that changes, good will follow.

We have to learn to change the trajectory of our lives. This begins where we are at with whatever we have. Below is a list of nine ways you can begin your journey of self-investment.

## 1. Join Automobile University.

Check this out... A study done by the University of Southern California showed that if a person drives 12,000 miles a year. (Which is the equivalent to most rush hour commutes to work and home again.) This person could acquire the equivalent of two years of college education in three years, simply by listening to educational information in your car.

Listening to podcasts and audiobooks is all that it takes. Bonus tip for you, most successful people find guidance and inspiration through the pages of a book.

## 2. Dare to dream!

Visualize. Sit down and see yourself with your dream fulfilled. What does that look like, feel like, sound like etcetera? Take time to experience it. Your subconscious mind doesn't know the difference between faux or real. This will activate your Reticular Activating System (RAS) causing the Law of Attraction to go to work for you.

The Law of Attraction is a universal law. Simply put, it is the ability to attract into our lives what we are focusing on. The Law of Attraction uses the power of our marvelous mind to materialize our thoughts into reality. In basic terms, all thoughts turn into things eventually. This is echoed in the definition of the Hebrew word Davar: meaning words or things.

## 3. Vision Boards.

As my body healed, I used vision boards to help keep my dreams and goals in front of me. Mr. Les Brown says, "Your blessings are looking for you". Vision Boards keep those blessings in the front of our minds and hearts. A Vision Board is a personal reminder of where we want to be. They help us identify and clarify our dreams and goals. Vision Boards are tangible and help us focus on our future.

## 4. Morning Rituals (routine)

For years, I lost the battle of the bed. Which came at a great cost to me, in the area of time and success. Here is an example. Pushing that snooze button for 30 minutes of extra sleep will cost 10 waking hours every month. Successful people across the board choose to guard their mornings. They cherish those as hours to invest in themselves while everyone else hits the snooze button. Choose to start your day right.

- First spiritually, with prayer, devotions, gratitude, or meditation. Everything begins from within. When we begin our day right spiritually everything else will fall into place.

- Next your marvelous mind. Educate, stimulate, and think. Listen to an audiobook, learn a new language, watch a self-help video, or whatever sounds educational. Theta brain waves are strong in the morning. This is important for processing information (learning) and memories (appropriating what you learn)

- Finally, your body. Do something physical. Take a walk, run, dance, do yoga etcetera, AND hydrate. Physical activity makes you feel strong. When a person feels physically strong their self-worth goes up. Which means you are in a better state of mind for whatever the day brings. Exercise also improves your mindset and your emotional health.

## 5. Evening Rituals (routine)

Having an evening routine allows you the time and space to decompress physically and mentally. This ritual will allow you to unwind and organize your thoughts for tomorrow.

Choose to end your day right.

- First spiritually through meditation, gratitude, journaling, worship, or prayer. These activities will center you and activate peace.
- Next your marvelous mind. Organize and Review. Review your day and organize your tomorrow. Listening to or reading something inspirational is a great way to prepare the mind for rest.
- Finally, our body. Stretch, do gentle yoga, or just breathe. Our bodies need to unwind and release from the day. This will alert the body, "It is bedtime."

## 6. Learn and Grow.

"Live as if you were to die tomorrow. Learn as if you were to live forever." - Mahatma Ghandi. Is there a class you have been wanting to take? A language you want to learn. A new form of exercise you would like to try. Learning is a fabulous form of self-investment. The UCLA Basketball Coach, John Wooden said, 'When I am through learning then I am through." In other words, don't ever stop learning.

## 7. Accountability

Accountability will eliminate non-productive activities and behaviors that would normally be a distraction. I encourage you to find an accountability partner. Whether that be a coach, minister, mentor, or a fellow peer. An accountability partner will help us stay committed to our purpose.

## 8. Community - Where are my "peeps"?

No one needs to feel alone. When a person connects with a thriving community, they find a home. These communities can be found in masterminds, self-help communities, classrooms, health clubs, religious organizations, book clubs, etc. In today's world, many of these communities are virtual, making weekly gatherings very easy. Do not hesitate to self-invest your time, talent, and finances into these communities.

The benefits you will reap are worth the investment. I searched for years for a community that felt like a family. A community where we are united in thought and heart. I found this through The Power Voice and Thinking Into Results Communities. I promise you; it is priceless!

## 9. Arise and Build

As we begin to wrap up this chapter, I would like to reference a Master Builder from my favorite Book. His name is Nehemiah. Nehemiah was commissioned to rebuild the walls of Jerusalem. He gathered his team and went to work. They were ridiculed continuously! "You can't build this wall", "This wall is going to fall down", "little animals will crush this wall". Did Nehemiah and his team quit? No, they did not. Hear the words of Nehemiah, "I am doing a great work and I will not stop or come down!" Friend, it is time to 'Go build your wall! This is where our self-investment pays forward to the world.

- Create that Website
- Build the YouTube Channel
- Create that course
- Start that podcast
- Design that masterclass
- Build your online business
- Write that book

Why? Because you are a world changer. Your story and your voice matters.

If you don't Boss Your Lane who will?

Lives are hanging in the balance. Those lives are waiting for you, my friend.

Invest in yourself because you are here on purpose with a Purpose by Design, not by default. Now, go out there and be the Salt and the Light everywhere you go.

I have two FREE Self-Investment opportunities for you. Just go to my website www.purposewithpamela.com

Free Purpose by Design Mini Course (click on courses)

Download My Empowerment/Morning Routine (top of main page)

# About
# Dr. Pamela Henkel

Dr. Pamela Henkel is the Founder/CEO of Purpose with Pamela. She is the host and producer of the TV broadcast, "The Pamela Show", International radio show, and podcast "Purpose by Design." Pamela is a results coach, visionary author, inspirational speaker, and minister. Pamela loves to cheer people on to "Dream Again". If you are around her long, she will have you talking about your Purpose and making a vision board. Pamela is a motivator, and she will convince you that finding your Niche` is simple. Although success is a daily upward climb, Pamela will give you the strategies you need to succeed. Pamela will always be there cheering you on (pom-poms in hand LOL). Because your Best You is the Next You. Pamela shares her personal experiences, her education, and her life as a woman in leadership. Her "let's have coffee and chat" approach, will awaken your dreams and Purpose by Design.

Pamela and her husband James have been married since 1995. They have 6 beautiful children and one amazing Grand. Along with their dog Bailey, 3 cats, and 7 birds. Minnesota is where they call home.

https://www.purposewithpamela.com

# Success Strategies for Bossing Up in Business

## By Nadia Francois

Going into business is a huge leap of faith and financial risk that is sometimes frightening for a new entrepreneur. Having a background of over 20 years of building my business in the hair care industry I have learned that this journey is not for the weak or faint at heart. If you give up easily, this is not for you. Entrepreneurship is a lot of hard work and sacrifice. But on the other hand, it is one of the most rewarding occupations one can ever have. Freedom alone is what is most valuable to me. I am a single parent to four sons that I have raised on my entrepreneur's salary for the past 15 years and we have not missed a beat. So, to achieve the income required to maintain my household as a single parent, I had to BOSS UP!!

I bossed up in every area of my life including my spiritual life. I decided to put God first in life and business, and this was a game-changer. I then became very disciplined with my time, energy, and resources being more intentional with my business moves. I developed a strategy to help me generate an income that can always be increased with more effort yet sustainable when life happens. I discovered that the key to building a successful business required some essential elements no matter what industry or field. These strategies are as follows:

## Build on a Solid Foundation

In business there is room for error but not in ensuring that your business foundation is solid. When building a business, certain aspects cannot be overlooked, or half-done. These aspects include being recognized as a legitimate business. Registering with the city, state, and federal agencies that are relevant to your industry and obtaining a business license, setting up a business bank account and setting up tax accounts by consulting an accountant for the best choices in tax reporting, and determining your branding. Whether your business is for-profit or non for profit, these steps are very important.

## Operate using Policies & Procedures

Policies and procedures are essential in any business or organization making decision making, compliance, and employee management much easier. Policies and procedures serve as a roadmap for day-to-day operations. They help prevent confusion and disorders when unexpected events occur. Any business that has employees should have a clear set of policies and procedures breaking down the daily task step by step, along with an explanation of what to do on occasions where compliance and regulations are being violated. Most businesses have a regulatory agency that provides guidance on the rules and regulations of their industry. Policies and procedures also help set the level of expectation for conduct, performance, and behavior and provides guidance for employee management.

## Always have a Plan

If you stay ready, you won't have to get ready! Business can be a true rollercoaster ride at times and as the owner, you must be able to pivot and adjust to change at any time. Having a clear plan helps make this transition a smooth, well-executed one that your business can potentially profit from. A business plan is the most essential part of your business toolbox because it includes the plan for each leg of your business such as identifying your target audience, a clear financial plan with supporting documents, a marketing strategy, employee management, growth planning, and more. Business plans help you focus on your business goal and maps out your strategy to success. The business plan is also a vital part of securing funding for your business. Potential investors want to know that you have a solid plan to produce a return on their investment and if that plan does not work, that you have a backup plan

## Maintain a Positive Mindset

Over the years I have learned that the energy that you give to a certain situation is the energy that you will receive in return. So, approaching all things with a positive mindset will help produce positive outcomes. Mindset is everything and is very essential to the growth and success of your business. Taking the positive mindset approach is the key to moving forward even when the outcomes are not favorable. Risk-taking is very important and goes with the territory of being a business owner, therefore making it necessary to have the correct mindset. Optimism and positive thoughts drive success which is fueled by the information that we consume. The use of positive affirmations, listening to an uplifting and informative podcast or messages, and surrounding yourself with positive people that are doing big things can change a negative mindset into a positive mindset.

## Build and Cultivate Business Relationships

There are several areas where networking and building business relationships are important. Mentorship provides major help for novice entrepreneurs through positive feedback, answering important questions and genuine encouragement to stay focused. Secondly, industry professionals are valuable assets to your network. Industry professionals help you to stay abreast of regulations, changes, and opportunities in your area of expertise. The final valuable business relationship includes vendors that are specific to your business needs and will assist in business growth. The combination of these relationships within your network will help your business to grow and thrive. Nurturing and valuing these relationships by staying connected and showing support always makes for a strong bond and lasting impression that will have your business mentioned in rooms you have not set foot in.

## Be a Forever Learner

Lifelong learning is essential to business success. The world moves at such a fast pace one can easily fall behind in new trends and practices in business. Change is constant and we must continue to learn to adapt and pivot to grow and sustain in business. Enriching your mind with the knowledge necessary to remain relevant and recognized as an expert in your field is always the goal. Enrolling in continuing education courses, participating in webinars, and obtaining trending certifications are all ways to enhance your knowledge base and remain up to date in your field.

## Don't Despise Small Beginnings

Sometimes in business, we must crawl before we can walk but that doesn't mean that we won't arrive! Remember that small steps toward the goal are still progressing. Building a business in the early 2000s was rather difficult and very expensive. I had to be very resourceful and extremely disciplined. Everything costs but when starting small you must be very smart with your resources. Nowadays thanks to technology, information is readily available along with many tools that the business owner can implement themselves with a little practice. Don't despise small beginnings, if you have to create your own graphics or build your own website or sell from your trunk just DO IT!! Your hard work will pay off.

## Invest in your Business

Always remember most times to make money you must spend some money. Don't be cheap doing business, be smart. There are several investments we must make in our businesses from consultants to licensing, insurance, and inventory so it is very important that we spend wisely. Some tips to remember before spending large amounts include research the company, ask for reviews and examples of work, and pay through a secure source. Taking advantage of opportunities to invest in your business can seem overwhelming at times but is a necessary action that ensures business growth and sustainability.

Building your business on a solid foundation, operating with policies and procedures, always having a plan, maintaining a positive mindset, building professional relationships, being a forever learner, starting small, and investing in your business are key strategies to bossing up in business. In business, whatever you put into it is what you will get out of it. There are no shortcuts, but hard work definitely pays off. If you believe, you can achieve whatever it is you want to do in life.

# About
# Nadia Francois

**Nadia Francois**
**Business Strategist| Media Maven| Author**

Nadia Francois is a serial entrepreneur with a heart for people. A hairstylist by trade, Nadia holds current licenses in Cosmetology and Barbering and a B.S. in Business Administration. The Baton Rouge native began her entrepreneurial journey at the age of 19 and has used her experiences and knowledge to help other business owners start and grow their ventures. Nadia continues to thrive and expand in her beauty endeavors, Heiress Haircare Systems and Heiress Beauty Lounge Online Beauty Supply Boutique which she describes as her passion. Because "people may not always remember what you said but they will always remember how you made them feel." As the founder and Executive Director of SOE, she has developed a series of programs and workshops that contribute to personal and entrepreneurial growth. Under her leadership, SOE grew from what started as a group of friends who wanted to give countless acts of community service, into a thriving sisterhood that incorporates motivational and business workshops, youth confidence and esteem pageants, and mentorship. The beautypreneur and non-profit founder became a first-time author in August of 2018, publishing The Entrepreneur Activity Workbook as her first project, which is very close to her heart. She created this workbook to help entrepreneurs have a clear business plan and understanding of their business goals. After participating in two additional book projects, Nadia attained the esteemed recognition of International Best-Selling Author for Better Woman Better World Book One. Her latest writing project includes her own faith-based compilation, What's Your Superpower Anthology.

In December 2020, this trailblazer stepped out on faith and became the channel owner of What's Your Superpower TV (WYSP TV), which also houses her talk show by the same title on Exposure TV Network, Nadia and her guest hostesses interview powerhouse women and spotlight minority business owners. The WYSP TV Channel also houses five additional empowering series that span from cooking, spiritual wellness, talk shows, and wealth creation. In 2021, Nadia continues to enhance her digital footprint with the addition of Power Conversations Podcast and Power Conversations Magazine which are extensions of her media empire that caters to entrepreneurs and the advancement of their brands. July 26, 2021, Nadia's latest visionary book project, Powerful Affirmations for Fempreneurs, was released and ranked #1 on Amazon's Best Seller and New Releases lists. This goal-getter contributes her success to grace and mercy. Her number one assignment is being the mother and sole provider for her four sons, the driving force behind her persistent hustle and diligent pursuit of greatness. Follow her at www.nadiafrancois.com.

# Proficient Use of Behavior and Experience

## Exudes Excellence

### By Kristin Brooke

Being successful in life requires dedication, determination, action, and knowledge of self. Of these, the most often overlooked area is knowledge of oneself. Discovering how you or your team are perceived and learning to use those perceptions to your advantage is key to success in any arena. Playing the game of life without vision leads us to bumps and bruises from the challenges we encounter, rather than having our eyes wide open and playing with vital strengths to win in the game of life. Rather than trying to fit someone else's leadership mold, it behooves us to understand how we behave and how we are perceived. This awareness allows us to alleviate the tension of not fitting the standard. This awareness allows us, instead, to begin to define the standard. From there, we can seek other behavioral styles to create a well-rounded team. When you uncover your behavioral style and play to your strengths, you will naturally begin to see success come into your life quickly.

One day, I received a call that was life changing. A few hours prior, my then one-year-old daughter's father had left work on a Wednesday... At 5pm, he hopped onto his motorcycle and before he could make it from the parking lot to the road, he fell over and died. He was 38 years old and at 5 pm on a Wednesday, a heart attack immediately ended his life. As I faced the reality of being a single mother yet again, I was angry and sad. The trauma of losing a man I once loved and the fragility of how significantly life could change in an instant was overwhelming. Although I had been through other traumas like miscarriage, divorce, and even sexual assault, this trauma, this new challenge, rocked me to my core. Because now, I did not get to decide. My destiny had changed in a moment. Despite all we had been through, that phone call dashed even the smallest ray of hope to raise our family together. The chance to see my daughter and her father bond, to go to daddy-daughter dances, bowling, and see her off on her first date, was lost in an instant. I began to imagine what conversations might be like with her daughter in 4 years when she heads to school and sees two-parent families and how she will cope with sharing her father's death among her peers. I initially cringed at the idea of telling my daughter that her father was dead in the future. At work, I was perceived as rebellious and careless when it came to routine and procedures. Unable to fully grasp how I was being perceived, I continued to focus on my team of people and clients. Paperwork became an afterthought. My reality shifted as I saw more value in people than tasks. I rejected the idea that rules can be more important than the impact we make on people. For some, thriving means maintaining and socializing with people while others thrive in maintaining compliance and quality. At the time, I could not value other perspectives. I did not know how to utilize my behavioral style to achieve the goals laid out before me without feeling tension.

As other managers and executives poured resources and mentors into me, I viewed it as humiliating and potential microaggressions. What my leadership and I did not understand was that my behavioral style had shifted due to the trauma. Now valuing life more than ever, I adopted the attitude that rules are a guidepost and interacting with people should come first because no moment is guaranteed. Unable to communicate my need for a position that allowed me even more people interaction, less paperwork, and routine, my strengths went unaddressed because I did not know how to voice them for myself along the way. After completing a behavioral DISC assessment with Eric Thomas' Extreme Execution coaching and training team I was able to understand and explain clearly what was happening at work. Before I learned behavioral style, my work environment felt pressured and suffocating to me. Despite being a people person, I could not express my requirements to thrive, and I did not know how to frame who I am as a strength to my counterparts and in my family. My story reminds us that if we cannot enumerate our strengths our full value is not shared with others. It is important to know and be able to communicate our strengths to ensure professional success.

Even more so, when faced with a sea of challenges, what behaviors would come naturally to you and your team even when the waves of trauma and grief surround you? Does your team understand how clients may perceive them? Even as we face challenges that hold us back from our fullest potential, even after we find ourselves recovering from traumas that others don't survive, do we know how others see us? Most people do not. Most people imagine, hope, and at times even strive to be something that is not authentically them because we tell ourselves we can change without embracing the actual strength of who we are in the moment. We hope our strengths fit the challenge instead of knowing for sure what our strengths are and who on our team can balance with us to become a force to be reckoned with.

When we as leaders learn there is nothing wrong with each person's behavioral style, we can mitigate turnover and the financial and emotional toll of termination. Why are some of us seen as driven, while others are viewed as patient, outgoing, or perfectionists? It is because we naturally have varying behavioral styles and life experiences that have shaped us. So, how do we effectively assess our team so that we can take action to ensure the right people are in the right places? We can utilize the qualitative and quantitative data that is provided from the DISC assessment and a knowledgeable coach. With that coach, we allow our team to understand that the challenges we face are building emotional strength, resilience, and behaviors that help us become power players. Eleanor Roosevelt was a huge proponent of looking fear in the face; she said, "We gain strength each time we look fear in the face and say, I survived this horror, I can face the next thing that comes my way." Knowing one's behavioral style allows us to optimize their usefulness and eliminate corporate waste of time and resources. We can position our companies and even our families to understand how to proactively build resilience to bounce back from difficult times when we allow the opportunity to thrive in our behavioral strengths.

Often, personal and professional challenges overlap. With approximately 70 percent of the world's population experiencing a lifetime trauma, and about 1.5 million children losing one or both parents by 15, trauma will undeniably impact our team and our outcomes. This prevalence of trauma and challenges means that leaders are very likely to encounter the effects of trauma themselves or have a member of their professional team that is affected. In business, we can proactively prepare by placing people on teams where their strengths shine. Not only does this allow confidence to be built, but it builds resilience also. Trauma and challenges do not define us as a team or individually, but they shape how we view our place of business, the world, our reactions, and behaviors.

No matter what someone has been through, people desire to share their strengths. A strong leader understands that each person exhibits behavior types, and that value is inherent and ever-present if placed in the proper roles within the team. Knowing who on your team is the natural-born decision-maker versus the analytical quality-focused person, or the outgoing, people-focused person versus the person that is supportive and steady with completing tasks, can allow your business to flourish with less tension and greater team satisfaction because everyone has a purpose tied to their strengths. TD Jakes said, "If you can't figure out your purpose, figure out your passion. For your passion will lead you right into your purpose." Once we uncover that passion and align our natural strengths, we can easily and joyfully share immense value with others. A person's purpose can be identified by recognizing their passions and strengths when doing what they love. When helping yourself or others uncover purpose, ask the following questions: What makes you happiest? What do people often thank you for, are impressed by, or say are your talents? Is there a cause for which you would be willing to fight? Do you have experiences that could help others? The answers to these questions along with a DISC assessment can better assist a company's success.

Experience breeds success. Whether it is failures, minor setbacks, or even trauma, a leader that knows their team's strengths will have more experiences with profitable outcomes. Rick Warren said in The Purpose Driven Life that "Experience is not what happens to you. It is what you do with what happens to you. Don't waste your pain; use it to help others." When you or your team members work in their passion and enjoy what they are doing, the result is joy and peace for everyone. We can more readily achieve accountability from our team and ourselves when we remember that success is defined individually based on beliefs, experiences, and behavioral styles. Knowing and understanding everyone's strengths makes way for team success with ease and confidence by alleviating anxiety to fit what is not natural. It also encourages excitement to achieve group goals. The mentality on how things should get done can hinder or help a team but placing the proper behaviors and strengths in the appropriate roles allows the team to soar in group and individual achievement.

Execution within each person's natural strengths, allows the company, the team, and each individual to succeed with ease. As team leaders, we can align our team with the corporate vision by learning about behavioral styles and ensuring that we are placing people in positions that allow them to utilize their strengths. Uncovering our strengths and behavioral techniques within our personal and professional lives will enable us to have more efficient and effective communication and reduce friction within the team. Communication based on how it is received within a group allows everyone to thrive because the information is conveyed in ways that all team members can find helpful. Goals will be achieved steadily and completed with proper systems and quality checks in place, leaving the team and clients motivated, inspired, and excited.

# About
# Kristin Brooke

**Kristin Brooke** combines a love for diplomacy and justice with compassion and dedication to success. She holds a Bachelor's Degree in Political Science from Michigan State University. Kristin passionately believes in helping others achieve success, as shown by her dedicated commitment as past chair for Southfield Young Professionals and Ambassador for Southfield Chamber of Commerce. Kristin Brooke is known for her resilience in overcoming many obstacles in her life, most prominently, her grit in sharing her own experience of sexual assault and escaping human trafficking. Kristin Brooke's dedication and commitment to helping others overcome their challenges moved to the forefront after experiencing the loss of loved ones and the end of her career in hospitality sales and management. Kristin Brooke is the author of "I Choose Joy: An Overcomer's Guide Through A Secret Journey," Certified Les Brown Speaker, Certified Extreme Execution Coach, and Certified Trauma and Resilience Trainer. Kristin firmly believes success can be found in the power of mindset, overcoming fears, and taking action. Kristin Brooke passionately advocates for others through writing, speaking, and entertaining. When Kristin Brooke is not writing to change worldviews book-by-book, she enjoys dancing, traveling, and comedic entertainment.

**Kristin Brooke. Author. Advocate. Champion**.

# Worldwide Wealth
# Digital Currency Conversations

Crypto "BIG BAG" Karmen

I n 2021, there are so many ways to create wealth outside of the traditional workforce. My name is Karmen Trice, and I was first introduced to Cryptocurrency right before the pandemic. Because of budget cuts, I lost 2 of my clients, had to close the doors to my salon, and was left figuring out how I would/could continue to build the financial dynasty that I had set out to build. I knew I still needed to provide for my family. I happened to be in Mexico finishing up some business and decided to sit in on a cryptocurrency seminar that I found very intriguing. Once I got home, I immediately followed up with the instructor to set up a time to begin learning how to trade and navigate the foreign exchange market. While learning, I made $700.00 on my first trade and that was all I needed to decide to go even further. As my understanding, as well as earnings, increased, I began telling everyone that I knew, about how easy it was for me to apply the principles and make money. Many people thought it was a scam, while others saw it as an opportunity to learn a new skill set during the pandemic, with the hopes of not returning to work. The people that thought it was a scam had dealings with people that unfortunately used the foreign exchange to mislead people. There will always be the select few that ruin the good in anything.

- *What is Cryptocurrency? According to Time magazine, Cryptocurrency is a type of currency that's digital and decentralized. Cryptocurrencies can be used to buy and sell things, and their potential to store and grow value has also caught the eye of many investors.*

- *There are thousands of different cryptocurrencies available today. The most popular — and the original — is Bitcoin, which was created in 2009. Other common cryptocurrencies include Ethereum, XRP, and Bitcoin Cash. Each of these currencies serves a different purpose, with some optimized for use in place of cash, and others designed for private, direct transactions.*

Bitcoin happens to be the most popular coin that most of the altcoins pattern themselves after. In this wealth conversation, we talk a lot about Bitcoin. Bitcoin is a digital monetary system. Instead of "dollars," the unit of currency is referred to as a "Bitcoin." Like traditional money, bitcoins can be used to store and transfer value among other bitcoin users within the bitcoin community. Bitcoin is considered a cryptocurrency. The currency utilizes cryptography for the management and creation of the currency.

There is a bitcoin protocol, which resides primarily on the internet. It's possible to utilize the protocol on your smartphone, computer, tablet, and other computing devices. It's easily accessible to anyone with commonly available technology.

Essentially, anything that can be done with conventional currencies can be done with bitcoins. It's possible to buy and sell goods and services, give money to other individuals or organizations, or even provide credit to others. Bitcoins can be bought, sold, and exchanged for other currencies.

Bitcoin is considered by many to be the ideal currency. It's secure, free from borders, and very fast.

Bitcoins are virtual. There are no physical bitcoins to be found anywhere in the world. The bitcoins are merely an idea to convey value. All that's required is that other bitcoin users accept the same premise.

Interestingly, bitcoins are a peer-to-peer system. There is no central authority, computer server, or control point.

## History

As with the founding of Facebook, the history of bitcoin is a little fuzzy, but these are the high points:

1. In 2008, someone named "Satoshi Nakamoto" published a paper titled, "Bitcoin: A Peer-to-Peer Electronic Cash System." To the best of anyone's knowledge, the author's name is an alias. It has even been suggested that several people wrote the article.

- The premise combined the previous technologies and philosophies of HashCash and b-money. The idea was to create an electronic monetary system that was completely decentralized.

- The primary innovation was a global accounting process that would take place every 10 minutes. This would allow the entire network of users to reach a consensus regarding the previous 10 minutes of transactions worldwide. The advantage of this process is the elimination of users double-spending their currency.

- Previous attempts and electronic currency dealt with the double-spend issue by clearing transactions through a centralized clearing system. This is considered a weakness because a centralized location could be hacked.

2. The actual bitcoin network was launched in 2009. The first issuance of bitcoins was 50 coins. The value of the coins was negotiated by the users at that time.

3. The first notable transaction was 10,000 bitcoins for two Papa John's pizzas. The transaction was indirect and did not include Papa John's as one of the involved parties. The first bitcoins weren't worth much!

4. There has only been one significant exploited vulnerability. In 2010, 184 billion bitcoins were created. The transaction was quickly noticed, reversed, and the flaw was removed from the system.

5. By the beginning of 2013, over 1,000 merchants were accepting bitcoins as payment. Many charities also began accepting bitcoins for donations. The Internet Archive gave employees the option to receive their salaries in the form of bitcoins.

6. Bitcoins have ranged in value from less than a penny to over $1,200. The value of a bitcoin is very volatile. The value in November 2015 was roughly $400. Who knows where it will be in a few months?

7. The first government seizure of bitcoins occurred in June of 2013. The DEA seized 11.02 bitcoins as part of a raid and listed the bitcoins as a seized asset.

8. Also in 2013, Vancouver, Canada became the location of the first bitcoin ATM. The ATM allowed the purchasing of bitcoins.

9. In 2021 Many larger companies are now accepting bitcoins. These include Overstock, Zynga, several Las Vegas casinos, Amazon, some Burger Kings locations, Dell, Microsoft, Paypal, Tesla, and many more. There are even bitcoin ATMs and financial product on the U.S. Commodity Futures Trading Commission.

I can say, early on, Bitcoins had a somewhat shady history. If you recall, the infamous Silk Road drug website relied on the use of bitcoins. However, the use of bitcoins is becoming more accepted, and even mainstream companies are now getting involved. Even the US stock market has investment options for those interested in bitcoins.

*"I do think Bitcoin is the first [encrypted money]*

*that has the potential to do something like change the world."*

*- Peter Thiel, Co-Founder of Paypal*

# The Advantages of
# Using Bitcoin

Bitcoin is a unique currency. It's completely virtual. Bitcoin is unsupported by any central bank or other authority. It's not the official currency of any country. Yet all of these are both advantages and disadvantages. Whether or not bitcoin is an advantage for you is dependent on your situation.

Bitcoins have several advantages over conventional currency:

1. Bitcoins can't be physically stolen. There is nothing physical to steal. In theory, however, someone could force you at gunpoint to send your bitcoins to someone else.

2. It's possible to avoid taxes. The onus is on the taxpayer, to be honest about bitcoin transactions. There are many disagreements regarding the government's ability to track bitcoins through the system. Most of the investigative activity regarding bitcoins is centered on major crimes, such as drug trafficking.

3. Bitcoins are extremely flexible. You can pay anyone in the world at any time. Holidays, exchange rates, borders, and the time of day are irrelevant. Bitcoins have far greater flexibility than any other type of currency system.

4. There are no transactional costs. As there is no central authority, transactional costs are unnecessary. All of the computers on the system, including your own, are doing the heavy lifting. There's no one else to pay. You could send your child a million dollars worth of bitcoins without it costing a single penny. Try doing that with your local bank or PayPal.

   - However, providing a small transactional fee will guarantee that payments are processed more quickly.

5. Privacy is maintained. Your personal information isn't required as part of the transaction. There's no risk of identity theft. The entire process is encrypted. Keep in mind that it's not entirely anonymous. All transactions are recorded and posted for anyone to view. However, your name isn't publicly associated with your transactions.

6. Transactions cannot be reversed. This is good news for merchants, but maybe a disadvantage for consumers.

7. The bitcoin code is open source. There are no secrets, other than the identities of the parties involved in the transactions.

It's easy to see why bitcoins are useful in certain situations. You have a greater degree of privacy and a lack of transactional costs. Bitcoins can be used at any time and on any day. You can still make or accept payment on Christmas day at 2:00 AM.

## Disadvantages of Bitcoins

There's a little bad news, too. Bitcoins have certain disadvantages. The lack of governmental regulation and the limited supply of bitcoins create challenges. In addition, considering the total number of retail establishments, only a small percentage of them accept bitcoins.

Consider these disadvantages:

1. The value of bitcoins is very volatile. The number of bitcoins is limited, and demand can vary from one day to the next. So, the value of a bitcoin can change very quickly. It's possible to earn or lose a tremendous amount of value very quickly.

2. Bitcoins are not widely accepted at this time. While the number of merchants and individual users is increasing, bitcoins still are an uncommon form of currency. Bitcoins are becoming more mainstream all the time, though. The Federal Reserve Board reports that the number of bitcoin users is doubling every 8 months.

3. It's possible to lose your bitcoin wallet and all of your bitcoins. It's crucial to keep a backup of your wallet

file. A hard drive crash, virus, or corrupted file will cause your bitcoins to become permanently orphaned. You can never get them back. No one else can ever possess them, either.

4. There's a lack of buyer protection. If you pay for a product prior to receiving it, there's no recourse if the product isn't delivered. However, there are third-party escrow services that can protect buyers. If you're paying in advance with bitcoin, you may want to use one of these services.

5. Bitcoins make it easier to commit crimes, including fraud. The anonymity of bitcoin makes it attractive to those engaged in illegal activity. However, cash is still more widely used in illegal activities than bitcoins.

It's important to consider how the disadvantages of bitcoins dovetail with your situation. It's easy to lose all of your bitcoins if you're careless. You can also lose a lot of money quickly if the demand for bitcoins drops sharply.

## Liquidity of Bitcoins

The bitcoin system is capped at 21 million bitcoins. Currently, there are roughly 14,800,000 bitcoins in circulation. There is a lot of speculation about what will happen to the value when the 21 million-bitcoin limit is reached.

In general, the US stock market is very liquid. You can quickly sell most stocks, bonds, or mutual fund shares at the going rate without concern. There's always someone willing to buy from you or sell to you, provided the price is right.

Given the limited number of bitcoins and users, it's not as easy to sell your bitcoins if you wish to cash out. Even if you can find a buyer, even relatively modest transactions can create volatility in the price for a bitcoin.

## • How Bitcoins are Created

Bitcoins are created through a process called "mining." The first computer to solve a puzzle receives a certain number of bitcoins. Unfortunately, many other computers are competing against yours. And you probably don't have a computer that can compete.

Mining bitcoins is extremely challenging. There are companies with powerful computer networks designed to solve the puzzles. The typical home user has no chance of winning.

When a puzzle is solved, bitcoins are created and awarded to the owner of the winning computer. The number of bitcoins provided decreases as the number of bitcoins in circulation gets closer to the 21 million-bitcoin limits.

With an adequate computer, the puzzles take approximately 10 minutes to solve. The winning solution requires quadrillions of operations per second. The difficulty of the puzzles can increase or decrease to match the current environment. Winning computers now utilize dedicated circuits rather than software to solve the puzzles.

Most of those competing spend more on electricity than they win in bitcoins!

How to Sell Your Bitcoins

There are several options for selling your bitcoins. The process can be quite simple or a little more complicated, depending on the method. More options are becoming available as bitcoins become more popular.

Selling bitcoin online:

1. Some websites offer direct trades. A few examples include Coinbase, Local Bitcoins, and BitBargain. Most direct trade sites require you to register as a seller. This means you have to reveal your identity. The website will post your wish to sell your bitcoins and buyers can accept your offer.

2. Exchange trades are another way to sell your bitcoins online. You'll still have to identify yourself, but exchange trades require less work on your part. You list the

number of bitcoins you wish to sell and your desired price. When someone else places a purchase order that matches your requirements, the exchange will complete the transaction.

- Most exchanges charge a small fee of roughly 0.2%.

- Many investors choose to store their bitcoins on exchanges since their only interest in bitcoins is speculative. While the bitcoin system is essentially hack proof, this isn't true for the exchanges. You could lose all of your bitcoins by storing your funds on an exchange site that gets hacked.

3. Peer-to-Peer trading marketplaces can also be used to sell your bitcoins online. The most popular sites are Brawker and Purse. Instead of selling your bitcoins for a more conventional currency, you can exchange your bitcoins for products you wish to purchase. Consider this example of peer-to-peer trading:

- Mary posts her Amazon wish list to the trading marketplace, along with the desired discount. The discount can be up to 25%.

- John wishes to buy Mary's bitcoins and is agreeable to her terms. He will then purchase the items and have them delivered to Mary's address.

- When the goods have been delivered, Mary will then notify the marketplace and the bitcoins will be released to John. The exchange takes a small fee, and everyone is happy.
- It's also common for the purchaser to purchase a gift card instead of purchasing the goods directly.

The advantage of selling online is convenience and safety. The websites do the heavy lifting for you. There can be a fee for using these websites, but it's minimal. Selling online is the most popular option for unloading bitcoins, but it's not the only option.

You can also sell your bitcoins in person:

1. Selling your bitcoins in person can be the simplest solution. All that's required is to scan a QR code on the other person's phone and accept your cash payment. Nothing could be simpler.

2. Agree on the price. The common practice is to make use of one of the bitcoin exchanges to determine the price. There are apps available to determine pricing.

3. Attend bitcoin meet-ups. At meetup.com, you can find others interesting in bitcoin. It can be a great place to buy and sell bitcoins.

4. Be safe if you're dealing with cash. A public place is much safer than an abandoned warehouse. You're not doing anything illegal, so stay visible. Bring along a friend, too. If possible, sell your bitcoins to a friend or family member.

5. There are websites available to help you find local bitcoin buyers. The most popular website is localbitcoins.com. Buyers and sellers are rated based on their previous transactions.

There are several ways to sell bitcoins, from established online platforms to local meetups. Selling your bitcoins can take some time, depending on the current demand in the marketplace. Remember to be safe when dealing with cash. A public place is a preferable option.

- How to Purchase Bitcoins

The options for purchasing bitcoins are similar to those for selling them. You're just on the other side of the transaction. Follow the same methods and do your research to ensure you're paying a fair price.

**How You Can Get Started**

Now that you know how to purchase and sell bitcoins, you may wonder how to get started. There's little to be done once you have the software on your electronic device. The software is referred to as a wallet.

Get started with bitcoins in just a few minutes:

1. Create a bitcoin wallet. There is a variety of wallets available for different platforms: mobile, web, and desktop. Different wallets have different features. Be certain to understand the features and choose your wallet wisely.

2. Secure your wallet. It's important to back up your wallet regularly. Remember, if the file is lost, your bitcoins are lost forever, too.

- Encrypt your wallet. Encryption ensures that no one can use your wallet without knowing the password, including you. Use a password that you can remember.

- An offline wallet is safest. If your wallet is stored offline, only those with physical access to the storage location can gain access to your wallet. Online storage is inherently riskier.

3. Keep all software up to date. Just as with any other type of software, bugs can appear from time to time. Keep your software up to date and you'll always have access to the latest features.

4. Obtain bitcoins.

- Buy bitcoins from an exchange.
- Accept bitcoins as payment for a good or service.
- Purchase bitcoins directly from another party.

That's all there is to it. There are countless online resources available to fill in the details. There are also many physical books on the subject. Much of the necessary information will depend on the wallet you choose. You can quickly learn all you need to know to use bitcoin as a currency.

## Bitcoins as an Investment

Investing in bitcoins is becoming more popular. Many millionaires have been created through the buying, holding, and selling of this currency. It's also possible to lose a lot of money. Bitcoin is becoming more mainstream every year, and even Wall Street is taking an interest.

There are two primary ways to invest in bitcoin at this time:

1. The Bitcoin Investment Trust. If you want to invest in bitcoins but leave the decisions to the experts, this is one option. Other similar investment options are popping up. You don't have to worry about

maintaining a bitcoin wallet or make decisions about when to buy or sell.

2. Invest directly in bitcoins. This is very similar to investing in any other currency. The low volume of bitcoins ensures significant volatility. From mid-September 2015 to early November 2015, bitcoin prices nearly doubled!

- If you have a strong stomach, it's possible to make a lot of money with bitcoins. However, it's questionable whether there is any way to make accurate predictions about the value of bitcoins. Many websites are claiming the ability to predict bitcoin prices. None, however, has a proven record of accomplishment.

- Many experts consider investing in bitcoins to be similar to gambling.

Currency investing is always exciting and rarely predictable. Bitcoin investing is even more so. It's definitely not the place to put your entire nest egg. However, if you're bold and stay informed, bitcoin is one way to invest with high risk.

## Conclusion

Bitcoin is a unique currency and community. The users of bitcoin are often attempting to avoid the prying eyes of others. It appeals to conspiracy theory types. However, bitcoin is also growing into a respectable and acceptable form of currency. Larger companies and banks are becoming more accepting of and interested in bitcoin.

Consider your situation and determine if bitcoin makes sense in your financial life. If you would like to learn more about Cryptocurrency, you can contact Karmen Trice at karmen@karmentricellc.com.

# About
# Crypto "BIG BAG" Karmen

Karmen Trice is a software engineer and serves as a worldwide consultant to many hospital systems. Karmen Graduated from Lindenwood University, where she received a BA in science technology.

Shortly after working in the field of information technology, Karmen launched her very own self-titling consulting agency, Karmen Trice LLC. This was an opportunity to travel the world gaining additional knowledge to keep current with the integration of medicine and technology. As a software engineer, Karmen was afforded the chance to program medical software for some of the world's top healthcare systems. The software captured the patients' medical records, provider compliance, patient safety, and much more.

While owning and managing her consulting agency, Karmen has also opened Worldwide Wealth better known as 3W (digital currency academy), and a home health agency. Karmen is also a 3x author, an International best-selling author, a tax service corporation, and the Karmen Kloset Boutique that serves both men and women. Karmen among many others has deemed herself a serial entrepreneur.

# Quick Guide to Turning Your Vision Into a Nonfit Organization

## By Daphine Priscilla Brown-Jack

S o, you have a vision, and you want to change the world or just make a difference in your community, ah ha the first thought comes to mind, *let's start a nonprofit.*

Let me first be honest with you. It can be difficult, and you can't do it alone. I am speaking from experience.

The first thing you want to do is not think dollar signs but think about how you can be a beacon in your community and put a dent in changing the world. In other words, your focus is your mission and vision, not money!

In this quick guide, I am going to provide you with some quick tips on how to build your nonprofit from the ground up.

**Objective:**

1.  Teach you how to create a master plan
2.  Tell you the documents you need to have before applying for your 501(c)3

3. Explain what is the 1023EZ – Streamlined Application for Recognition of Exemption Under Section 501(c)3

4. Explain what happens after you get approved

## SO, LET'S BEGIN OUR JOURNEY TO CHANGING THE WORLD!

### The Master Plan

The average timeline for a nonprofit to start seeing the money is usually between two and five years.

When I was thinking about doing a nonprofit, I started researching anything that had something to do with nonprofits. **STOP STAY CALM!**

The first thing you want to do is create a master plan. A master plan consists of 10 important reasons why your nonprofit will make a difference in the community.

1. Mission Statement – is a short statement of why your organization exists, what its overall goal is, identifying the goal of its operation; what kind of product or service it provides. – WIKIPEDIA

2. Vision Statement – is an inspirational statement of an idealistic emotional future of your nonprofit. WIKIPEDIA

3. Core Value – a word that describes your nonprofit and can use them in a sentence that relates to your mission.

4. Statement for Sponsor – is telling how your nonprofit can have a successful partnership.

5. Brand Value Statement – tells why your nonprofit is important

6. Brand Culture – can be defined as the inherent DNA of your nonprofit brand and it tells how your brand can solve a problem in our society.

7. Purpose Objective – list at least four objectives as to why your nonprofit exists.

8. Brand Uniqueness – list at least six words or phase that makes your nonprofit different.

9. SWOT – S- Strength (9 words); W – Weakness (8 words); O – Opportunity (9 words); T – Threat (8 words). Think of words that describe your SWOT.

10. Value Proposition (VP) and Unique Selling Point (USP) – VP is a promise of value to be delivered to your program or services. USP is the marketing strategy of informing the community and/or clients about your brand is greater. List three VP words; Make VP statement; List three USP words; Make a USP Statement.

Add to your master plan 10 strategic partners; 10 centers of influence; list 7 short-term goals (3-6 months); list 9 long-term goals (6 months – 2 years); prepare a five-year projected budget; list of potential board of directors. My recommendation is four to nine board members.

If you choose to have family members on your board, I recommend no more than two. Make sure you select board members who are part of the community and people who can relate to your mission and vision.

**Required Documents Before the Official Filing for Tax Status**

- Article of Incorporation (Certification of Formation - Texas) and you must have your official board members selected.
- By-laws
- Fundraising Policy
- Conflict of Interest Policy
- Contributions and Donations Policy

**DO NOT APPLY FOR AN EIN BECAUSE ONCE YOUR TAX STATUS IS APPROVE IRS WILL ASSIGN ONE TO YOUR NONPROFIT.**

**Streamlined Application for Recognition of Exemption Under Section 501(c)3 – 1023-EZ**

A new Form 1023-EZ was released in July 2014 to help smaller organizations seeking exempt status. Upon approval, the organization will receive a determination letter from the IRS. The determination letter provides written assurance that the organization qualifies to receive tax-deductible contributions.

## What is the 1023-EZ Form?

In response to complaints about severe delays in approving exempt applications, the IRS issued Form 1023-EZ in July 2014. This form is significantly easier and shorter than Form 1023. The IRS promises to approve these applications within 6-8 weeks of filing. The Form 1023-EZ must be completed and filed online. An eligibility worksheet must be completed to determine whether an organization is eligible to use Form 1023-EZ. In general, organizations must have gross revenue below $50,000 and total assets below $250,000 to qualify for the 1023-EZ. Private Foundations do not qualify for the 1023-EZ. Form 1023-EZ should take no more than one hour to prepare.

## Congratulations in advance for your 501(c)3!!!!!!!

## Officially Approved

Now that you are official, I would like to share three things that you need to know!

1. Do not become overwhelmed with the many nonprofit information that you will begin to get after you are approved.
2. Find one good nonprofit resource (National Counsel of Nonprofit) and select your state.
3. Your nonprofit is now our nonprofit. Although you founded the nonprofit, it now belongs to anyone who has become involved.

As I stated earlier, I begin researching how to start a nonprofit, but I still needed the guidance to help me build a successful solid nonprofit.

Here are a few helpful tools and information to get you started:

- Get a website (Wix works well for me). If you are doing it yourself, visit other nonprofit websites to get some suggestions such as www.preventionzoneinc.org. If you don't know how to build a website, stay in your LANE and hire someone to build your website.
- Register with GuideStar www.guidestar.org
- Register with TechSoup www.techsoup.org
- After you register with TechSoup, apply for a $10,000 ad grant from Google for Nonprofit

Now you have it, a quick guide to starting a nonprofit.

Let us do a recap of the objectives:

1. You should know how to put together a master plan for your mission and vision.

2. You should be able to put together the necessary documents needed prior to applying for your 501(c)3.

3. You learned how to apply for your tax-exempt using the 1023EZ application and,

4. Utilizing tools and resources to get you off to a good start to serving your community and making an impact on the world.

**Reference**

https://www.wegnercpas.com/form-1023-form-1023-ez-faqs/

https://www.thegideongroupllc.com/

Wikipedia

# About
# Daphine Priscilla Brown-Jack

Daphine Priscilla Brown-Jack is from Houston, Texas. She is a retired Parole Officer, Parole and Author Consultant, Private Investigator, Author, Inspirational Speaker, Podcast Host "If Emmet Was Alive Today Podcast" owner and manager of Brown Jack Books, LLC, and the Founder and CEO of nonprofit Prevention Zone Inc.

Daphine has been speaking for over 20 years. She also taught Sixth Grade Social Studies for four years. She was the speaker for the Prison Entrepreneurship for a few years, she was one of the seminar speakers for the Ultimate Women Expo 2016, the keynote speaker at the Texas Voices Annual Conference 2016, a guest speaker at North Harris County Criminal Justice Association, Presenter at the InterNational Prisoners Family Conference 2019 and has spoken at other local conferences. She has served as a panelist at various conferences. She has been a guest on a radio show, Conscious Mindset KPFT 90.1FM, BlogTalkRadio Show with Funky Writer, Source Nation with Kathy B., Janeane Bernstein with Get the Funk Out Radio Show, Gospel Radio Nation with Dr. Lorelle Strong Rich Show, Real Talk with Dr. Lisa Talley on Rhema Gospel Radio KOER 101.5FM and guest on Life is Not Complicated, You Are Podcast with Carlos Wallace. She has appeared in the February 2016 issue of Women of Distinction Magazine She has hosted and emceed many church and secular events as well as being a DJ on internet radio. Daphine also has performed in local stage plays.

Daphine has various topics she speaks about and enjoys speaking to women, men, and youth. She can be able to articulate her expertise on parole and the criminal justice system (plea bargaining, bonding, court procedures, etc.).

Some of her latest topics are "Keeping Life Simple", "Face Your Fears, Accept your Fears, and Move Around", just to name a few.

She wrote her first book titled, "**The Other Side of the Story**". It was published on April 9, 2015. On September 28, 2017, Earthshine Media announced that "The Other Side of the Story" has been named a Winner in the **John E Weaver Excellent Reads Award for Non-Fiction: Inspirative.**

She currently volunteers for the Houston Livestock Show and Rodeo, the Houston Art Festival, and the Social Media Ambassador for the Mayor's Office of Special Events. She is a member of the Non-Fiction Writers, Story Circle Network, North Harris County Criminal Justice Association, the Academy of Criminal Science and a former mentor for Pass the Torch, and a former member of Triple "D" Society Club.

She earned a B. S. in Public Affairs with a concentration in Administration of Justice and a Master's in Public Administration both from Texas Southern University and Certification in Nonprofit Management at Texas A & M-College Station. Daphine is currently pursuing her second master's in Criminal Justice Leadership and Management from Sam Houston State University. Daphine enjoy astronomy, traveling, different genres of music, stage plays, and enjoying life. Daphine is a wife and mother of four children two boys and two girls. Three live in Texas and one lives in California.

Social Media

Facebook:

https://www.facebook.com/DaphinePriscillaBrownJack/

Twitter: daphinebjack,

Instagram: DaphineJack

Website: www.daphinebjack.com

Press Release:

http://www.prweb.com/releases/DaphinePriscillaBrownJack/TheOtherSideoftheStory/prweb12691840.htm

Women of Distinction Magazine

http://go.epublish4me.com/ebook/mobile?id=10087649#/0

# Quid Pro Quo

## By Angela Singletary

Y ou scratch my back and I'll scratch yours. But are you only scratching my back so I will scratch yours? Or do you care about my needs?

You may be thinking "Uh, doesn't she know she's in a book about business??". Touché my friend. I am, indeed, speaking about business. In fact, I get to share with you what is, in my opinion, the most important part of a business – giving stuff away! Of course, the point of business is to make money. I love making money! But one thing I love more is serving, and when I can serve via my passions and gifts it is all the more fulfilling for me!

#GiveItAllAway is more of a mindset than a program. When you are addressing your clients/audience you want a pure, warm connection. You don't want them to feel you are trying to sell them something (even though eventually you are). The best way to do that is to remain humble and serve. Connect with them via social media and newsletter. Respond to comments and messages. Reach out to those who show interest in your business and simply thank them – no ask at all. Thanks and asks should always be two different things.

Never thank someone then turn around and ask them for a sale (unless the client initiates of course). When you show your clients/audience that they are your priority and you are happy to serve them, then you will gain their trust and their interest (and hopefully soon after, their money!).

Every single business relies on selling and marketing in order to make it in this world. They may not literally purchase airspace or impressions, but if you run a business or have a professional career, then you are selling and marketing every single time you open your mouth. With that in mind – how's that going? In this day and age where the line between reality and virtual is hair-thin, you and your business are also one and the same. You can have your professional brand refined and pristine but if you have a gunky personal brand, you can do some damage to your business.

No matter how fancy or cool something is, people will be much more likely to buy it based on people than they will be based on want or need. Homo Sapiens are very social beings. We were made to connect with others and build things together as a community. This is one of the reasons that humans purchase things based on the people, not the product. Building relationships is a core element to a successful business or career. Networking, getting to know people, and expanding your reach is business 101. What isn't often included in the basics is *how* you should network and connect. Are you meeting people and looking for someone that you feel could help you out either now or in the future? Do you decide how you will invest time into someone based on their position and what you think they can do for you? If you are doing this, then this is the wrong way to network. Next time when you are meeting new people, look for someone that YOU can help. I promise you, you won't regret it.

Networking gives us the chance to find like-minded humans with who we can connect. Connecting could be just a friendly convo, partnering with a project, help to promote an event, etc. Connecting could also be recognizing when you can do something for someone else. That person that just opened up a similar business to you on the other side of town. Reach out to them and congratulate them. Give them a little support and love and that will come back to you. Success isn't pie and no one can take away what is truly meant for you. Not only are you putting deposits into the karma bank, but you are also forming true connections that may end up benefitting you in a way you never expected.

As a business owner/professional, it is absolutely key that you utilize whatever platforms you wish to be able to showcase your particular skill set and expertise. Give your client/audience a taste of what you do. Leave them with something they can apply or use, but just a little bit. This makes them feel special because you're sharing with them, and it also gives them a chance to see what you're all about.

Think about your relationship with your audience/client as if it were a loved one. You wouldn't appreciate it if cousin SueMae showed up out of nowhere and asked you to buy this new thing she's doing, now, would you? You don't want to be that person.

Be the person who is always encouraging and educating their clients and audience. The one that stays in touch with them and provides value to them at no cost.

The most beautiful part of the #GiveItAllAway plan is that not only will it build you a better, more loyal audience and client base, but it will make you a happier person! When you give joyfully you get tenfold in return. With the #GiveItAllAway plan, you would map out your campaigns/sales and then reverse engineer it to create your marketing plan. Make sure that for every ask you #GiveItAllAway at least four times. This doesn't mean give your packages for free. This doesn't mean you have to have a bunch of tchotchkes and stuff that no one really uses. Be intentional and strategic with content and you can have your clients/audience feeling like you are giving away state secrets when really, you're just giving the basics. Your people want to be engaged so connect with them on social media. Keep them up to date via the newsletter. Start a Facebook group (or whatever the cool thing is at the time you're reading this).

Lastly, I'll leave you with this to consider – Do unto others as you would have them do unto you. That sentence has always held so much power to me. When you zone into that kind of mindset, you can implement #GiveItAllAway easier. It's easier to see what someone wants, what you can do for them when you're looking through their eyes.

# About
# Angela Singletary

Standing at just under 4' tall, Angela has a commanding and comforting presence. Often told by strangers that they can tell her anything, she takes pride in showing others how she sees them in place of the negative self-image they carry around. Angela combines her love for people, her natural gift for counseling, and her passion for whole wellness in her Life & Wellness Coaching business, Purpose by Ang where she helps women over the age of 35 get unstuck and live their best life. She carries a bachelor's in Health and Wellness from Tulane University and certifications in Life Coaching, Health Coaching, Nutrition, Personal Training, Cognitive Behavioral Therapy, and Crystal Therapy.

Being a person with dwarfism she understands the struggles of marginalized communities and fights for equity, equality, accommodation, and advocacy.

Angela Singletary is also the owner of A Little Perspective - a communications company with a focus on advocacy for all humans with a disability.

Angela regularly conquers her fear of public speaking by addressing crowds to motivate, educate and inspire.

She interviews local, national, and international guests with a focus on disability awareness on her podcast, *A Little Perspective*. You can find it on YouTube, anchor.fm, and Spotify.

In her advocacy book series "A Little Perspective" she brings awareness through real-life stories of various members of marginalized communities. Authors contribute their experiences in their own words to bring *true* awareness to the world.

The first publication in the series, "ALP: Real Stories of Little Ladies", is a collection of chapters written by women with dwarfism about their real-life experiences pertaining to their stature. Women with dwarfism face very unique challenges in dating, social settings, growing up, employment, and even in the day-to-day activities. These stories are raw accounts, firsthand from each of these women and their particular struggles and, naturally, they're overcoming these challenges. It is our hope that these stories bring genuine awareness to the needs of the dwarfism community and help affect actual change to improve equality, equity, accommodations, and advocacy. These stories will also serve as encouragement for women of all sizes, shades, and shapes around the world.

"ALP: Special Delivery – Stories From Pregnancy to Toddlerhood" is a collection of chapters written by parents of children with dwarfism. These stories cover the period between pregnancy through toddlerhood. Most children with dwarfism are born to average height parents at a rate of 80%. These stories cover parents' various experiences from diagnosis in utero to medical complications their children have faced. With so many parents not having a medical history or even direct experience with someone with dwarfism, it is our hope that these stories bring knowledge and comfort to others who may find themselves in a similar situation

Angela is a 2x bestselling author with her first book, Finally Free, hitting #1 on four of Amazon's Best Seller lists.

She writes regularly for *LPA Today* (the official publication of Little People of America) and *Five Feet Four* (the official publication of Mississippi Rising Coalition) and occasionally contributes to two local publications – *Gulf Coast Woman Magazine* and *South Mississippi Living Magazine*.

Being a single mom of three kids, she strives to be a present and loving mom while juggling entrepreneurship, personal growth, and social justice work. Angela is always on the move and looking for ways to serve and help others.

She has held an officer's role on the Board of a local women's networking organization *Lighthouse Business and Professional Women* for the past two years. She is the Chair for the 2021 Woman of Achievement Awards Ceremony presented by Lighthouse BPW.

Angela is a founding member and current President of the Mississippi Chapter of Little People of America (Mighty Magnolias).

Additionally, she is also on the Development Committee for the Ohr-O'Keefe Museum of Art, was an Honoree for the inaugural Shuck Cancer event for American Cancer Society and has done some volunteer work with Mississippi Rising Coalition.

You can follow her on Instagram, FB, YouTube, and Linked In as @CoachAng and @PurposeByAng. You can sign up for her newsletter at www.PurposeByAng.com.

# Creating Cakers

## By Becky Barton

s Cakers even a Word? Yes, it is!

**The Entrepreneurs Guide to Starting a Cake Business!**

Let me shed some light on what it means to become an entrepreneur in the cake world or any business. If you are not afraid, then let us jump right in!

Businesses use a set of strategies to obtain their goals, but all business strategies can be categorized into one of four different strategies. Your choice will depend on the goals you set for yourself. These include cost leadership, differentiation, cost leadership focus, and differentiation focus. Example of what works for me: Differentiation is a non-price strategy. Instead of getting customers by providing the lowest price, I attract them by value-adding features. Increasing the quality of my cakes; for instance, premium ingredients and special recipes. You can create this with your own business and offer something to your audience that no one else is offering. Deliveries, rush services, healthier options, and loyalty programs to name a few.

Just know that I was just like you, always afraid of current trends; will my customers love my cakes, will I be compared to everyone else. These were just some of the fears I had! I felt like I was always striving to be the absolute best at what I do! Keeping up with current trends, practicing every new technique, and trying to acquire as much knowledge as I possibly could before beginning any new idea.

Can I help? Of course, I can.

Let me help you take some of the guesswork out of it. You can learn from my mistakes!

Nurturing a successful and profitable business organically can be an immense challenge. Implementing these business growth strategies requires time, it requires dedication, focus, and strategic demanding work from the cake entrepreneur who is very adamant about growing their business to an unparalleled level of profitability.

**How to build a business with strategies I have used in my own business to be successful.**

**How to start and run a profitable Cake Business:**

Creating a Cake Business for the novice baker starting at home. While approaching it can be limiting, contingent upon the size of your kitchen, it will appreciably cut out some startup costs. ("HOW TO START A CAKE BUSINESS - Outset Media") My initial startup costs were an investment of about $50.00-$200.00. This was a gradual process as I did not need a whole assortment of things to begin. As I progressed, I accumulated things along the way.

## Plan

Licenses in your state – Home Bakers: Cottage food license, check with your local government.

Insurance – Call around and get the best possible prices, you will not need this in the beginning however as you grow it will be beneficial.

Bakers supplies and decoration tools – Check around to find the best prices. Amazon is my friend.

Ingredients – sugar, flour, extracts, salt, butter, milk, and eggs. You know all those baking goodies.

Refrigerator – dedicated to your baking needs only to ensure no cross-contamination. You can purchase a used refrigerator for around $200.00 or less.

Shelving – for your ingredients, again you want to have a dedicated space for all your baking items.

Marketing Materials - while in the beginning, you do not need to spend a lot of money on this. Remember that your packaging is an especially important part of your product.

## Who is your target market?

You will want to research the industry and market in your area:

Research other bakers in your area and identify community needs, which other bakers may not be offering. Do any of those apply to you? Organic cakes can be a good place to start and vegan products, and gluten-free options are niches you may want to explore. Do you only want to make wedding cakes or are sculpted cakes more your thing? When you decide which direction most appeals to you, you can then launch, then build on your buyers and target them in your marketing efforts.

What makes your product special or unique? People will pay top dollar for your products if you know exactly what it is you do the best!

## What are the ongoing expenses for a cake business?

Aside from standard overhead costs, expenses will be minimal. Your license will renew annually, for a cottage food license, the cost runs about $100.00 -$200.00 a year depending on the State. Packaging and ingredients and an occasional promotion campaign will be the greatest portion of your budget. Depending on how busy you are the price will fluctuate. If you are going to offer delivery, you will also need to consider that in your budget, fuel, maintenance associated with your vehicle.

## How much do you charge?

The cost of ingredients is just a small portion of what customers are paying for. Baking and decorating skills, your time should always be considered with the pricing of each cake. Setting your price based on these is a fundamental part of curating revenue. Your skillset and time are valuable do not sell yourself short and undervalue your artistic creations. TIME IS MONEY!

Profit of your business, and managing your cost is the first step to profitability!

You must value your time understanding the value of both your time and your cake business starts with you! Value each creation you make. Because if you are not aware of these things you will end up with NO MONEY! Not trying to sound harsh, but it is the truth! A vast majority of small businesses go out of business simply because they do not know how to price themselves. You must remember every detail, material, time, and ingredient. Have a cake cost breakdown sheet that you use for everything. Price it out, how much was a bag of flour, sugar, and eggs? How much was the box, parchment paper, dowel rods, and cake boards? How much time did it take you to make the cake? What equipment did you use? Water and electricity! PRICE IT OUT! See below for more information on this.

## How does a cake business generate money?

Whether you open a storefront or focus on custom orders only from a cottage food bakery (at home), your cake business revenue will be generated from the sales of your cakes. Unique creations (custom orders) which I prefer, will have special pricing, based on a variety of factors. Pricing for cake will differ by area. How much money do you want to make per hour? You are working and deserve to be paid just like anyone else who goes to work at an 8 hour a day job! Price your cakes accordingly. This is how you make MONEY!

Below is a breakdown of how I create the cost and profit for my cakes.

Customer Service/ on the phone - 15 minutes or more speaking with a client

Designs - Cake Research - 30 min

Driving to get supplies - 20 min

Shopping - 30 min to an hour

Prepping - 20 min

Mixing - 20 min

Baking - 60 min

Cooling - 60 min

Filling/Frosting - 30 min to an hour

Creating Design - 20 min

Decorating – 4 to 6 hours depending on design could be more or less

Clean up - 60 min

Delivery - 30 min or more if you deliver

As you can see, I have already spent 10 ½ hours on this one cake.

10 ½ hours times what you want to make per hour.

Before just throwing a price out there make sure you are making a profit on each item and paying yourself.

EXAMPLE: 8-inch round 2-layer cake to feed 12 people. 12people x $6.00 per slice = $72.00 that is just for the cake, now what about your time? Let us say it took you 3 hours. You would then multiply 3 times your hourly rate. Base your hourly rate on your skillset. 3 x $15 = $45.00 so the price of the cake would be $117.00.

## How much profit can cake businesses make?

Cake business opportunity offers a significant profit, especially as your reputation grows within your community. This is an industry that is forever changing, and people rely heavily on word of mouth. Make sure you have a safety net in your bank account before any business venture, just in case things start to get busy you have money for supplies. You may need a lot of supplies as the word spreads. Choosing to remain small is ok, with only a home-based bakery report of a profit of $30,000 to $75,000 a year. Branching out and expanding to larger-scale report profits ranging from six figures to over a million. Revenue. s directly tied to how hard you are willing to work. Push yourself and the possibilities are endless. Above all else, practice, practice, and more practice. Get good at what you do.

## How can you make a Cake business more profitable?

The following strategies have helped me and can help you boost your profits!

Teach decorating and baking classes, where the students learn as they go. Be careful not to give away too many trade secrets. Consider offering another baked good when your cake schedule is low. Cupcakes, cookies, and pies are always a good filler. Play to your strengths as to not overwhelm yourself. Seek out partnerships with restaurants, coffee shops, and farmers markets in your area, contacting your local wedding venues, birthday party venues any place that holds events. Depending on your time, you could become their number one supplier for baked goods. You can also do pop-ups at local businesses to get the word out. You must put in the work; it is not going to drop in your lap.

**What will you call your Business?**

Choosing the right name is especially important and can be quite imitating. One suggestion is NOT to name your cake business after your first or last name. Katie's cakes, for example, there are so many of those already. Be original and think creatively outside of the box, check the online sources to make sure no one else already has that name in your state. Once you settle on a name if you operate a sole proprietorship, you might want to check with, 1. Your state business records 2. Federal and state trademark records 3. Social Media Platforms 4. Web domain availability. Use all the free resources available to you via the internet.

Once you have established a name for your business and have checked with your local government on the regulations and license required, you are now ready to jump in body and soul.

This can be the most exciting and rewarding career if you have a flair for art and have an inventive mind.

There are so many GREATS in this industry, extraordinarily talented cake artists.

**Guidance if you are using social media platforms:**

Your page needs to stay up to date and relevant. The cover photo must reflect the season. For example, if your cover photo is showing Christmas cookies and you are trying to sell Valentine's Day Cakes. This could confuse your audience or cause them to think your page is stale.

If you provide a teaser, sneak, peek, or a countdown of something amazing coming up, there might be more excitement if you post a presale! Be your own hype girl or guy!

Always use a CTA (Call to Action). By asking a simple question at the end of your caption (example: How are you celebrating the 4th Will you be watching fireworks this year? What is your favorite side to bring to a cookout?) you will tempt readers to answer, which will tell Facebook "Hey, people love this content, let's show it to more of her/his page followers!"

If you are only showing up when you have something to sell...which, I get it, is a business page. But showing up to SERVE your audience (by entertaining, educating, enlightening, or inspiring) in between the sale posts will keep your audience from thinking you are just trying to sell them for everything they have (which I know is not what you are going to do.) It will make them know, like, and trust you, then they will be a lifelong customer!

Post around 3 to 4 times a day! Do not post just one image of your goods! Post different angles, pics, and videos, until you are sold out!

Learn how to create opportunities for yourself first and foremost, always be open to innovative ideas!

# About
# Becky Barton

Becky Barton is a self-taught American Cake Artist, Decorator, and teacher known for her intricate sculpted cakes. She is the founder of Rising Star Bakery based out of Lula, Georgia. Becky wants her students to reach inside themselves and find that artist they knew as children, no boundaries no fear. Becky's mantra is simple; Create, Imagine, Challenge.

# Passion into A Paycheck through Network Marketing

By Latoya Griggs

Why I chose network marketing?

I have always had the heart to help people. It is rewarding to see other people reach their level of success based on what they see for themselves while reaching their own greatest potential.

Tony Bennet said, "if you follow your passion, you will never work a day in your life" and I found that to be so true in the network marketing industry. I believe in the products that I sell. This belief makes it easy to share with the world what I found and allows me to become a walking billboard for my brand. Time freedom is next. Enjoying the freedom to work my business from anywhere on my schedule, with my family, for my family, and around my family is rewarding, and last but not least is the residual income. Money that I continue to earn long after the work has been done.

Let's defined network marketing in the simplest term. Network marketing is an independent representative that forms a network of distributors or associates to sell a company's product. These individuals are encouraged to recruit other independent representatives or business partners to duplicate the process to reach as many potential clients or customers as possible. It's a win-win situation for both the company and the independent distributor. The company no longer has to pay for marketing and that savings can now be transferred to the pockets of the independent representative.

There are several levels to network marketing. I found that most brand new marketers come into the business to get rich quickly. This way of thinking can cause them stress when the money doesn't happen overnight or when they are not earning as fast as they hoped to at the beginning of starting their business. Some new marketers want fast money without putting in the time and energy that their Upline has already invested. New marketers in the business see their investment as a side gig or hobby instead of a company of their own... meaning they are in business for themselves but not by themselves. More like a CEO of your Brand.

After having the scare of my life which forced me to focus more on my own health, finding my true purpose in life, always sat in the back of my mind. I loved being a nurse and a retail store manager but the long hours and stress of missing all my family special moments had me questioning my career path often.

I started my network marketing business in 2015 while working 60 to 80 hours a week in a busy retail store. I saw this networking opportunity as a way out of corporate America after receiving my first commission check of $571 after only sharing my products with 3 individuals. At that moment, I knew this business could really provide an unlimited amount of income for my family, a way to better health and time freedom. This was everything I wanted for my life Despite all the great things that come along with being a network marketer, this business does have its own ups and downs.

Here are my 5 Top challenges that I've identified and the things I learned to help overcome them in this business.

1. To make the money you dreamed of in the business, you have to understand and learn how you are getting paid. Learn how the company's compensation plan works and break it down so that you understand how to earn top dollar. If you don't understand how you are paid, money could be left on the table. Learn how to break down the levels of payment and teach it to your team so simple that they can share it with the next person that comes aboard with

simplicity. Duplicate what is already working for those that are making Top dollar and has proof of their growing success. Keep it simple. There's no need to reinvent the wheel if it's already rolling and moving forward. Jump on the train and follow the clues of success. Keeping things simple and duplicatable allow others to follow in your footsteps while building their business in the nooks and crannies of their time. Remember most network marketers have a full-time job that they are trying to work their way out of. They need to be productive with results and not just busy in the small amount of time that they have.

2. Building the business with a team of people that see the same vision of the company. Recruiting other like-minded people is a major challenge in network marketing. How do you find the people that see the same vision that you display each day? Happy clients with a business mindset become one of your best business partners. They believe in the products, they have results and they're willing to share with the world what they've found. Those are the people you want on the team. So, you ask, how do you find those people... Who are excited about your products? Who is sending you referrals? Who's asking questions? Who shares your information? Start there and make a list of possible business partners. Share with them the opportunity and

benefits of being on the team and add value to what they can offer to the world.

3. Staying motivated is another challenge most network marketers encounter. Majority of the network marketers going into business wanting instant gratification and high hopes of waking up RICH. They want to start out at the top of their organization and skip the levels of building their own brand. With unrealistic goals, they lose motivation when their success isn't Instant. I've learned that setting small goals to success and tracking them weekly, monthly, and annually keeps me excited about the level in my business. Keeping my goals at the forefront of my mind helps me stay on track with my vision and dreams of success. Staying consistent with my Dream and working towards it a little each day allows me to stay focused and on track. Talking to excited business partners and clients gives me more motivation to stay the course. Happy people constantly remind me of my purpose and why I love what I do. Seeing my family enjoy the benefits of my time freedom also gets me motivated to go even further in business.

4. No means Next...The fear of rejection should not kill your vision or dreams as a business owner. When potential clients say no, they're not saying No to you personally but

simply saying, they are not interested in what you have to offer them at the moment. For every no that you receive, it brings you closer to the next "Yes." If you begin to take rejection in this business personally, you'll give up on all the goals you set for yourself. Success doesn't happen overnight, and you'll hear way more no's than a Yes! Go ahead and practice saying no to yourself and develop a comeback Thank you statement for when the No's arrive.

5. "Have an escape from all your excuses" this is the simplest way I've overcome all my challenges in business. I found a way to get things done, not an excuse for why I could not. It is so much support out there to help you reach all your goals but are you willing to learn, will be the determining factor in your success.

If you learn to help people solve their problems with the services your business provides, you will reach every business goal you've set for yourself ...

To live the life of your dreams and work what you love, step out on faith "Have an escape for all your excuses" and turn your Passion into your Paycheck.

# About
# Latoya Griggs

Latoya Griggs is a life enthusiast, inspirational speaker, transformational coach, and co-author of an Amazon bestseller book "Finally Free". Living life with a zeal for seeing lives transformed through the freedom of health and wellness. Her sincere passion for vitality is at the center of all she does, as Latoya is reputed for her great ability to aid women in their pursuit of wholeness, through the power and execution of *self-love*. Latoya's clients have experienced lives, once filled with exhaustion, irritability, and self-deprivation; evolve into a complete transformation of the soul.

**Free Spirit Health and Nutrition LLC** is an unconventional wellness company owned and operated by Latoya Griggs. Using the basic ethics of healthy eating, targeted supplementation, and an active lifestyle change, Latoya successfully provides, both life-changing strategy, and proven results to her client base.

She is valued as one who provides effervescence to all she meets; using the joy gained from conquering her own life's obstacles into provisional results for others. Her main goal in business is simple; *to help people find their "why", and to see them execute it, with both happiness and a will to win.*

Website: LatoyaCarr-Griggs.com

FreeSpirit4Health.com

Facebook: Latoya Carr Griggs

Instagram: Latoya Carr Griggs

Email: FreeSpiritHealthandNutrition@gmail.com

# Don't Put the Cart Before the Horse

## By Chandra Nicole

Depending on where you are from and how you were raised, the title of this chapter may make you recall an old saying by the elders in your family. Or maybe your immediate thought was "What does this title have to do with starting and running a business??? What is she even talking about???"

The "putting the cart before the horse" analogy describes doing things in the wrong order and expecting the best outcome, doing things before its time, building a house without a solid foundation, etc. By now you get where I am going with this. And when it comes to this entrepreneur thing, there is order needed to ensure your success and to prevent resentment and frustration.

I have started several businesses in the past. My first business was wedding and event planning. I started that business solely because I was already doing it for family and friends, and they expressed to me that I was great at it.

So, I looked for a training class because I wanted credentials and to look professional as possible. I became a certified event and wedding planner within six months and the only thing I had to start my business was a certification, a Google voice number (business phone), and social media pages...that's it.

No EIN, no business formation, no insurance, no website, no business plan, no marketing, no tracking of expenses. Just a whole bunch of people trusting me because I was good. But what if something major happened??? What if someone got hurt or sick? What if I caused damage to someone's property? I could have been sued. I could've lost everything I owned simply because my business affairs were not in order.

Next, I started a nonprofit mentoring program for young women called SisterNation, LLC. This time around I was more knowledgeable about business structure, business planning, and marketing, but the nonprofit sector is a horse of a different color. There were things like fundraising, finding a board of directors, figuring out how to pay myself, and other essential things I had to learn. I needed to hire help and pay them. I didn't have a clue what I was doing. I attended several training sessions to learn the information.

I learned some great strategies and skills that I used to this day. But honestly, I could have made better use of my time and hired a professional (we will talk about when and why to outsource later). Also, my mentors helped me tremendously for free but eventually, I needed to pay them for their time and effort. So, my mentoring program fizzled out and it left me frustrated and in debt.

I mean, "What was I doing wrong?" I totally loved planning events and mentoring girls. Why am I struggling so much?

Then I entered the social media space where millions of gurus promised that taking their training was going to skyrocket my business and that I could be a millionaire in 3 days lol (not saying it's not possible), but a lot of planning and executing would need to happen to accomplish that money goal. But it is totally possible.

This promise has made a lot of gurus rich, and a lot of new entrepreneurs frustrated and resentful about entrepreneurship after they discover that no amount of money will allow them to skip the process of building a sustainable business.

For years, I signed up for training after training. I mean I was swimming in information but didn't have a clue what to do with it. I became frustrated with the get-rich-quick schemes and gave up on being an entrepreneur.

Still unaware of what I was missing, I continued to ask myself "Why was I struggling to launch and maintain a business?" I desired to be an entrepreneur. I desired to own my time. I wanted to spend more time with my family. I wanted to do more community service work.

Then one day I had an ah-ha moment. I noticed out of all the training I had attended, and the coaches hired, not one guru was concerned whether I had a business plan or whether my financial outlook was good, or that I was legally ready to be a business owner. No one analyzed my business and said "No, I'm not taking your money. You are not ready. Let me refer you to someone who will teach you how to legalize your business and do a financial audit to see if you can afford to start a business right now, then come back and see me." They just accepted my payment. Training after training. Coach after coach. At this point, I had a wealth of information. So much so, I was advising others about business but could not figure out why I was stuck and struggling.

Don't miss the point I'm making here. Basically, I had not done enough research about starting a business and what it entails. I just knew I loved what I was doing, and I wanted to make money doing it. You will need to start with researching your business idea and the process of starting your business so when you enter the marketplace in search of help, you will know the lingo and you can interpret what is being communicated so you do not waste time and money thinking that you are going to skip steps in the process of business ownership.

The very next thing before you even consider starting is hiring a good and honest financial advisor to look over your finances to determine if it is possible to start a business based on your portfolio. When the advisor presents you with the analysis of your finances, take this opportunity to learn and understand the reasons why you should not start a business until certain criteria are met. It will be the best decision you will make in business and your financial advisor and accountant will both become your best friends. So do the numbers regarding your business before you start and don't let the numbers be the reason you start and fail because you were not honest about your assets and liabilities.

Becoming an entrepreneur has its perks.

There is something so powerful about business ownership.

There are certain virtues you will need to survive and thrive once you decide to go all in.

Here are the top five things in my opinion you need to get started on your way to being the creator of the life you desire and deserve.

**Passion**- If this is your dream business you will need passion. But passion alone will not sustain your business. Most people do not consider researching the market and finding a need and then building their first business around the need and using that business to fund your dream. Read it again. Your first business may not be your dream business. Even if you're not passionate about it, the business may produce rapid results and income that puts you in a position to go for your dream business. Please consider this when starting your first business.

**Plan**- If you want to be successful and want to position yourself for opportunities, you will need a plan. A business plan. A business plan is a document you draft up to forecast your business outlook. When someone reads your business plan, they should be able to see themselves inside your dream (business). The info you provide should connect in a way that investors want to take the next step and possibly invest in your business.

**Mindset**- The way you think can be one of the biggest roadblocks to running a successful business. You must adopt a CEO mindset. You must see your business in the future. You must understand that failing in different aspects of your business is likely and necessary for growth. Think of your business as an experiment that you are testing for the most probable outcomes. In the beginning stages, you are figuring out what works and what doesn't. Failing early and fast is the blueprint to building a business you can be proud of. CEOs measure their efforts, analyze their mistakes, make changes, shift their perspective and business then continue. You must think like a CEO.

**Finances**- Please consider how you handle your personal finances because it will show up in your business finances. Money habits don't change overnight. Thoroughly look over your credit reports. Check for all the bad habits that hold you back and may prevent you from obtaining business credit. Do the numbers. Write down every expense and equipment needed to run your business and plan for how you are going to pay for it. On the flip side, we think because we have a nest egg, 401K, savings, or stocks, that we can buy our way to success. Money is a major part of the equations, but it will not exempt you from the process.

**Consistency**- Showing up every day ready to do business is the only way you can measure true effort. Doing things for your business every day the same way can become boring and redundant sometimes. You are not going to feel like showing up every day, but you must. It is the only way to measure if your business idea is worth the time, effort, and money. Consistency sets the standard of your business. People expect you to be in a position so they can purchase your products and services. I suggest you be there. If you are not, I can guarantee you the belief in your business will dwindle and people will find others to service their needs.

Now that you have gotten started, there are other things you are going to need to keep you going and moving forward.

I like to call it MONEY MATTERS. You will need the following...

**M**otivation- Staying motivated will keep you going. You want to see your business grow and succeed, right? Keep the spirit of joy and expectation as you navigate the entrepreneur space. Things can and will get challenging, but you must push through the feelings of temporary defeat to see your dreams of business ownership become a reality.

**O**ptimism- Be optimistic about the future of your business. How will it change your life? How will it impact the lives of others? How it is different and unique from any other business? How do you plan to stay in business for years to come? Staying positive about your business and looking for the good in the people who decide to join you in building your business will create the atmosphere you need to grow as your business thrives.

**N**on-negotiable- When it comes to your business or business ideas, you must be decisive and non-negotiable. You must communicate to possible investors, business partners, and consumers that you stand on the mission and vision for your business and that you operate strictly from the goals of that mission and vision. If people suspect that you are not sure about your business or business idea, they may try to sway or manipulate you into doing things that may jeopardize or destroy your business. Be non-negotiable and forthcoming. You will only intimidate people who had ill intent from the start.

**E**nergy- The energy you possess is powerful to the success of your business. Your energy must be high, and heartfelt. If you are excited about your business so will potential investors, employees, and customers. You are a walking billboard. People are looking for you to show up fully for your business. If you're always frustrated and always complaining, you are going to repel the very people you need to take your business to the next level. Keep your spirit high and your energy higher.

**Y**ou- You go first. You show up for your business. Set the tone and expectation. You are it! Did you know that people buy into you, your personality, and what you stand for before they consider purchasing your products or services? Think about it. Are you sharing with the world what you do and why you do it???

**M**anagement- A business cannot run itself. You must manage the day-to-day processes of your business and those processes must be clear, concise, and easy to follow. You must manage your time, people, and money. Don't be afraid of communicating what is needed to make sure the business runs smoothly. Have regular staff meetings and training so that your help is in the know and the flow of things. Also document these processes in an employee handbook and a policy and procedure manual for the times you are not on-site and cannot be reached. The business must continue to operate even when you are not around. So, manage your business, don't let the business manage you.

**A**ssets- Assets are the things you own in your business that give it worth. How much is your business worth? Does the equipment, decisions, your team add to or take away from your business? You must analyze every business transaction to make sure that what you are doing benefits and fulfills the goals of the business.

**T**ime- Building your business is going to take time. New business startups will demand a great deal of your time and effort. If you have a job while you are building your dream, you must commit to spending time working on your business each day until you are up and running. Newsflash: It will require more time and energy when you finally launch, so be ready.

**T**eam- You've heard the saying "Teamwork makes the dream work." Having a high-functioning excited group of people who believe in the mission and vision for your business is priceless. Your team is your greatest asset. After all, you cannot run your business alone. Whether you have employees or outsource and contract your help if it were not for these people your dream business will not become a reality. Believing in your team and allowing them to show off the skills you hired them to implement will reduce your need to micromanage and set the business up for expansion if desired.

**E**nthusiasm- People are attracted to positivity. There is nothing like witnessing an entrepreneur who is sold out and excited about their business. When you are enthusiastic about your dreams and aspirations people want to know more. This is how opportunities are born. People generally don't know what they need until someone expresses its value. Remain enthusiastic about your business, products, services, and future even when you are having a bad or off day. Be honest with yourself about those days and keep pushing through with the same enthusiasm, and you will discover that bad days are the days you learn and grow the most in your business.

**R**eady- "If you stay ready, you don't have to get ready" I think that's how that saying goes. Your business plan is going to help you stay accountable and on track when it comes to your business. Being organized and prepared is going to ensure that you don't miss opportunities. Have you ever met a business owner that was so excited about their business, communicated its value but when you were ready to patronize the business, the business owner could not communicate the next steps? Like...How to get their products and services? How to pay? How to contact them in the future? nothing. Don't be that business owner. Entrepreneurs stay ready because they understand that the right connection or opportunities can catapult their business into the stratosphere and beyond. CEOs learn to expect opportunities regularly and are prepared when they show up.

Skills- There are skills you will need to have to run and maintain a successful business and there are some skills you will need to outsource to save time, money, and energy. Operating your business will require the most skills. You at least need to know simple skills like answering the phone professionally, sending professional emails, interacting with customers and vendors. Then there are skills that require a lot of time and effort and will slow you down because it requires intense training such as marketing and branding. You may want to find and hire a person who is passionate about the skills you need and who is performing those skills as a business. Having the right skills and hiring people with the right skills to fit your business will ensure that your business thrives and survives.

Your business matters and so does your money.

Passion only comes before a plan in the dictionary. That means without a plan you are simply dreaming and setting yourself up for failure. Adopt an abundance mindset, have your finances in order, communicate passionately about your business, plan your wins.

Don't get caught in the nice, curated pictures you see on the internet of successful businesses. Because behind all the pretty make-up, creative captions, great lighting, and photoshop, there is a person who has given up a lot to be where he/she is. They have failed forward and fast. They have discovered that passion alone will not sustain their dreams, but a well-thought-out plan and solid finances will.

They learned how to build a good enough cart(foundation), then they bought a horse(process) that pulled their dream business in the direction it was meant to go.

Reduce your anxiety and worries and get this one thing right from the start "Don't put the cart before the horse."

Happy launching and building your dreams!

Chandra Nicole

XOXO

# About

# Chandra Nicole

Chandra Nicole is the founder and CEO of the Urban Mom Society, a support community for moms with teen daughters. She is the proud mother of three amazing ladybugs— Norkeisha Denise, Demetria Chantrese, and I'mari Rhythm.

As the "Queen of Real Talk," she brings balance and bonding to moms who struggle to #pushthru the pain of guilt and shame by helping them break the cycle of brokenness, depression, and the fear of seeking mental wellness.

She believes when women are empowered, families are strengthened—thus creating emotionally strong and resilient daughters with high self-esteem and confidence.

She has worked as a mentor for teen girls and their moms for the past 10 years and has served as the executive director of SisterNation Inc. Mentoring Program.

Her goal is to teach urban moms and their daughters all over the world how to connect and communicate consistently and courageously while developing an undeniable life-changing bond.

Her big dream is to one day open a private practice as a Marriage and Family Counselor serving mothers and daughters while empowering families to persevere through challenging life events.

## Contact Info

Phone: 901-337-1960

Email: pointerchandra@gmail.com

Facebook: Urban Mom Society and Da Urban Girls Mentor

Instagram: Urban Mom Society and Da Urban Girls Mentor

# BO$$ YOUR LANE
# THE SPIRITUALITY OF BUSINESS

By Irma Matos

## BUSINESS HAS NO SOUL

An attorney I used to deal with once told me, "Business has no soul." I choose to believe that the soul of a business is the soul of the owner. The owner guides the employees and creates the business culture by working with core values. My core values are integrity, honesty, and loyalty. Those core values build credibility, which is priceless. I instilled those values in my employees because I operated by them myself. What are these core values and how can they be expressed?

Integrity is soundness of moral character or rectitude. It means looking out and doing your best for your clients.

Honesty is truthfulness, sincerity, frankness, and freedom from deceit or fraud.

Loyalty is faithfulness to your commitments or obligations, including being faithful to your clients.

Some people have two sets of standards when it comes to their personal life and their business when you should operate in business with the same core values of your personal life. If you are honest in your personal life, then you must also be honest in your business. Moral values are not interchangeable. They are part of who you are. Be authentic. Be yourself.

## BUSINESS IS BUSINESS

I am sure you have heard this phrase before. It leads to the belief that in business anything is permitted in order to make a profit. I have never liked that phrase. I believe you must live an authentic life and be your true self in all aspects of your life.

I realized many years ago that I work for God. He will reward me for my efforts and bless me. I learned that bosses don't always appreciate what you do, and clients don't either.

If you are not appreciated, know that you must always do the right thing no matter what. When your head hits the pillow, you must be able to sleep peacefully knowing that you did your best all day long. Peace of mind is priceless.

You also have to value yourself and be prepared to walk away if someone does not appreciate or value you and the situation turns toxic.

Don't wait for anyone to pat you on the back, that pat may never come. If you always do the right thing, then God will bless you.

I learned early in my career to listen to what I call "my little voice," the still, small voice we all have inside. It is my intuition, God speaking to me, call it anything you want, but it is very real. On one occasion I was renting a townhouse. My little voice told me not to rent to certain applicants, but I did it anyway because I couldn't have it vacant anymore. Those individuals were not good tenants and created all kinds of problems. I learned it is better to have a vacant property than to rent it to the wrong tenants.

From that point forward I always listen to my "little voice," my still, small voice. You must learn from your experiences and mistakes, otherwise, the same things keep happening to you until you learn the lesson. Awareness is king. You must be aware of your surroundings and the people around you. Not everyone that you meet is a good person and wants to help you. You must be in tune with your intuition to help you discern which way to go, what relationships to foster, and what decisions to make.

**WIN-WIN**

Live by the golden rule "always treat others as you would like them to treat you." As a leader, you must be respectful and courteous to others, so they won't have any other choice but to be respectful and courteous to you. Respect is earned by the way you treat people. This applies to employees as well, not just clients. Pay your employees what they are worth and treat them like family. It builds loyalty and you will not have to worry about turnover. There is a cost involved in training. Once trained, the employee is more valuable to the company. If they leave, you have to train someone else and, in the meantime, that person is not as productive as the one that just left. Having employees working in your company for many years is a sign that you have a stable business, something your clients appreciate. Clients don't like to deal with new employees all the time.

Be early for your meetings, because it shows you respect the time of others. Be a person of your word. Do what you say you are going to do. It builds up credibility and credibility is priceless. Be a person of increase. Leave everyone you come in contact with feeling better than before, happy that they had an encounter with you.

Part of creating a win-win situation is that your deals must be fair for all involved. Do not focus on just getting what you need or want. That willingness to be fair is key to building a reputation with others that they can respect. Praise in public and correct in private. Prepare a "to do" list the night before so you can be ready in the morning. Do the more difficult tasks first. Focus on one task until you finish it. Do the work quickly and well.

Concentrate on providing the very best service you can provide. Go the extra mile, and the money will come. Don't forget to be generous and give to good causes. The money you give will come back to you a hundredfold in blessings.

## THIRTY-THREE YEARS IN BUSINESS

Live a vision-driven life, focus on the end result. Write your goals down and pursue them every day. Don't worry about the "how." The "how" will take care of itself. Concentrate on the "what," and the "why." What do you want and why do you want it?

I always wanted to have my own business. When the company I was working for decided to move to Dallas, Texas, that was my opportunity to go out on my own. I started a photography business where I helped the Red Cross with their ad campaigns, did social events, etc. Then I started a patient transportation service where I would pick up patients that were part of a medical study, take them to the hospital, and then take them back home. Finally, I started my property management company in which I worked for 33 years of my life. I built it from scratch. My sister is running it now with the help of her daughter, my niece. It became a family business, my legacy to them.

During the 33 years, I was building my property management company I was investing in real estate. I purchased properties. Many of them were purchased at auctions. Afterward, I renovated them, rented them, and sold them.

I bought the properties with partners, mostly friends and family. We all profited when the properties were sold.

Take calculated risks. When I went to buy the house I live in, I did not have the money for the down payment in the bank. The money was invested in the other properties, which I was in the process of selling. By the time I closed on my house, the properties were sold, and I had the money I needed for the down payment. You must have faith.

Don't mix business with pleasure. Keep your professional life separate from your personal life. Don't use a client to solve another client's problem. If it doesn't work out, you will have two upset clients instead of one.

I have always gone by the old adage: If it ain't broke, don't fix it. However, at times you must go outside of your comfort zone in the interest of growth. If you are not growing, then you are disintegrating. Most people resist change because it makes them uncomfortable. If you find yourself in a situation where you need to make some changes, then explain it to your employees and bring them into the project. When people feel that they are a part of something, then they are more willing to cooperate.

## IT CAN'T BE ALL WORK

At age 40, I decided to learn the French language. I had studied French in high school but this time I was taking it seriously. I signed up at the French Alliance in Miami. For seven years, I went to school religiously every Saturday morning for 2 hours. That was my way of disconnecting from work. I used to say it was less expensive to learn French than to go to the psychiatrist. I became friends with my French teacher, Dominique, a wonderful lady, and a beautiful soul. We ended up going to France together with other classmates. It was a magical trip. We went to Paris, Orleans, the Loire Valley, and Dunkirk, where her father once lived. It was in Dunkirk where Dominique taught me to eat mussels. It was 1999 and the Eifel Tower had a luminous sign counting down the number of days to the millennium. Those memories are ones that I cherish but would never have happened if I didn't decide to take a much-needed break from work every Saturday.

Find a hobby or learn something new to help you manage the stress of work. Most importantly, work at something you love and master it. A job is something you get paid for, but a calling is something you are made for.

Take time off often, even if it is a couple of days to disconnect from the routine and the stress from work. Take a day's drive and connect with nature. I live close to the Florida Keys and the Everglades. Often, I drive to Key Largo just to have lunch and return home or drive to the Everglades to see if I can spot an alligator. This practice is important for your mental health.

## HONOR AND PAY HOMAGE

Honor and pay homage to those who have helped you, taught you, and cared for you. Gratitude is a beautiful quality to have. It is the gate to abundance. We must be grateful for everything, the good and the not-so-good. The good makes you happy. The not-so-good teaches you lessons.

You can be grateful by serving, by being a mentor to someone. Serving and mentoring others bring out the most rewarding feeling inside you. A feeling of accomplishment, a rewarding feeling of knowing that you have helped someone conquer a fear or a limiting belief and have set someone free to soar like an eagle. What a feeling!

It was Maya Angelou who said: "People will forget what you said, people will forget what you did, but people will never forget how you made them feel." So true, so profound.

I serve in several ministries of my church, as well as having gone to Mexico as a missionary. You'll be surprised how much you learn about yourself, and how much you grow personally and spiritually. You realize you don't need much to live and be happy. It is all within you. By giving of yourself and your time you receive a lot more than you give. The blessings pour in.

I am a Cuban refugee who came to the United States at the age of 14, had to learn English, and get used to a new country and new customs.

When I arrived in Miami, I had to live in an efficiency with 11 people. I had to overcome a lot of challenges, but I didn't let the challenges stop me. I made the American Dream happen for me. You can make it happen for you.

Best wishes and God bless your new business.

# About
# Irma Matos

Irma Matos is the author of the upcoming book, *A Noble Profession: Life Lessons To Inspire Your Soul & Live In Abundance*, as well as an entrepreneur, property management consultant, real estate investor, life coach, speaker, and missionary. She immigrated to the United States from Cuba in 1970. After completing her formal education, Irma created a property management company, which she ran for 33 years. Today, she serves as a consultant for her former company and its clients. In addition, she is a Certified Life

Transformation Dream Builder Coach, guiding her clients in the fulfillment of their goals and dreams.

In 2006, Irma was honored to be invited to the President's Dinner in Washington D.C. as the Business Advisory Council Honorary Chairman. She received the Congressional Medal of Distinction in recognition of her Outstanding Meritorious Service. Integrity, honesty, and loyalty are three pillars that define Irma both personally and professionally.

Irma remains active in several ministries of the Catholic Church, including the Emmaus Retreat and Life in the Spirit. She has also traveled to Mexico as part of several missions. Her goal is to inspire people to live a vision-driven life and impart the many life lessons she has learned to others, including the importance of gratitude and service in order to live in abundance.

Today, she lives in Miami, where she continues to write, consult, coach, and serve others.

## CONTACT INFORMATION FOR IRMA MATOS

Facebook: facebook.com/irma.matos.7

Email address: IrmaMatosAuthor@gmail.com

# BEFORE AND AFTER THE LEAP

By Eseverere

Some people dream of becoming an entrepreneur, they desire to be their own boss, but they never take action. And one of the consequences of not taking action is staying on the sidelines forever. So, I would like to use this opportunity to commend you for conquering the fear and making the bold move to "Boss Your Lane."

I still recall fantasizing a few years back about how I couldn't wait to leap, go all in and start my own business. The after feeling was always a mixture of excitement and anxiety. When we attempt anything new or go into unfamiliar terrain, there's always that fear, doubt, and uncertainty you will have to deal with. You never know what to expect.

My breakthrough came during the pandemic in 2020 after reading the book titled "The Pursuit of Happiness." I realized from the story that to define your own happiness, you must pursue it! And, if you've got a dream, you must protect it! I sensed it was time to face my fear and leap! I was hungry to be my own boss, build my brand, make an impact and unveil my influence. So, I said to myself, "there will never be a perfect time," and I gave it a shot: I'm glad I leaped!

Looking back, I have learned a lot on this journey, and now I coach and speak on most of the things I will be sharing with you in this chapter.

## MINDSET IS KEY

When it comes to starting a small business, it all begins with having the right business mindset. It will play a significant role as you journey into the entrepreneurial world. The right business mindset was something I got introduced to early in my business, and I'm glad I took steps to work on it.

How you think and act can affect your business, and most times, our mindsets can be a massive hindrance to the goal and growth of our business.

## VALUES ARE THE ROOT

### Courage

"All of our dreams can come true if we have the courage to pursue them." – Walt Disney

I learned that one way to overcome fear is to show courage. Courage is not the absence of fear. It's acting despite the fear. Being courageous allows you to take chances, pursue your dream and get what you want out of life.

Being a successful entrepreneur is having the courage to try something outside of your comfort zone even though it may seem unrealistic at first, you must believe in yourself, your business and get moving.

## Confidence

"So much of starting a business or affecting change is the confidence and courage to simply try" – Simon Sinek.

Confidence and Courage go hand in hand. Confidence may come easy to some people, while others will have to develop it. During my teenage years to young adulthood, I didn't have a lot of confidence, so this was something I had to develop over time and have carried on to my venture.

Building your confidence is an integral part of the entrepreneurial journey. It may be one of the first and most essential tools to have in your toolbox.

You will need confidence to succeed in all areas of your business - sell your product or service, adopt new business ideas, find new clients, request and close deals, etc.

## Persistence

As a young entrepreneur or someone just starting their own business, your "Why" plays a significant role when it comes to persistence. Inspiration will get you started, but it's not enough to last you through the rough times. Therefore, a lot of people start but are not able to finish.

In my case, there were times when the thought of all the things I had to figure out early in my business made me so overwhelmed that I considered giving up and taking the easier route, but what kept me on track was my "Why."

Quite frankly, the journey is going to be tough sometimes. There will be hard days and seasons but what keeps you going is what got you started initially. So, if your "Why" isn't strong enough, there might not be enough good reason to persist.

## Passion.

I love to talk about passion. I believe people should do what they are passionate about to enjoy life and have fulfillment. Everything in life and business done with passion triumphs.

Passion will help you persevere through challenges in your business, and it gives you purpose. Passion is evident and can be contagious. If you choose a business solely for the money, with time, people can tell.

Let your passion come through in a way that when people see you, they see the passion in your eyes. When they can't see you, they hear the passion in your voice, and when you show up, people can feel it in your actions.

"Having passion for what you do lights you up and reveals your best version" – Eseverere.

## INVEST TIME IN YOUR BUSINESS

### Invest time to Plan

My suggestion is to keep it simple at the beginning. Your plan should be clear and concise.

A good business plan will convey the vision and purpose of your business.

You may be tempted to put off planning until later, but it's better to get things ironed out at the early stages of your business to give some clarity.

You have the option to hire experts to help with this; however, as a small business most likely on a budget, there are free business plan templates online that you can utilize, and they will serve the same purpose.

### Invest time to Research

Doing the initial research on the product or service you want to provide saves you a lot of headaches which is where Business Branding comes in. Research has shown that some people do not consider branding their business in the early phases; they only omit to realize 5,10 years down the line and finally return to the drawing board.

Invest the time and effort needed early. It may be ideal to partner with a business branding expert who can help you research your brand and the longevity of your brand. They can help you drill down on your business why, the need, vision, and core values of your business. You want to be clear at the beginning on why you are in business, who your business will serve, how you will render your service and what value you will provide.

One of the primary goals of any business is to solve a problem hence the need for proper branding and analysis. Once this is taken care of, it will benefit other areas of your business, especially sales and marketing.

**Invest time to Learn New Skills**

Personal development is the bedrock of any entrepreneur. We cannot give what you don't have. When you make time for personal development, you are investing in yourself and also your business.

Take time to learn a new skill necessary to move the needle in your business towards your business goal. If entrepreneurs stop growing, they tend to grind to a halt, which is why personal development is vital. Learning new skills has been made easier in recent times. You can find free resources or digital courses and programs online at affordable prices.

Every successful entrepreneur is constantly learning, growing, and striving for more. However, because there's a lot to be done initially, your best bet might be to start by learning the skills which you enjoy doing first and gradually progress from there.

## Invest time on your Strengths

It is easy to get stuck in the initial phase of your business because you are struggling to do everything. You could quickly become overwhelmed and burnt out from wearing too many hats – from learning new business tactics to keeping tabs with trends. My suggestion will be to identify your strengths and take note of the things you struggle with within your business.

For instance, one area I struggle with is the administrative part of my business. I see myself dropping the ball constantly in this area. To keep tabs, I must outsource that aspect to be more productive and build a successful business.

We have to learn to concentrate on our strengths and leverage other people's strengths in areas we have challenges. It will not only help maximize your time but keep the momentum going in your business.

## INVEST IN YOURSELF

"The best investment you can make is in yourself." – Warren Buffet

### Attend Events and Network

This area cannot be under-emphasized. You're the number one asset in your business. Investing in yourself increases your value as an entrepreneur.

"You are the average of the five people you spend the most time with." – Jim Rohn.

When you network with other successful entrepreneurs in a mastermind, workshop or event, you master the mindset of successful people. You will be surrounding yourself with like-minded individuals, which can help you see things from different angles in your business.

I have lost count of the number of events I have attended to network. These weren't events I got invited to for a speaking engagement. I intentionally paid to attend and expand my network, and it paid off in the end.

The goal is to build relationships. People do business with people that they know, like, and trust. Your best source of support sometimes will come from complementary businesses and fellow successful entrepreneurs.

## Hire Coaches and Mentors

Find yourself a coach. It is unwise to go somewhere unknown without a GPS. It would help if you had someone who would walk you through the jungle to find your treasure quickly.

I couldn't have come this far in my journey if I did not invest in coaches and mentors because I'm committed to my growth in business. If you're not growing in business, you are struggling.

Why re-invent the wheel when you can partner with a mentor to collapse time and avoid costly mistakes. Suppose you find a very successful entrepreneur with a good business result; nine times out of 10, they have a coach or mentor. Success is easier when you decide to learn from those that know more than you.

"One of the greatest values of mentors is the ability to see ahead what others cannot see to help them navigate a course to their destination." – John C. Maxwell.

YES! You read this to the end. Congratulations! You're on the right path. The first step is usually the hardest. You have taken the first step to seek knowledge and start building a business that will last a lifetime.

Welcome on board! Embarking on my entrepreneurial journey is one of the best things that happened to me. I can categorically say that one thing that lights me up more often is when I wear my entrepreneurial hat.

GO, BOSS, YOUR LANE!!! If this chapter resonates with you, don't hesitate to reach out. Let's see how I can be of help and support you on your journey. In the meantime, continue to do what lights you up and be the CEO of your life.

# About

# Eseverere

Passion, tenacity, and clarity are the appreciated traits of any growing entrepreneur. Advising current culture on maximizing these values through the power of positivity and discipline; is the energetic professional, Eseverere.

Eseverere is an author, speaker, multidimensional coaching expert, and consultant. She is the CEO, and founder of **The 5-9 CEO Brand and The CEO Empire, LLC**, a multifaceted coaching and consulting conglomerate centered around empowerment, lifestyle transition, education, and advising of growing entrepreneurs looking to achieve success while doing what they love. Having combined skillful entrepreneurship with a successful career in the corporate workforce for several years, Eseverere has positioned herself as a quintessential influencer amongst her growing clientele.

**Her mantra is clear: She empowers her clients to do what they are passionate about, so they can live a happy and fulfilled life.**

High regard backs Eseverere's dynamic contribution to the success of her brand for empowerment, education, and personal achievement. She holds a Graduate of Mathematics, a Master's in Business Administration, several Business certifications, including a Power Voice certification, from world-renowned motivator Les Brown.

Affectionately known as the "Queen" on her social media broadcast, **The 5-9 CEO**, Eseverere, impacts a global audience to hold fast to their personal entrepreneurship goals while maintaining a reputable relationship with their professional vocation. Over the years, she has had a successful career as a Marketing Manager in Global Retail, an

Operations Executive, in the Aviation Industry, in Nigeria, and an IT Business Professional in the US.

She is commonly recognized as one polarizing, energizing, motivating and inspiring viewers to replace their comfort zones with the passion, clarity, and positivity needed to achieve their highest dreams. Impressing a global audience, Eseverere has featured in several podcasts, local and international (Canada, UK) radio stations, and magazines such as Pretty Women Hustle Magazine, In The City Magazine, and many more.

Eseverere remains fastened to her goal of creating *a liberated space* for entrepreneurial hopefuls around the world by leading the masses with her unequivocal effervescence. When Eseverere is not motivating others to be their best, she enjoys traveling and meeting new people, sharing her story, singing, dancing, modeling, and hanging out with her kids.

**Queen Eseverere. Leader. Innovator. Tenacious. Motivator. Energizer.**

# Bought Sense

## By Misty Stevenson

As much as I hate to admit this, there are people that make a living getting over on other people, and this has gone on since the beginning of time. Do you recall the older movies the snake oil salesman? The one that promised the miracle cure in a bottle. Well, those people still exist however social media has made it much easier and has expanded those people's reach. Be careful of the wolf in sheep's clothing. Thinking about the new entrepreneur in the movies, there is always a scene that shows them being taken advantage of or overcharged because they simply do not know any better. This leads me to my expert advice. I call myself an expert because my sense was not taught instead it was bought.

I will start by saying that I am a firm believer in investing in yourself and your business. One cannot expect anyone to spend money with a business owner that is not willing to spend money on themselves or their business. You must pay for marketing, certifications, training, coaching, etc, However, this is where it can become somewhat tricky, and if you are not careful you may find yourself spending more than what is required. This can make start-up hard on a novice entrepreneur.

When deciding to open our first business Stevenson Elite Renovations, I will admit we were lucky. We had support and people were very eager to help us get our business up and running. We had family and friends offer advice, making start-up easy for both me and my husband. So, when I decided to branch out on my own and open Sophisticated Elite Décor, I was not so lucky. I was working full time, managing our already established business, and writing a book. I found myself time-poor and needing assistance with several things related to startup. I became desperate because I already had jobs waiting on me. I reached out to a lady who claimed she did business consulting, training, coaching, etc... and before long I found that I spent money on service that I could have gotten for either free or cheap. I later found that this lady was known for scamming people out of money. Luckily, I did not go under contract with her, but I have friends that did. This happened to me because I was in a rush and therefore, I trusted everything this person said. I even brought her into my circle of successful friends. If I had taken my time, took a step back, and did my research I would have found that this lady was not at all who she said she was. I could have saved myself money and undue frustration. That was an expensive lesson.

My advice to the novice entrepreneur is when dealing with people in business and in life remember the Phrase "every good tree bears good fruit, but a bad tree bears bad fruit." Matthew 7:17 NIV. Jesus warns us of false prophets and to beware of sheep that are wolves. You can identify them by their fruit. If you decide to hire someone to help you such as a coach or consultant please ask for references, websites, and thank God for Google. Do not go into a contract with anyone that you have questions about. Do not pay anyone until you are comfortable and ready to start working. Always ask for a contract first. Take your time, read it over, before signing or paying. Slow down! If your plate is full take your time and clean a few things off before attempting to open your business. Your business is your ideas, and it is not going anywhere. While in the waiting process there are several things you can do but slow down because opening a successful business is a process, not a race. Most importantly pray about it. Ask God to show you the way. He never fails us. I hope that my advice helps someone on the way to successful entrepreneurship.

# About
# Misty Stevenson

Misty Stevenson is an International Best-Selling visionary author, blogger, communal advocate, and the CEO and Founder of **Sophisticated Elite Décor;** a premier interior design company, and owner of **Stevenson Elite Renovations**; a premier construction company; by which she serves as an interior decorator; alongside her husband, CEO, and licensed contractor. Both businesses service a diverse clientele on the Mississippi gulf coast.

Misty Stevenson brings an impressive 20 years in nursing and healthcare. Misty knows all too well the importance of clarity, education, and servant leadership, centered, at the core of her business structures. Having a high respect for education, Misty received her bachelor's in science and a nursing degree from Loyola University. After receiving high honors in nursing school, she was inducted into both Sigma Theta Tau, International Honor Society of Nurses, and Sigma Alpha Pi, the National Society of Leadership and Success.

Misty's mantra is simple: wherever there is exclusivity, her name is top on the list.

Living out her mantra as a matter of simplicity, Misty is a highly decorated professional, recognized as a well-respected member of her local community. Misty is a proud member of the illustrious sisterhood **Delta Sigma Theta sorority inc.** She currently sits on the advisory board of Empowerment for the next generation. She is also a member of the **NAACP**, *The Gulf Coast Chapter of the Like-minded Ladies*, and a beloved member of the *Pow-her Group*, where her wisdom and ideas are valued amongst elite professionals. Misty is also a leader at the *Black Nurses Rock for the Mississippi gulf coast*, where she received an award for Service Excellence during the *National Black Nurses Rock Annual*

*Conference in 2018.* Remaining an impeccable example to business peers and communal leaders alike; Misty received the *Top influencer* Award for the Success conference in both 2019 and 2020; nominated as a woman of achievement for 2019, and 2021. Misty was a finalist for "Mississippi's Best" as a Registered Nurse, in 2020 and was named "Nurse of the year for 2021.Misty was named as one of the *100 most successful women of the Mississippi Gulf Coast, in 2020.* Proving herself as a woman driven by impactful accomplishment, Misty was called upon by the American Cancer Society as an honoree along with 17 other professionals and asked to fundraise to provide transportation grants for cancer patients along the Mississippi Gulf Coast. Misty was amongst the Top 5 honorees that surpassed her goal. Misty Stevenson aims to be a figure that other women can glean from; a narrative she has lived up to, very well.

Misty Stevenson devotes the best influence on her loved ones; as she is a devoted mother, wife, and friend.

Elevatewithmisty@yahoo.com

IG:@themelanatedhomemakerlife

Melanatedhomemaker.life

FB: Misty Stevenson

# To Change From Within

## By Joanna Kleier

CTACC Certified Transformational Life
Coach/Transformational Speaker/Author

Edmund Burke said, *"The only thing necessary for the triumph of evil is for good men to do nothing"*.

I was born in Burbank, CA, USA, on the floor in a triplex on October 17th, 1970. I am the fifth child out of eight pregnancies. That was back in the day when women used midwives to deliver babies in their homes.

I grew up with one brother and three sisters and unfortunately, my parents tragically lost my brother at the age of 7 due to complications from Lymphoma in 1966. I have to give my parents credit for persevering through a very turbulent time and pushing through till the end. Their strength and courage taught me to do the same for myself.

On the surface, I was living the American Dream, but deep down I was in a nightmare, trapped in a state of autopilot as a high-functioning alcoholic.

Have you ever felt like everything on the outside of your life looked entirely different from what was happening on the inside? Well, that's what happened to me.

Les Brown says, "Shoot for the moon cause even if you miss, you will land among the stars."

Coming from a generational curse of Mental Illness, Alcoholism, and Domestic Violence, I realize now at 50 years of age, I have to stop the insanity and perpetual victimization.

In 2014, I put myself in inpatient and outpatient addiction program because my addiction had reached its peak. I was a mess and fallen down the rabbit hole with no end in sight. I realized it was time to stop what I was doing because I would not have survived and so I took 100% responsibility.

Until I accepted my responsibility and stopped blaming everything and everyone for my problems that's when I realized how much control I do have over my life. Since the sudden death of my momma in 2018 (in front of me), and my bottom with my addiction and recovery, I was able to break the generational curse that had limited my family for centuries to rise up and live my dreams!

As I said, I had the American Dream, with the house, husband, two beautiful children, two dogs, and my first job for 32 years but I was dying inside with low self-esteem which included shame, guilt, alcohol addiction, being scared, and running away from any deep intimate relationships with those in my own family

Les Brown says, *"Life happens for you and not to you"* and that *"a breakdown leads to a breakthrough"*.

Elevation began for me after I hit my bottom and learned that I could get the help I required for recovery. Les Brown says *"If you take responsibility for yourself, you will develop a hunger to accomplish your dreams* Building a foundation on "Rock" for myself with self-love was the next step for me in my recovering journey to wellness.

They say that if you help others, it helps you and they are correct! When I achieved sobriety, approximately one year into it, and attended support group meetings regularly, the clouds of despair started to lift, and I felt the rush of energy for life. I saw that I could turn the dark tunnel into a vast blue endless ocean. I've been traveling into my dream of a beautiful beachside home as I work on myself each day. Rock bottom for me started in 2014, where my alcohol addiction had increased over time from its beginnings when I was 21 till the age of 48. With each additional stress of adulthood piling up, I would eventually find myself out of work for five months, in bed for four, and voluntarily put myself in an outpatient program for substance abuse. I was diagnosed with Major Depression and Bipolar Disorder.

Once I had two and a half years of sobriety, the ultimate life-changing moment was on February 8, 2018, when my mom and I left the hospital after her three-week tumultuous emergency surgery and recovery. This was the second emergency surgery in 14 months. I had decided to stay with my mom for 6 weeks to aid in her recovery but because of her sudden death within 20 minutes of us coming home from the hospital that was not going to happen. We were supposed to hang out in our pajamas and slippers and party together. This was the ultimate trial any person could ever face, and it happened to me. It taught me how strong I really could be. I want to let you my readers know is that you can get through anything.... I did. My friend, Michele Mupo, says, "Tomorrow is never promised so make every day count!"

There is a saying from Mr. Les Brown, "When you fall, fall on your back because if you look up you can get up."

I was introduced to Danette May, a Health and Wellness Expert in 2019. This turn of events changed my life forever!

Danette May wrote the book, "The Rise: An Unforgettable Journey of Self Love, Forgiveness, and Transformation. It was about her story and her rise to self-love. This is a must-read for women who desire to find inner peace in such a chaotic time working, raising children, running a household while trying to care for herself.

Danette May introduced me to meditation and visualization, healthy food combinations, exercises, and a tribe of women supporting each other in their journey to self-love. This is where the beginning of love for myself started, and it brought me out of the pit of despair and for that, I am so grateful.

*"Your job is to fill your cup up, so it overflows. Then you can serve others joyfully from your sauce,"* says Lisa Nichols. I have spent the last seven years working on being honest with my problems and getting help. I realize I can't help others until I take care of myself. In our past generation, we have been taught that it is selfish to please oneself, but self-love is not selfish!

Please take a moment every day to do self-care first. Try to, meditate, pray, visualize, get into motion and eat healthy live foods so you can live a long healthy prosperous life.

Reconnecting to oneself is key to success! Also ignoring negative people can be of great help as well.

*Don't let anyone's opinion of you become your reality,"* Les Brown.

Successful people only hang around quality people, and I find this to be very helpful.

Unfortunately, even family members can limit our exposure to a healthy environment at times so that we can maintain a healthy outlook on life. I suggest you find only quality people to spend your time with and limited or remove the toxic people from your life.

As Mahatma Gandhi has said, *"A man is but a product of his thoughts, what he thinks he becomes."* I have been studying "Mindset, Meditation, and Visualizations with Danette May and Fitrise 365." It has been a Life-Changing Program.

I recently found a program called "Thinking Into Results" created by Bob Proctor and Sandy Gallagher. I learned how to wake up each day and go into gratitude and learn through constant repetition of new information over and over again to shift old paradigms to new paradigms. This creates a new way of thinking. In three months, I saw a great shift in my thinking from negativity to positivity. This is an awesome program and I highly recommend it for those who are struggling during these stressful times.

Thriving to achieve my dreams I never thought was possible until now! Now that I think positively, I fill my cup up with goodness and surround myself with only quality people. I can be and do whatever I desire. Les Brown says, "*Shoot for the moon and you'll land among the stars!*"

Helping people is something my parents and I have always done, and it brings me immense joy. My father had a morning ritual every morning to make his day go smoothly and I do as well. Make sure you take the necessary steps to ensure you have taken care of yourself first and remember it is not selfish to do so.

I love my daily regimen for myself of reading the self-confidence formula, making a gratitude list, meditation, reading something uplifting for 30 minutes, listening to something inspirational, walking in nature, and eating live foods. This has brought me great joy and true happiness that I never had before. I truly can now say I love Joanna!

As Mahatma Gandhi says, "*Live as if you were going to die tomorrow. Learn as if you were going to live forever*".

Just because you find yourself at your bottom does not mean you can't dust yourself off and get up and start your life all over again.

There is a saying I came up with and that is when you are at your bottom there is only one way to go.... Up!

When I lost my mom, I decided that life was short and that I needed to explore entrepreneurship because after I met Danette May, finished Life Coaching Certification, Training by the Power Voice System with Les Brown, and became a Motivational Speaker, I started to build confidence.

I talk to a business leader named Tina Paulas-Krause about opening up an L.L.C, and she made it seem easy, so I bit the bullet and jumped right in. I printed business cards for the FLYING CAMILIAN L.L.C. and decided my niche would be helping women with separation from children to find self-love and self-confidence. I had helped all my friends over the last 26 years, and I was so proud of these women because they decided to protect their children from toxic relationships that would eventually destroy them and their little ones.

After receiving my business cards, I actually was afraid to pass them out. I thought I had worked through a lot of things, but I realized that if you don't face your fears, you will never achieve greatness. Each fear I push through allowed me to divide and conquer.

My first client named Jennifer I met camping a year before told me as soon as I started my business, she wanted to be my 1st client It was awesome to see her transform from her divorce to freedom. It's a hard transition for anyone but she did it with my support.

My second client by the name of Olga was a customer of mine at the grocery store. She was suffering from major anxiety. I knew anxiety all too well, so I said yes to helping her even though I was scared to death because I didn't even do any studies on anxiety or work through my own, but I wanted to do everything that scared me. I knew that if I did it, I would be really good if I just believed in Myself and just do it!

There are all sorts of things that will go through your mind and many fears that will pop up. If you just work on a daily practice of meditation, visualization, mindset, movement, and determination you will be able to do anything you choose. You will eventually find your why for living through this process of growth and turn your pain into your passion. Some opportunities pop up that will blow your mind. Always and I mean always invest in yourself no matter what!

I am now a Producer of my own show called Jojo's Mojo under the wonderful leadership of Michele Mupo of Mupo Entertainment as well as being her "Lovely Assistant." Michele has such an awesome heart and wants to teach all of her crew everything she knows about the entertainment business. Her goal is to buy buildings and house the Disabled Veterans with Handicap Accessible as well as providing therapy dogs for them.

I also have another show called "Your Voice Your Story Your Legacy" with the Believe In Your Dreams Television Network with CEO Dr. Nichole Ebullience Peters and Vice President Taneisha Ramsey where I interview people that have overcome adversities and feature my children, Mira Kleier, where she performs the songs that she has written. Lyssa Kleier and her drawings, digital art, and hip hop with the Duarte Teen Center and in Mob HQ Studios where I have a huge fondness for Mob HQ where they teach Hip Hop and other dance styles.

I have to say what Forest Gump says, "Life is like a box of chocolates, you never know what you are going to get." For years, there had been many obstacles, trials, and tribulations for half of my life, but I always had the courage that my parents gave to me. They also taught me not to give up and get help when there seems to be no hope left. I have been at my bottom for too long but since the death of my mom, I realized then how short life was!

You will find everything you want in life! It is already there; you just have to find it. Set goals, think positively, and dream big! You are enough!!

I am very proud to be able to write my story in the "BO$$ YOUR LANE" Book Compilation with such an elite group of resilient women and men. Our belief in ourselves and each other is making it possible for us to help millions with our stories and our voice. We are building a legacy for all future generations to be able to pass down stories of loss, strength, perseverance, and triumph. You too can do anything you want. You just have to believe in yourself and surround yourself with OQP, Only Quality People!

# About

# Joanna Kleier

The entire world encounters heroic grace, when unconventional leaders materialize pathways of success, for others. Displaying this ethic in unconquerable measure; is the ardent professional, Joanna Kleier.

Joanna Kleier is an Author, Transformational Life Coach, Motivational orator, and CEO and Founder of **The Flying Camilian, LLC**; a multidimensional coaching practice aiding professionals, managerial specialists, and entrepreneurial hopefuls along their diverse paths towards success. Having more than 25 years of reputable expertise in social advocacy, rehabilitation, and recovery, Joanna delivers compassionate and heartfelt results, to a global audience.

**Her mantra is clear: She helps clients alleviate annoyances that are weighing them down; creating the momentum needed, to help achieve lasting results, and to set better goals, while freeing up more time and energy**.

Joanna's expertise is emboldened by a sincere regard for humanity, advocacy, and community service. Having overcome a long battle with alcoholism and personal adversity, Joanna uses lessons reformed from her own life, to inspire others. Joanna spearheads "Standing Up Against Bullying"; a campaign positioned to reduce bullying in the workforce, and local school sectors. Her propensity for leadership is highlighted through trusted relationships with several communal influencers, such as: **The Mainseed Mastermind Group,** by which Joanna is a key consultant, and **The House of Helping Hands**, by which she is the president; helping Domestic Violence Survivors and their children with therapy, job training, and guaranteed job placement. Joanna combines her philanthropic vernacular, with a love for orating. She is a proud Motivational Speaker of **Les Brown's "Power Voice System"**, and a client of **Jon**

**Talarico's 6 Month "Thinking into Results" Mindset Coaching Program.**

When Joanna is not out speaking, educating, and advocating for victims' rights, she is an asset in her community of Duarte, and a loving member of her family and friendship circles.

**Joanna Kleier. Leader. Advocate. Philanthropist.**

Joanna Kleier

1337 Marand St.

Duarte CA 91010

Jojokleier@gmail.com

FB Joanna Bricker Kleier

IG jojokleier

Linked In Joanna Kleier CCTA

# The Time is Now!!

By EL'Nadeana Patterson

In the art of entrepreneurship, no one knows the right answer or the right way to go about becoming an entrepreneur. There is no blueprint when becoming an entrepreneur. I have always wanted my own business; I just did not know where to start or how to start. I have always worked and put my best into what I did. The thought of being an entrepreneur kind of scared me in a way because I would doubt myself or didn't feel like I had the necessary funds to start. A little about how I got to where I'm at now, I started as a retail worker. I was attending college at USM and working. After I graduated, I started working for a company that changed my outlook on life and taught me a lot of life lessons. I was working as an office manager, and let's be honest, going from a retail salesperson to an office manager is a big jump. I was nervous, but I took the leap of faith and followed my heart, and I'm glad I did. I met some of the most amazing inspiring business-minded women that made me look at life on a different level. After working as an office manager and administrative assistant for five years, I began to learn more and more about starting a business. Now I can share what I have learned with you.

One of the most important factors to have when starting a business is your WHY! Yes, your why. Make sure the reason you are starting any business is to help better someone else and yourself. Determining what your why is will help you know where to start and how to start. If you are just starting a capital business and it's not something you are really passionate about, you should think really hard about why you are starting this business. Once you find the true reason, you will start to feel different. I know I did.

I started my business which is a family-owned online boutique that has now grown into an actual retail store that specializes in providing the latest but affordable children's clothing and accessories. The reason I started this business is that I love children. I also have 2 young sons that I would have a hard time finding nice and affordable clothes for. I wanted to help parents find nice and affordable clothes for their children. Another factor to consider when starting your business is your niche. What special "sauce" do you have that separates you from any other business in the same field as you. Finding your target market and who your business will cater to is one of the most important factors to figure out.

How would you find your target market you might ask? For example, if you sell women's clothing your target market will be women. If you sell men's clothing, your target market will be men, and so on?

OK, now it's time for the fun part. You should now know your WHY, target market, and your niche or "special sauce." Now it's time to do a blueprint of your business. You now can come up with your company's name. Once you have your company's name and you love and are sure about it, it's time to register your business with the state and get an EIN with the IRS. Please make sure you are confident and sure about your business name. I have changed my business name two times, and it can be a headache to get it changed. So please make sure it's a name you love and has meaning to your business and its purpose.

Now, let's do your mission statement and purpose for your business. This will have in your blueprint. Your mission statement is a short statement that tells what kind of business you have, the products that you will have, and who you will be serving. You can create your own saying or logo that will set you apart from other businesses.

Lastly, it's time to look at the capital you will need to start your business. Start making your business budget and expenses. Research how much it will take to start the kind of business you are wanting to start. Decide if you want to save up the money or try to get an investment loan to help get it going. Always remember your business does not have to be like everyone else's. You are made to be different so don't be scared to step out on faith and follow your heart. Start the business you want to start. Do not worry about what anyone else is going to say or if it's going to fail. You will only get in your own way when you let fear stop you. You have the power to do whatever you set in your heart and mind to do. And always remember the time is NOW!! What are you waiting on???

I pray that this helps someone!

# About

# EL'Nadeana Patterson

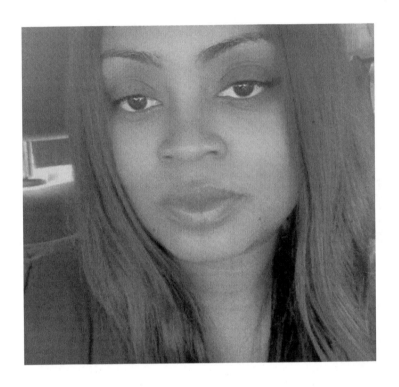

ElNadeana "Deana" Williams- Patterson was born in McComb, Mississippi to Emma Dean Williams and Ronnie Williams. She has one sibling, Ricky Williams. Growing up as a child. She enjoyed spending time with her grandmother learning different things and helping her cook. Sadly, she passed away 22 days after ElNadeana's second born.

ElNadeana attended Tylertown School in Tylertown, Mississippi. After graduation from high school, she interned at B&D Consultation. She received her associate's degree in Business from Jones County Junior College. After receiving her degree from Jones County Junior College, she attended The University of Southern Mississippi located in Hattiesburg, MS. There, she was a member of the Student Entrepreneurship Club and received her bachelor's degree in Entrepreneurship in 2016 while carrying her 1st born.

She married her high school sweetheart with whom she has two children, Germarion and Elijah Patterson. Germarion is 6 and Elijah is 2. She is currently an office manager/administrator assistant at L&L Homemaker Inc and also a business owner for a children's clothing boutique, G&E Children's Fashion. She is a devoted wife and mother who loves God.

Her favorite quote is by Maya Angelou: *"Whatever you want to do, if you want to be great at it, you have to love it and be able to make sacrifices for it."* She lives on this quote daily with whatever task given to her by striving to do her absolute best.

Her favorite saying is: If you make ONE step, GOD will Make TWO!!! She understands that "I can do all things through Christ who strengthens me." She states, "My story is currently still being written, and I know there is a great purpose for me to fulfill in my life."

EL'Nadeana Patterson

6013413094

Elnadeana_williams@yahoo.com

# THE CEO MINDSET

By Sher Graham

L ife is wonderful! Whatever choices your mind makes for your life is up to you – YOU ARE THE CEO OF YOUR LIFE! Your MINDSET as CEO determines your life journey, each moment of the day.

As you read, I hear your brain's left and right hemispheres spinning asking the question, "What is the mindset, and how do I make it work for me?" Great question!

I asked myself that question when I began my journey, as opportunities appeared. The kaleidoscope of my young life's journey and all I accomplished was lost in my personal valuation of my self-worth. Yes, there were accomplishments in writing, speaking, and volunteerism. Yet, I did not appreciate those accomplishments nor realized the impact they would have on my life journey until much later in life.

I was my own promotions and public relations agency. I learned the mechanics of writing press releases – Who, What, When, Where, How, Why – the newspaper contacts, and that a photo was required. My press release was typed on my Blackwood typewriter, mailed to the local newspaper with my photo and magically it would appear in the local newspaper days later. I was my own agent! And then one day, I became a 'stock photo.' That meant that the newspaper kept my photo in their stock because I was sending news releases to them on an ongoing basis for journalism award announcements, writing accomplishments, and my volunteer service. Somewhere beneath the surface, I was still with a sad heart.

During my high school junior year, I chose a college two hours away from my hometown, giving me space to discover my own mindset and to encourage myself to find me somewhere in the middle. My decision was the best choice I made that sent me on the trajectory of my life script as it is today. A love for writing, music, speaking, and sharing with others led me to choose a path in behavioral science, communications, and education. I combined all my gifts, my passion, and my talents into an adventure that continues to fire my inner child by putting knowledge into action and lifting thousands of others who use their inner child motivation to achieve their dreams. Now that is my CEO MINDSET.

Has my own CEO MINDSET been through the ovals of opportunity? YES. I have learned about myself (my strengths and weaknesses), how I choose my choices, how behavior impacts results (positive and negative), how to continuously maintain a healthy mindset, and how to thrive in the middle of chaos.

I am sharing with you the process I began so many decades ago, and with revisions along the way, still use.

STOP!!! Get a journal or notebook and pen to write with as you progress through these steps. Write each question down and take time to answer it.

### Discover Your CEO Mindset

Choosing to take time to discover Your CEO Mindset is the first step.

## 1. Defining Mindset – YOUR DEFINITION

Understanding your NOW mindset is your first critical step. What is your mindset? What are your values? What are your ethics? What is important to you?

Your mindset began at birth. Your opportunity is to decide if your mindset is working to achieve your dreams in your life journey. If it is, then great, maintain the mindset course. If it is not working, then it is time for your Mindset SHIFT. Shift into a definition mode.

Here is my perception of 'mindset' based on a short definition found in _Oxford Languages_: "the established set of attitudes held by someone." Or my CEO MINDSET definition: 'the established way of thinking or feeling about someone or something that is reflected in a person's behavior."

There are other synonym words and phrases that include a way of thinking, frame of mind, outlook, mentality, what makes someone tick, thoughts, ideology, and mind. Pick one that resonates with your thought process or mindset. What is your CEO MINDSET definition? Write it down and memorize it. Write it where you can see it daily.

NOTE TO SELF 1: Two thought processes that positively enable and enhance your mindset:

- 'mindfulness' – a mental state achieved by focusing one's awareness on the present moment, while calmly acknowledging and accepting one's feelings, thoughts, and bodily sensations; and,
- 'meditation' – a written or spoken discourse expressing considered thoughts on a subject.

## 2. Transformation Mindset – YOUR WHY?

Now that you have written down your definition of YOUR CEO MINDSET – you are ready for the second step. Discover YOUR WHY. Why do you want to create Your CEO MINDSET? Determine your NOW mindset. What is YOUR NOW WHY? What needs to be changed in Your WHY? If your mindset is working, continue to follow your life script. If it requires change or enhancement, be flexible in identifying and creating new actions. What will you create and implement in your IMPROVED plan to transform old thoughts and habits into new thoughts and new habits?

NOTE TO SELF 2: This takes energy, perseveration, planning, and CONSISTENTLY doing it daily, as well as checking and rechecking to make sure it is working. And, if not, creating alternative actions to replace the thoughts and actions that are not working. Trial and error? Trial by fire.

## 3. Transformation Process – YOUR WHO

Whether you take a personality test, a behavioral communications assessment, or explore forms of neurolinguistic language, you will find elements that describe you in each of these experiences. From over fifty years of my entrepreneur experience and adventure, my research and observational study have identified four CEO MINDSET Archetypes:

- Chief Enthusiasm Officer: Person who leads through positive reinforcement (whether authentic or fake), supports team members with rewards whether justified, loves to schedule team-building activities and out of office trips, but provides no written nor verbal communications for long-term planning, financial sustainment, and vision for people, products and process. Everything is in 'my head.' Expectation: You are a mind reader.

- Chief Effectiveness Officer: Person who leads through micro-management techniques, supports team members through daily 'short' meetings in their office to get status of every assigned task/project, views team building activities as a waste of money and time, overly goal-oriented, uses only yearly review process to determine success, but only provides project management goals for long-term planning, financial sustainment, and vision for people, products and process. Expectation: Follow company goals/objectives and complete written reports.

- Chief Enigma Officer: Person who allows the business to manage them, does not take ownership for lack of business success, chooses to communicate through email, text or not at all, isolates self in office, lack of participation in company events or meetings, but provides no formal written or verbal communications for long-term planning, financial sustainment and vision for people, products and process. Everything is working perfectly. Expectation: No changes needed, even if we are not financially solvent.

- Chief Executive Officer: Person who manages business responsibly with a formal written business model that is communicated to all employees, exemplifies how all employees are a part of the business team, provides a nourishing culture, leads the ideation, planning, and implementation of new and long-term business strategies, recruits, trains and maintains a strong management team, manages assets and liabilities ensuring financial sustainment, directs the growth of the company through a formal written and verbal communications strategic plan for long-term planning, financial sustainment and vision for people, products and process.

Which CEO has more traits that describe your CEO Mindset?

How you choose to manage or business or let your business manage you establishes your NOW mindset. There will be parts of each CEO archetype that may fit your management style. Who is YOUR WHO?

NOTE TO SELF 3: Write down the traits you recognized in each of the CEO archetypes. What traits need to be changed? Write down one action for changing that trait. What traits are working? Write them down. Celebrate them with a WOOHOO shout!

## 4. Transformation Process – YOUR 7 TRAITS FOR CEO MINDSET SUCCESS

These traits are part of my personal/business values, ethics, and transformation checklist. Each day, I make sure I am following these seven traits for my CEO MINDSET SUCCESS.

- Authenticity: Be who you are. What you say is important. How your body behaves reflects your thoughts more than you realize. Authentic Communications are powerful.
- Empathy: Learn to understand the feelings of another. Try to walk in their shoes and footsteps. Understanding others is powerful.
- Ownership: Take responsibility for everything happening. No excuses nor blaming anyone else. You are responsible for your life script. Owning Responsibility is powerful.
- ActiveObservingListener: Be active in observing and listening to others. Use eyes and ears more than the mouth. Clarify and connect, not respond and react. Active Observing Listener is powerful.

- Influencer: Maintain a positive attitude. Persuasion is inspiring others to motivate themselves to dream and reach for success. Influence is persuasion in action. People see what you do, not always by what you say. Influence Actions are powerful.

- Creativity: Use creativity to create solutions to business opportunities and challenges. Be curious when others have ideas. Listen and be open to new methods of problem-solving.

- Resilience: Tenacity builds resilience. Getting up each day and being happy brings healing to each person in your influential sphere. Resilient in small steps is powerful.

## YOUR CEO MINDSET TRANSFORMATION

These four steps are designed for you to begin your NEW journey in creating your CEO MINDSET transformation or guiding you to continue your NOW mindset life script that is working for you.

May your CEO MINDSET transformation bring you peace, calm from the chaos, and a transformation plan inspiring you toward success.

# About
# Sher Graham

As the Executive Vice President, NeuroBehavior, OSBI/Synergy Solutions Collab, Mobile, AL, she is a co-active neurobehavior coach and Business Solutions Consultant. Her experience in human behavior and system dynamics has given Sher

Graham opportunities to coach thousands of individuals and consult with companies in achieving their dreams and success since 1970.

Sher has spent her life learning and sharing with others through education, training, and as an international speaker and writer. An Ohio native, she is a journalist, poet, 3X international/best-selling author, and the host of Real Talk community mental wellness programs. A life-long community activist, she has received national and local recognition for her volunteer service. Graham serves as Co-Chair, Gulf Coast Mental Health Coalition, and Safe Kids Now National Network Board.

Self-care is a priority in her life and includes prayer, laughter, music, meditation, volunteering, and having a daily adventure. Her mantra: Breathe. Smile. Laugh. Pray. Read. Repeat if necessary.

### Contact Information:

Sher Graham

EVP, NeuroBehavior

OSBI/Synergy Solutions Collab

www.shergraham.com

synergytosoar@gmail.com

Telephone: 251.404.3924

LinkedIn: https://www.linkedin.com/shergraham

Instagram: https://www.instagram.com/sherg49

Twitter: https://www.twitter.com/shergraham

Facebook: https://www.facebook.com/shergraham

# You Are What You Think; It's All About The Mindset

By Sharm Ieshie McInnis

I'm so thankful to be able to share my thoughts with you. I hope there's something that I discuss in my chapter that helps you along the way— congratulations to you on deciding to start a business.

Many entrepreneurs start their own businesses to follow their dreams and also to fulfill their passion. When you follow your dreams, you will satisfy yourself in a way that working for someone else may not. You're in charge of creating your business from the ground up, so you can shape your company to be something you're proud of and that you may even be able to pass on to your children as your legacy. Many people commit to starting a business with the dream of financial comfort. While it's true that getting your company off the ground can take a lot of grit and result in some challenging times while you're getting started, the goal of being your own boss is cultivating financial independence. With determination and hard work, there's no cap on how lucrative your own business can be. If you aspire to build wealth, there's no reason why you can't achieve that goal.

One of the most important things to remember first and foremost is that Life and Death are in the power of the tongue Proverbs 18:21. You must speak life over yourself and to your situation. This would give you the courage that you didn't know you had to move forward. When you are thinking of opening a business, the most important thing to keep in mind is to treat people the way you want to be treated. Let's talk about respect; respect means honoring and valuing other people even if you don't agree with their views or actions. Respecting yourself is also crucial because it lays the groundwork for respecting other people. When being a respectful person, is it a valuable quality that will help you both personally and professionally? Although you may disagree with someone, you can still talk to them and treat them with respect. When you act respectful towards others, this encourages them to treat you with more respect.

Fairness means that a leader will treat everyone appropriately and individually, based on circumstances and contribution, not just for who they are. The best thing to do is to use sound judgment about the employees. There are numerous ways for you as a leader to ensure that you're creating a fair environment for your employees. The first thing to do is be sure to explain your expectations clearly to all employees. What kind of performance or results will be deemed excellent? What kind of rewards can employees who exhibit this outstanding performance expect? Make sure each employee has the chance to reach these personal and organizational goals on their own terms.

Your employees also need to feel valued beyond members of your team. You must meet their unique working situations with understanding and respect. If one of them is going through a tough time or situation, then their performance will likely waiver as a result. Knowing these circumstances is a direct result of having a solid and trusting relationship with your employees. Of course, all while keeping it professional.

Lastly, holding yourself accountable is another way to ensure your employees are being fairly treated. Changing your mind or your attitude on a day-to-day basis will do nothing to foster trust with your employees.

Of course, equality, diversity, and inclusion should remain a critical focus as you also move toward treating employees more fairly. Equality and fair treatment lead to happier employees who engage themselves more and productive employees who are proud to vouch for your company.

Starting your own business has several financial benefits over working for a wage or salary. First, you're building an enterprise that has the growth potential – and your wallet grows as your company does. Second, your business itself is an asset. As your business grows, it's worth more and more. You may decide to sell it or hold on to it and pass it down to your heirs. Either way, it's valuable.

The master key to a successful business, you must put yourself in the client's shoes. This is the only way that I know. When handling a situation, first ask yourself, is this a way I would like for someone to treat me? Being in business since 2006 has taught me so much, like making sure that each client knows and feels that you appreciate them. There would be no you without each client. They must know and understand that they're not just a number; they are a priority. You then deny yourself most times to ensure that you take care of your clients. This is the motto I live and drive my business each day by, and so far, it has been effective.

# About
# Sharm Ieshie McInnis

Sharm grew up in a small, rural town of Tylertown, Mississippi but later counted places such as El Paso, Texas, Izmir, Turkey, Newport News, Virginia, Killeen, Texas, and Colorado Springs, Colorado. She attended Tylertown High School in Tylertown, Mississippi; she received her Bachelor of Science and Master's Degree from Liberty University and now pursuing a Ph.D. Sharm is married has three children. After many years of living in other states, she settled back in Tylertown, Mississippi. She has over a decade of experience in entrepreneurship and multi-business platforms in areas of healthcare, housing, and event supplies such as party signage and equipment. She continues to build on to her business platform and inspire others as along the way.

For more information on how to contact Sharm McInnis. She can be reached at sharmbrown32097@yahoo.com or Facebook under Sharm Ieshie McInnis.

Bestselling author **Tess Gerritsen** is also a physician, and she brings to her novels her first-hand knowledge of emergency and autopsy rooms. But her interests span far more than medical topics. As an anthropology student at Stanford University, she catalogued centuries-old human remains, and she continues to travel the world driven by her fascination with ancient cultures and bizarre natural phenomena. Now a full-time novelist, she lives with her husband in Maine.

# GIRL
# MISSING

## TESS GERRITSEN

### BANTAM PRESS

LONDON · TORONTO · SYDNEY · AUCKLAND · JOHANNESBURG

TRANSWORLD PUBLISHERS
61–63 Uxbridge Road, London W5 5SA
A Random House Group Company
www.rbooks.co.uk

First published in the US
in 1994 by HarperPaperbacks
a division of HarperCollins Publishers
under the title *Peggy Sue Got Murdered*

First published in Great Britain
in 2009 by Bantam Press
an imprint of Transworld Publishers

A CIP catalogue record for this book
is available from the British Library.

ISBN 9780593062753

Addresses for Random House Group Ltd companies outside the UK
can be found at: www.randomhouse.co.uk
The Random House Group Ltd Reg. No. 954009

The Random House Group Limited supports The Forest Stewardship Council
(FSC), the leading international forest-certification organization. All our titles that
are printed on Greenpeace-approved FSC-certified paper carry the FSC logo.
Our paper procurement policy can be found at
www.rbooks.co.uk/environment

Typeset in 11.5/17pt Arrus by
Falcon Oast Graphic Art Ltd.
Printed and bound in Great Britain by
Clays Limited, Bungay, Suffolk

4 6 8 10 9 7 5 3

**Mixed Sources**
Product group from well-managed
forests and other controlled sources
www.fsc.org  Cert no. TT-COC-2139
© 1996 Forest Stewardship Council
FSC

# AN INTRODUCTION
# FROM THE AUTHOR

Years before I built my reputation as a thriller writer, I had another life – as a romantic suspense author. Fans of my crime novels may be surprised to learn that I launched my career by writing stories in which romance shared equal billing with murder, where characters struggle with both fear and sexual tension. At the time, I was working as a doctor in a hospital, a job in which I saw far too much pain and heartbreak at work. At the end of the day, I drew comfort from reading – and writing – romance novels.

But over the course of writing nine of those novels, I found that the thriller elements began to dominate my plots. I was evolving into a crime writer, and in *Girl Missing* (first published in 1994 under the title *Peggy Sue Got Murdered*), that evolution is well underway. Yes, it's a romance. But it's also a crime novel, featuring a female medical examiner who must track down the cause of an epidemic of mysterious deaths. I consider it my 'bridge' novel, a moment in time when I was poised to step from one genre into the next.

Recently updated for today's readers, *Girl Missing* will give you a glimpse of the thriller writer I would one day become. I hope you enjoy the look back!

Tess Gerritsen
May 2009

# 1

An hour before her shift started, an hour before she was even supposed to be there, they rolled the first corpse through the door.

Up until that moment, Kat Novak's day had been going better than usual. Her car had started on the first turn of the key. Traffic had been sparse on Telegraph, and she'd hit all the green lights. She'd managed to slip into her office at five to seven, and for the next hour she could lounge guiltlessly at her desk with a jelly doughnut and today's edition of the *Albion Herald*. She made a point of skipping the obituaries. Chances were she already knew all about them.

Then a gurney with a black body bag rolled past her doorway. *Oh Lord*, she thought. In about thirty seconds, Clark was going to knock at her door, asking for favors. With a sense of dread, Kat listened to the gurney wheels grind down the hall. She heard the autopsy room doors whisk open and shut, heard the distant rumble of male voices. She counted ten seconds, fifteen. And there it was, just as she'd anticipated: the sound of Clark's Reeboks squeaking across the linoleum floor.

He appeared in her doorway. 'Morning, Kat,' he said.

She sighed. 'Good morning, Clark.'

'Can you believe it? They just wheeled one in.'

'Yeah, the *nerve* of them.'

'It's already seven ten,' he said. A note of pleading crept into his voice. 'If you could just do me this favor . . .'

'But I'm not here.' She licked a dollop of raspberry jelly from her fingers. 'Until eight o'clock, I'm nothing more than a figment of your imagination.'

'I don't have time to process this one. Beth's got the kids packed and ready to take off, and here I am, stuck with another Jane Doe. Have a heart.'

'This is the third time this month.'

'But I've got a family. They expect me to spend time with them. You're a free agent.'

'Right. I'm a divorcee, not a temp.'

Clark shuffled into her office and leaned his ample behind against her desk. 'Just this once. Beth and I, we're having problems, you know, and I want this vacation to start off right. I'll return the favor sometime. I promise.'

Sighing, Kat folded up the *Herald*. 'Okay,' she said. 'What've you got?'

Clark was already pulling off his white coat, visibly shifting to vacation mode. 'Jane Doe. No obvious trauma. Another body-fluid special. Sykes and Ratchet are in there with her.'

'They bring her in?'

'Yeah. So you'll have a decent police report to work with.'

Kat rose to her feet and brushed powdered sugar off her scrub pants. 'You owe me,' she said, as they headed into the hall.

'I know, I know.' He stopped at his office and grabbed his jacket – a fly-fisherman's version, complete with a zillion pockets with little feathers poking out.

'Leave a few trout for the rest of us.'

He grinned and gave her a salute. 'Into the wilds of Maine I go,' he said, heading for the elevator. 'See you next week.'

Feeling resigned, Kat pushed open the door to the autopsy room and went in.

The body, still sealed in its black bag, lay on the slab. Lieutenant Lou Sykes and Sergeant Vince Ratchet, veterans of the local knife and gun club, were waiting for her. Sykes looked dapper as usual in a suit and tie – a black homicide detective who always insisted on mixing corpses with Versace. His partner, Vince Ratchet, was, in contrast, a perpetual candidate for Slim-Fast. Ratchet was peering in fascination at a specimen jar on the shelf.

'What the hell is that?' he asked, pointing to the jar. Good old Vince; he was never afraid to sound stupid.

'That's the right middle lobe of a lung,' Kat said.

'I would've guessed it was a brain.'

Sykes laughed. 'That's why she's the doc and you're just a dumb cop.' He straightened his tie and looked at her. 'Isn't Clark doing this one?'

9

Kat snapped on a pair of gloves. 'Afraid I am.'

'Thought your shift started at eight.'

'Tell me about it.' She went to the slab and gazed down at the bag, feeling her usual reluctance to open the zipper, to reveal what lay beneath the black plastic. *How many of these bags have I opened?* she wondered. A hundred, two hundred? Each one contained its own private horror story. This was the hardest part, sliding down the zipper, unveiling the contents. Once a body was revealed, once she'd weathered the initial shock of its appearance, she could set to work with a scientist's dispassion. But the first glimpse, the first reaction – that was always pure emotion, something over which she had no control.

'So, guys,' she said. 'What's the story here?'

Ratchet came forward and flipped open his notebook. It was like an extension of his arm, that notebook; she'd never seen him without it. 'Caucasian female, no ID, age twenty to thirty. Body found four A.M. this morning, off South Lexington. No apparent trauma, no witnesses, no nothing.'

'South Lexington,' said Kat, and images of that neighborhood flashed through her mind. She knew the area too well – the streets, the back alleys, the playgrounds rimmed with barbed wire. And, looming above it all, the seven buildings, as grim as twenty-story concrete headstones. 'The Projects?' she asked.

'Where else?'

'Who found her?'

'City trash pickup,' said Sykes. 'She was in an alley between two of the Project buildings, sort of wedged against a Dumpster.'

'As if she was placed there? Or died there?'

Sykes glanced at Ratchet. 'You were at the scene first. What do you say, Vince?'

'Looked to me like she died there. Just lay down, sort of curled up against the Dumpster, and called it quits.'

It was time. Steeling herself for that first glimpse, Kat reached for the zipper and opened the bag. Sykes and Ratchet both took a step backward, an instinctive reaction she herself had to quell. The zipper parted and the plastic fell away to reveal the corpse.

It wasn't bad; at least it appeared intact. Compared to some of the corpses she'd seen, this one was actually in excellent shape. The woman was a bleached blond, about thirty, perhaps younger. Her face looked like marble, pale and cold. She was dressed in a long-sleeved purple pullover, some sort of polyester blend, a short black skirt with a patent leather belt, black tights, and brand-new Nikes. Her only jewelry was a dime-store friendship ring and a Timex watch – still ticking. Rigor mortis had frozen her limbs into a vague semblance of a fetal position. Both fists were clenched tight, as though, in her last moment of life, they'd been caught in spasm.

Kat took a few photos, then picked up a cassette recorder and began to dictate. 'Subject is a white female, blond, found in alley off South Lexington around oh four hundred . . .' Sykes and Ratchet, already knowing what would follow, took off their jackets and reached into a linen cart for some gowns – medium for Sykes, extra large for Ratchet. The gloves came next. They both knew the drill; they'd been cops for years, and partners for four months. It was an odd pairing, Kat thought, like Abbott and Costello. So far, though, it seemed to work.

She put down the cassette recorder. 'Okay, guys,' she said. 'On to the next step.'

The undressing. The three of them worked together to strip the corpse. Rigor mortis made it difficult; Kat had to cut away the skirt. The outer clothing was set aside. The tights and underwear were to be examined later for evidence of recent sexual contact. When at last the corpse lay naked, Kat once again reached for the camera and clicked off a few more photos for the evidence file.

It was time for the hands-on part of the job – the part one never saw on *House*. Occasionally, the answers fell right into place with a first look. Time of death, cause of death, mechanism and manner of death – these were the blanks that had to be filled in. A verdict of suicide or natural causes would make Sykes and Ratchet happy; a verdict of homicide would not.

This time, unfortunately, Kat could give them no quick answers.

She could make an educated guess about time of death. Livor mortis, the body's mottling after death, was un-fixed, suggesting that death was less than eight hours old, and the body temperature, using Moritz's formula, sug-gested a time of death of around midnight. But the cause of death?

'Nothing definitive, guys,' she said. 'Sorry.'

Sykes and Ratchet looked disappointed, but not at all surprised.

'We'll have to wait for body fluids,' she said.

'How long?'

'I'll collect it, get it to the state lab today. But they've been running a few weeks behind.'

'Can't you run a few tests here?' asked Sykes.

'I'll screen it through gas and TL chromatography, but it won't be specific. Definitive drug ID will have to go through the state lab.'

'All we want to know,' said Ratchet, 'is whether it's possible.'

'Homicide's always possible.' She continued her external exam, starting with the head. No signs of trauma here; the skull felt intact, the scalp unbroken. The blond hair was tangled and dirty; obviously the woman had not washed it in days. Except for postmortem changes, she saw no marks on the torso either. The left arm, however, drew her attention. It had a long ridge of scar tissue snaking down it toward the wrist.

'Needle tracks,' said Kat. 'And a fresh puncture mark.'

'Another junkie,' sighed Sykes. 'There's our cause of death. Probable OD.'

'We could run a fast analysis on her needle,' said Kat. 'Where's her kit?'

Ratchet shook his head. 'Didn't find one.'

'She must've had a needle. A syringe.'

'I looked,' said Ratchet. 'I didn't see any.'

'Did you find anything near the body?'

'Nothing,' said Ratchet. 'No purse, no ID, nothing.'

'Who was first on the scene?'

'Patrolman. Then me.'

'So we've got a junkie with fresh needle marks. But no needle.'

Sykes said, 'Maybe she shot up somewhere else. Wandered into the alley and died.'

'Possible.'

Ratchet was peering at the woman's hand. 'What's this?' he said.

'What's what?'

'She's got something in her hand.'

Kat looked. Sure enough, there was a tiny fleck of pink cardboard visible under the edge of her clenched fingers. It took two of them to pry the fist open. Out slid a matchbook, small and pink with raised gold lettering: 'L'Etoile, fine nouvelle cuisine. 221 Hilton Avenue.'

'Kind of out of her neighborhood,' Sykes remarked.

'Hey, I hear that's a nice place,' said Ratchet. 'Not that I could ever afford to eat there myself.'

Kat opened the matchbook. Inside were three unused matches. And a phone number, scrawled in fountain pen ink on the inside cover.

'Think it's a local number?' she asked.

'Prefix would put it in Surry Heights,' said Sykes. 'That's still out of her neighborhood.'

'Well,' said Kat. 'Let's try it out and see what happens.' As Sykes and Ratchet stood by, she went to the wall phone and dialed the number. It rang, three times, four. An answering machine came on, the message spoken by a deep male voice:

'I'm not available at the moment. Please leave your name and number.'

That was all. No cute music, no witty remarks, just that terse request, and then the beep.

Kat said, 'This is Dr. Novak at the Albion medical examiner's office. Please call me back, in regards to a . . .' She paused, unwilling to reveal that she had a corpse whom he might know. Instead she said, 'Please call me. It's important,' and left her number. She hung up and looked at the two cops. 'We'll just have to wait and see who calls back. In the meantime, do you both want to stick around for the autopsy?'

It was probably the last thing the men wanted to do, but they remained stoically by the table, wincing as she stabbed various needles into the corpse, collecting blood from the femoral vein, vitreous fluid from the eye, and urine from a puncture through the lower abdominal wall. After watching a needle pierce an eyeball, a blade does not hold nearly as many horrors. Kat picked up the Henckel knife and this time neither man flinched, even as her blade sliced into the torso. Even as she snapped apart ribs and lifted off the sternum, releasing the odor of blood and offal.

Inside the chest, organs glistened.

Kat put down her knife and picked up a far more delicate scalpel. Reaching into the cavity, her gloved hands registered the neutral temperature of those organs. Neither warm like the living, nor chilled like a refrigerated corpse. As Goldilocks would have said, *Not too hot, not too cold, but just right* – this description suitable for a corpse

15

that had been lying exposed on a spring night. She sliced through the great vessels, freeing the heart and lungs, which she lifted out of the chest cavity.

'These lungs feel pretty heavy,' she noted. She set them on the scale and watched as the dial confirmed her judgment.

'What would cause them to be heavy?' asked Ratchet.

She noticed the fleck of froth that had leaked from the bronchi. 'There's foamy edema. The lungs are filled with fluid.'

'Meaning what? She drowned in an alley?'

'In a sense, she did drown. But the fluid came from her own lungs. Foamy edema can be caused by any number of things.'

'Like a drug OD?' asked Sykes.

'Absolutely. This could certainly happen after an overdose of narcotics.'

She sliced open the heart, examined the chambers. Except for the soggy lungs, the organs appeared grossly normal. The coronary vessels were healthy, the liver and pancreas and intestines undiseased. Cutting open the stomach, she found no food remnants, only 20cc of bilious fluid.

'Died with an empty stomach,' said Kat.

'Look at how skinny she is,' said Sykes. 'When you're shooting crap into your veins, I'd guess eating takes second priority.'

Kat moved on to the vagina and rectum. It was one aspect of the postmortem that made her uncomfortable, but only because two men were in the room. As she inspected the external genitalia, as she inserted swabs to collect body fluids, they were watching intently, and it was more than just Jane Doe's privacy that felt violated. 'I don't see any evidence of sexual assault,' she said.

She turned her attention to the head. Of all the parts of a corpse, the face is the most personal, and the most disturbing to contemplate. Until that moment, Kat had avoided looking at it too closely, but now she was forced to. In life, the young woman might have been pretty. Shampoo her hair, animate those facial muscles into a smile, and she would probably have caught the eye of more than a few men. But death had made her jaw droop, her mouth gape open, revealing coffee-stained teeth and a tongue dried out from exposure. It was a blank face, revealing no secrets.

Neither did her cranium provide any answers. Kat sawed open the skull and the brain within showed no signs of hemorrhage or stroke or trauma. It was a healthy-looking brain, a young brain, and it should have given its owner many more years of service. Instead that brain, with its lifetime of memories, was now dropped into a bucket of formalin. And the body – what was left of it – would go into a refrigerated drawer, dubbed with the name shared by far too many other unidentified women who had come before her.

Jane Doe.

Kat was sitting at her desk later that morning when her phone rang. She picked it up and answered: 'Dr. Novak, Assistant ME.'

'You left a message,' said a man. She recognized at once the voice from the answering machine. Its deep timbre was now edged with anxiety. 'What's this all about?' he demanded.

Kat at once reached for pen and paper. 'Who am I speaking to?' she asked.

'You should know. You called *me*.'

'I just had your telephone number, not a name—'

'And how did you get my number?'

'It was written on a matchbook. The police brought a woman into the morgue this morning, and she—'

He cut in: 'I'll be right there.'

'Mister, I didn't catch your—'

She heard the click of the receiver, then a dial tone. *Jackass*, she thought. What if he didn't show up? What if he didn't call back?

She dialed Homicide and left a message for Sykes and Ratchet: 'Get yourselves back to the morgue.' Then she waited.

At noon, she got a buzz on the intercom from the front desk. 'There's a Mr. Quantrell here,' said the secretary. 'He says you're expecting him. Want me to send him down?'

'I'll meet him up there,' said Kat. 'I'm on my way.'

She knew better than to just drag a civilian in off the street and take him straight down to the morgue. He would need a chance to prepare for the shock. She pulled a white lab coat over her scrub suit. The lapel had coffee stains, but it would have to do.

By the time she'd ridden up the basement elevator to the ground floor, she'd rearranged her hair into a semblance of presentability and straightened her name tag. She stepped out into the hallway. Through the glass door at the end of the corridor she could see the reception area with its couch and upholstered chairs, all in generic gray. She could also see a man pacing back and forth in front of the couch, oblivious to her approach. He was nicely dressed, and didn't seem like the sort of man who'd be acquainted with a Jane Doe from South Lexington. His camel-hair jacket was perfectly tailored to his wide shoulders. He had a tan raincoat slung over his arm, and he was tugging at his tie as though it were strangling him.

Kat pushed the glass door open and walked in. 'Mr. Quantrell?'

At once the man turned and faced her. He had wheat-colored hair, perfectly groomed, and eyes a shade she'd never seen before. Not quite blue, not quite gray, they seemed as changeable as a spring sky. He was old enough – his early forties perhaps – to have amassed a few charac-ter lines around those eyes, a few gray hairs around his temples. His jaw was set with tension.

'I'm Dr. Novak,' she said, holding out her hand. He shook it automatically, quickly, as though to get the formalities done and over with.

'Adam Quantrell,' he said. 'You left that message on my answering machine.'

'Why don't we go down to my office? You can wait there until the police—'

'You said something about a woman,' he cut in rudely. 'That the police brought in a woman.' No, it wasn't rude-ness, Kat decided. He was afraid.

'It might be better to wait for Lieutenant Sykes,' she said. 'He can explain the situation.'

'Why don't *you* explain it to me?'

'I'm just the medical examiner, Mr. Quantrell. I can't give out information.'

The look he shot her was withering. All at once she wished she stood a little straighter, a little taller. That she didn't feel so threatened by that gaze of his. 'This Lieutenant Sykes,' he said. 'He's from Homicide, right?'

'Yes.'

'So there's a question of murder.'

'I don't want to speculate.'

'Who is she?'

'We don't have an ID yet.'

'Then you don't know.'

'No.'

He paused. 'Let me see the body.' It wasn't a request but a command, and a desperate one at that.

Kat glanced at the door and wondered when the hell Sykes would arrive. She looked back at the man and realized that he was barely holding it together. *He's terrified. Terrified that the body lying in my refrigerated drawer is someone he knows and loves.*

'That's why you called me, isn't it?' he said. 'To find out if I can identify her?'

She nodded. 'The morgue is downstairs, Mr. Quantrell. Come with me.'

He strode beside her in silence, his tanned face looking pale under the fluorescent lights. He was silent as well on the elevator ride down to the basement. She glanced up once, and saw that he was staring straight ahead, as though afraid to look anywhere else, as though afraid he'd lose what control he still had.

When they stepped off the elevator, he paused, glancing around at the scuffed walls, the tired linoleum floor. Overhead was another bank of flickering fluorescent lights. The building was old, and down here in the basement one could see the decay in the chipped paint, the cracked walls, could smell it in the very air. When the whole city was in the process of decay, when every agency from Social Services to trash pickup was clamoring for a dwindling share of tax dollars, the ME's office was always the last to be funded. Dead citizens, after all, do not vote.

But if Adam Quantrell took note of his surroundings, he did not comment.

'It's down this hall,' said Kat.

Wordlessly he followed her to the cold storage room.

She paused at the door. 'The body's in here,' she said. 'Are you . . . feeling up to it?'

He nodded.

She led him inside. The room was brightly lit, almost painfully so. Refrigerated drawers lined the far wall, some of them labeled with names and numbers. This time of year, the occupancy rate was running on the high side. The spring thaw, the warmer weather, brought the guns and knives out onto the street again, and these were the latest crop of victims. There were three Jane Does. Kat reached for the drawer labeled 373-4-3-A. Pausing, she glanced at Adam. 'It's not going to be pleasant.'

He swallowed. 'Go ahead.'

She pulled open the drawer. It slid out noiselessly, releasing a waft of cold vapor. The body was almost formless under the shroud. Kat looked up at Adam, to see how he was holding up. It was the men who usually fainted, and the bigger they were, the harder they were to pull up off the linoleum. So far, this guy was doing okay. Grim and silent, but okay. Slowly she lifted off the shroud. Jane Doe's alabaster-white face lay exposed.

Again, Kat looked at Adam.

He had paled slightly, but he hadn't moved. Neither did his gaze waver from the corpse. For a solid ten seconds he stared at Jane Doe, as though trying to reconstruct her frozen features into something alive, something familiar.

At last he let out a deep breath. Only then did Kat realize the man had been holding it. He looked across at her. In an utterly calm voice, he said, 'I've never seen this woman before in my life.'

Then he turned and walked out of the room.

# 2

Kat shut the drawer and followed Adam into the hall. 'Wait. Mr. Quantrell.'

'I can't help you. I don't know who she is.'

'But you *thought* you knew. Didn't you?'

'I don't know what I thought.' He was striding toward the elevator, his long legs carrying him at a brisk pace.

'Why did she have your phone number?'

'I don't know.'

'Is it a business number? One the public might know?'

'No, it's my home phone.'

'Then how did she get it?'

'I told you, I don't know.' He reached the elevator and stabbed the Up button. 'She's a total stranger.'

'But you were afraid you knew her. That's why you came down here.'

'I was doing my civic duty.' He shot her a look that said, *No more questions.*

Kat asked anyway. 'Who did you think she was, Mr. Quantrell?'

He didn't answer. He just regarded her with that impenetrable gaze.

'I want you to sign a statement,' she said. 'And I need to know how to reach you. In case the police have more questions.'

He reached into his jacket and pulled out a card. 'My home address,' he said, handing it to her.

She glanced at it. *11 Fair Wind Lane, Surry Heights.* Sykes had been correct about that phone prefix.

'You'll have to talk to the police,' she said.

'Why?'

'Routine questions.'

'Is it a homicide or isn't it?'

'I don't know yet.'

The doors slid open. 'When you make up your mind, call me.'

She slipped into the elevator after him, and the doors shut behind her. 'Look,' she said. 'I have a dead body with no name. Now, I could just call her Jane Doe and leave it at that. But somewhere, there's someone who's missing a sister or a daughter or a wife. I'd like to help them out, I really would.'

'Fingerprints.'

'I've done that.'

'Dental X-rays.'

'I've done that, too.'

'You sound capable. You don't need my help.' The doors slid open and he stepped out. 'It's not as if I don't

24

care,' he said, leading her on a brisk chase down the hall, toward the reception area. 'But I don't see why I should get dragged into this, just because my number happens to be written in some – some restaurant matchbook. She could've gotten it anywhere. Stolen it—'

'I never told you it was from a restaurant.'

He halted and turned to her. 'Yes, you did.'

'No, I didn't. I *know* I didn't.'

He fell silent. Their gazes locked, both of them refusing to yield ground. *Even a guy as smooth as you are can slip up,* she thought with a dart of satisfaction.

'And I'm sure you're wrong,' he said evenly. He turned and went into the reception area.

Sykes and Ratchet were standing by the front desk.

Sykes tuned to Kat and said, 'We got your message . . .' His gaze shifted to the man with her, and he reacted with surprise. 'Mr. Quantrell. What brings you down to . . .' Suddenly he glanced back at Kat.

'It was his phone number, Lou,' said Kat. 'But Mr. Quantrell says he doesn't know the woman.'

'Talk to her, Lieutenant,' said Adam. 'Maybe you can convince Dr. Novak I'm not some ax murderer.'

Sykes laughed. 'Novak giving you a hard time?'

'Since I can see you two already know each other,' said Kat in irritation, 'I'll just take Mr. Quantrell at his word.'

'I'm so relieved,' said Adam. 'Now, if you'll excuse me . . .' He gave Kat a brief nod. 'Dr. Novak, it has been . . . interesting.' He turned to leave.

'Excuse me, Mr. Q.?' called Sykes. 'A word, please.'

As the two men moved to a far corner of the room, Kat

caught Adam's glance. It said, *This has nothing to do with you.*

'We'll see you downstairs, Lou,' Ratchet said. Then he gave Kat a nudge. 'C'mon. You got anymore of that god-awful coffee?'

She could take a hint. As she and Ratchet walked to the elevators, she looked over her shoulder. The two men were still in the corner, talking in low voices. Adam was facing her, and over the head of the shorter Sykes, he caught sight of her backward glance and he returned it with a look of cool acknowledgment. The tension in his face was now gone; he was back in full control.

In the elevator she said, 'Okay, Vince. Who is he?'

Ratchet shrugged. 'Owns some pharmaceutical company. Cyrus, something or other.'

'Cygnus? He owns the *Cygnus* Company?'

'Yeah, that's it. He's always in those society pages. You know, this or that black-tie affair. Surprised you haven't heard of him.'

'I don't read the society pages.'

'You should. Your ex was mentioned in them the other day. He was at some campaign benefit for the mayor. Had a nice-looking blond on his arm.'

'That's why I don't read the society pages.'

'Oh.'

They got out of the elevator and headed to Kat's office. The coffee machine was doing overtime today. The glass pot had already been emptied twice, and what was left in it now looked positively vile. She poured out a cup and handed it to Ratchet.

'How does Lou know Mr. Society?' she asked.

Ratchet frowned at the evil brew in his mug. 'Some private thing. Quantrell asked Lou for a little police assistance. Something to do with his daughter.'

'Quantrell has a daughter?'

'That's what I hear.'

'He didn't strike me as the daddy type. Not a guy who'd let sticky little hands anywhere near his cashmere coat.'

Ratchet took a sip from the mug and winced. 'Your coffee's improved.'

'What sort of help did Lou give him?'

'Oh, the girl dropped out of sight or something. You'd have to ask Lou. It happened a while back, before we got paired up.'

'Was he working South Lexington?'

'Been on that beat for years. That's where his partner went down. Drive-by. Then I lost mine in Watertown, and Lou got stuck with me. The rest, as they say, is history.' He took another sip of coffee.

'Adam Quantrell doesn't live anywhere near South Lexington.'

Ratchet laughed. 'That's for sure.'

'So why did he tap a South Lexington cop for help?'

'I don't know. Why don't you ask Lou?' Ratchet's cell phone rang. Automatically he glanced down at the number on the display and sighed. 'Ratchet here,' he said. 'Yeah, what have you got for us now?'

Kat turned her attention to the stack of papers on her desk. They were the request forms to be sent with the body fluid samples to the state lab. If she wanted to make the three o'clock pickup, she'd have to fill them out now. She sat down and began checking the appropriate boxes: Gas chromatography/UC; immunoanalysis. Every test that might possibly identify the drug that had killed Jane Doe.

She looked up at the sound of footsteps. Sykes walked in. 'Sorry to brush you off,' he said. 'It was sort of a personal matter for Mr. Quantrell.'

'So I heard.' She resumed filling out the forms.

He noticed the papers. 'Is that for Jane Doe?'

'Courier comes by at three. I know you want quick answers.' She gathered up the slips, wrapped them around the test tubes, and stuffed it all in a lab envelope. 'So here it is, off to the races.' She dropped the bundle into the basket marked *Pick up*.

'Thought you were going to run some tests here.'

'I'll do them when I do them. First, I've got deadlines on a few autopsy reports. Court dates coming up. And my ex has already sent me nasty messages over voice mail.'

Sykes laughed. 'You and Ed still at each other's throats?'

'Lou, love is fleeting. Contempt is forever.'

'I take it you're not going to vote for him.'

'Actually, I think Ed's got the right temperament for a DA. Don't you agree he's got that striking resemblance to a Doberman pinscher?' She went to the filing cabinet and began rummaging for papers. 'Besides, Ed and the mayor deserve each other.'

'Hell,' grunted Ratchet, snapping shut the phone. 'Now we'll miss lunch.'

'What is it?' asked Sykes.

'We just got a call. They found another one. Female, no signs of trauma.'

Kat looked up from the file drawer. Ratchet was already scribbling in his notebook. 'Another OD?' she asked.

'Probably. And my stomach's already growling.' He kept writing in that matter-of-fact way of his. *Too many corpses, too many deaths, and this is what it does to us*, Kat thought. *A dead body means nothing more to us than a canceled lunch.*

'Where's the vic?' she asked.

'South Lexington.'

'What part of South Lexington?'

Ratchet shut his notebook and looked up. 'Same place we found the other one,' he said. 'The Projects.'

Adam Quantrell walked briskly across the street, his shoulders hunched against the wind, his hands thrust deep into the pockets of his raincoat. It was April already, but it felt like January. The wind was cutting, the trees skeletal; people on the street wore their winter pallor like masks.

He unlocked his Volvo, slid into the driver's seat, and shut the door.

He sat there for a moment, safely hidden behind tinted glass, relieved to be in a place where no one could read his face, divine his thoughts. It was cold inside; his breath misted the air. But the real chill came from within.

*It wasn't her. At least I should be thankful for that.*

He started the engine and guided the Volvo into city traffic. His first inclination was to head for Surry Heights and home. He should call his secretary and tell her he wouldn't be in the office today. What he needed was a chance to regain his composure, something he'd lost when he'd first heard that doctor's voice on his answering machine.

What was her name again? Novak. Yes, that was it. Vaguely he wondered what Dr. Novak's first name was, thought it had to be something blunt and to-the-point, like the woman. She was a straight shooter; he appreciated that. What he hadn't appreciated were her sharp eyes, her keen antennae. She'd seen far more than he'd intended to reveal.

He merged onto the freeway. Still a half hour to Surry Heights. He wanted out of the city, out of all this gray and gloomy concrete.

Then he passed a highway sign that said: *South Lexington, exit ½ mile*.

What came next was a snap decision, a crazy impulse that rose purely out of guilt. He turned onto the ramp and followed the curve until it eased into South Lexington Avenue. Suddenly he was driving through a war zone. The area around the ME's office had been shabby, but at least the buildings were occupied, the windows intact.

Here, on South Lexington, it was hard to imagine anything but rats residing behind all this red brick and shattered glass. He drove past empty warehouses and dead businesses, reminders of the city's better days. Two miles south, beyond the abandoned Johan Weir tannery, he came to the Projects. He could see them from blocks away, those seven gray towers propped up against an equally gray sky.

They were relics from an earlier age, born of good intentions, but doomed by location and design. Built miles from any jobs, constructed of monolithic concrete, they looked more like prison towers than public housing. Even so, they remained occupied. He saw cars parked on the road, clumps of people gathered on corners, a man huddled on his front stoop, a kid shooting baskets in an alley hoop. They all glanced up as Adam drove past, every pair of eyes taking note of this territorial incursion.

Adam drove another block, pulled over to the side, and parked in front of Building Five.

For an hour he sat in his car, watching the sidewalks, the alleys, the playground across the street. Mothers shuttled babies in strollers across broken glass. Young kids played hopscotch on the pavement. *Even here*, he thought, *life goes on*. He knew people were watching him; they always did.

Someone tapped on his window. He glanced out through the lightly tinted glass and saw a young woman. She had a wild mane of uncombed black hair, dark eyes, a white face heavily caked with makeup. Upon closer scrutiny, he realized it was just a young girl under all that rouge and powder.

Once again, she tapped on the window. He rolled it down a few inches.

'Hey, honey,' she said sweetly. 'You lookin' for me?'

'I'm looking for Maeve,' he said.

'Don't know any Maeve. What about me?'

He smiled. 'I don't think so.'

'I'm open to anything. Indulge your fantasies.'

'I'm really not interested. Thank you.' He rolled up the window.

At once her smile transformed to a scowl. She muttered an obscenity, audible even through the closed glass, then she turned and walked away.

He watched her blue jean-clad hips sway as she headed down the street, saw her pause by a gathering of young men. Automatically she tilted her head up in a smile. No interest there either. With a shrug, she kept walking.

Something about that young woman – her raven-colored hair, perhaps, or that walk, announcing to the world: *I can take care of myself*, reminded him of someone. Dr. Novak, the woman with no first name. She had hair that color, a thick and glossy black, just long enough to lap at her shoulders. And her gait, what he'd seen of it in the dim basement corridor, had that confident spring to its step. He suddenly wished he'd told her the truth, about the matchbook, about Maeve. He knew she knew he'd been lying. It was necessary to hide the truth, but he felt uneasy about it. And it troubled him that Dr. Novak now considered him some sort of miscreant, whose word was not to be trusted.

*Why should it bother me? I'll never see the woman again.*

At least he hoped he wouldn't. A trip to the city morgue wasn't the sort of experience he cared to repeat. He wondered how she could stand it, dealing every day with death, probing the contents of those ghastly refrigerated steel drawers. How did one live with the images? He himself was having trouble dealing with just one image he'd confronted an hour ago – the dead woman, the one who'd been clutching the matchbook.

Thank God it wasn't Maeve.

He reached for the car phone, dialed his office, and told Greta he wouldn't be coming in. She sounded surprised; it was unlike him to skip work, even for a day. 'Let Hal hold the fort,' he told her. After all, what were senior vice presidents for?

Outside, a police car slowly cruised by and continued down South Lexington. Children, just out of school, skipped along the pavement, kicking glass. Adam told Greta he'd see her in the morning, and hung up the phone. Then, grim-faced, he settled back against the seat and resumed watching the street.

Dr. Davis Wheelock, the chief medical examiner, had an office on the fourth floor, in a distant corner of the facility. It was about as far as one could get from the grim day-to-day business of the morgue and still work in the same building. The brass plaque on his door was a gift from his wife, who had been distressed by the cheap plastic version provided by the city of Albion. If one must be a public servant, so her reasoning went, at least one could do so in style.

Dr. Wheelock shared his wife's view, and his office was a reflection of his expensive and eclectic taste. In various places of honor were displayed Kenyan masks, Egyptian papyruses, Incan statuettes, all acquired during his travels. The office faced east, toward the river. On this overcast day it was an unremittingly depressing view. The gray light through the window seemed to cloak Wheelock and all his primitive artwork in gloom.

'Drug ODs are a fact of life in this town,' said Wheelock. 'We can't chase them all. Unless you're sure it's something new, I can't see getting distracted—'

'That's just it,' said Kat as she sat down in the chair across from him. 'I don't *know* if it's something new. But I think you should notify the mayor. And maybe the press.'

Wheelock shook his head. 'Aren't you overreacting?'

'Davis, in the last twenty-four hours, I've had two come in, young women, no signs of trauma. Both found in the South Lexington area. Since they both had tracks on their arms and recent needle punctures, I was ready to call them ODs.'

'Heroin?'

'That's the problem. I can't identify it. I've sent blood, urine, and vitreous to the state lab for immunoassay, but that'll take a week.'

'What have you run here?'

'Thin layer and gas chromatography. Subject One had a positive ethanol. Subject Two turned up salicylates, probably just aspirin. Both subjects had the same peak on gas chromatography – it looks like a narcotic.'

'There's your answer.'

'Here's the problem. It's a weird peak, biphasic. Not quite an opiate, not quite cocaine. I've never seen it before.'

'Impurities. Someone cut two drugs together.'

'Maybe.'

'Wait till the state IDs it. It'll just take a week.'

'And in the meantime?'

'You've only got two victims.'

She leaned forward on his desk. 'Davis, I don't *want* any more victims. And I'm afraid we're about to get more.'

'Why?'

'After the second woman rolled in, I got on the phone. Called around town to all the hospitals. I found out Hancock General admitted three ODs yesterday. Two were obviously suicide attempts. But the third was a young man brought in by his parents. He had a cardiac arrest in the ER. They managed to pull him back. He's in the ICU now, still unconscious and critical.'

'Hancock's a busy ER. You'd expect ODs to show up there.'

'I spoke to the hospital lab. They ran a routine gas chromatography on the man's blood. It turned up a biphasic peak on the narcotics screen. Not quite an opiate, not quite cocaine.'

Wheelock said nothing. He simply sat there, frowning at her.

'Davis,' she said, 'we're seeing the start of an epidemic.'

# 3

Wheelock shook his head. 'It's too early to call,' he said. 'Too early to go to the press. You've only got three vics—'

'Guess where the young man lived? South Lexington. Within five blocks of where the two women were found. I'm telling you, there's something new, something that's killing off junkies. And South Lexington seems to be its point of origin. Here's what I think you should do, Davis. Get on the phone to the mayor. Call a joint press conference. Get the news out before we get more John and Jane Does cluttering up my basement.'

'I don't know.'

'What don't you know?'

'It could be a single batch. Maybe that's all it is.'

'Or maybe there's a whole ton of the stuff sitting in some pusher's warehouse.'

Agitated, Wheelock sat back and ran his hand through his gray hair. 'All right. I'll talk to the mayor. It's a bad

time to be bringing this up, what with the city bicentennial and all. He's launching his campaign this
week—'

'Davis. People are *dying*.'

'All right, all right. I'll call him this afternoon.'

Satisfied that she'd made her point, Kat left
Wheelock's office and headed down to the basement. In
the corridor, two of the overhead fluorescent lights
flickered like a strobe flash. Everything seemed to be
wearing down, wearing out. The building. The city.

And there they were, celebrating the bicentennial. *What
are we celebrating exactly, Mr. Mayor? Two hundred years of
decline?*

Back in her office, Kat considered drinking the last
dregs of the coffee pot. No, she wasn't that desperate.
Two files lay on her desk, files she couldn't complete, perhaps would never be able to complete. One was Jane
Doe's. The other was for Xenia Vargas, the second woman
from South Lexington. She, at least, had been found with
ID in her purse, though they hadn't yet confirmed Vargas
was really her name. Nor had they been able to contact
any relatives.

Two dead women. And no one who could tell her how –
or why – they had died.

On a corner of her desk was a notepad, with the name
*Dr. Michael Dietz* scribbled on it. He was the ER doctor
she'd spoken to earlier, the one who'd admitted the male
overdose victim at Hancock General.

It was five o'clock; she could hear the evening
morgue attendants laughing in the prep room, enjoying

the brief and blessed lull before the madness of nightfall.

Kat changed into her street clothes, pulled on her coat, and left the building.

She didn't drive home. Instead, she drove to South Lexington, to Hancock General Hospital.

It sat like a fortress in a war zone, its parking lot surrounded by a barbed wire fence, the front entrance overhung by surveillance cameras. The ER clerk was sitting behind glass – bulletproof, Kat surmised. He spoke through a microphone; the tinny voice coming through the speaker made Kat think of a McDonald's drive-through. 'How can I help you?' he asked.

'I'm Dr. Novak,' she said. 'ME's office. I want to see a Dr. Michael Dietz. It's about a patient of his.'

'I'll page him.'

Dr. Dietz emerged a few minutes later, looking like some weary veteran of the trenches. A stethoscope was looped around his neck, and his scrub pants were splattered with blood. 'You just caught me,' he said. 'I was going off shift. You're from the ME?'

'We talked earlier. About that overdose.'

'Oh, yeah. He's up in Intensive Care. I can't remember his name . . .'

'Can we go up to the Unit?' she asked. 'I'd like to look over his chart.'

'I guess it's okay. Seeing as you're official and all.'

They headed to the elevators. The hospital looked the same as Kat remembered it, dingy linoleum floors, halls painted a bizarre aqua color, gurneys shoved up against the walls. Through the doorway on the right was the cafeteria, with its echoes of clinking dishes and scraping chairs. On the overhead paging system, a bored voice read out a list of doctors' names and extension numbers. Dr. Dietz moved like a sleepwalker in tennis shoes.

'I see the place hasn't changed any,' said Kat.

'Did you use to work here?'

'No. I did my residency over at St. Luke's. But I knew a patient here. A relative.'

He laughed. 'I'm not sure I'd want any of *my* relatives here.'

'Didn't matter to her. She didn't know where she was, anyway.'

They stepped into the staff elevator and crowded in beside nurses and orderlies. Everyone stared straight ahead, as though mesmerized by the changing floor numbers.

'So are you from the city?' asked Dietz.

'A native. And you?'

'Cleveland. I'm going back.'

'Don't like it here?'

'Let's put it this way. Compared to this town, Cleveland is the Garden of Eden.'

They got off on the third floor and headed into Intensive Care.

The Unit was set up like a giant stable, with stalls marked out by curtains. Only two beds were empty, Kat noted; not much preparation for an unexpected disaster. And there was a full moon. That was always a harbinger of a busy night.

The patient was in bed thirteen. Only comatose

patients went into that bed, Dietz said. Why scare some conscious patient? When you're fighting for your life, even dumb superstitions take on frightening significance.

The man's name was Nicos Biagi. He was a husky fellow, about twenty, with biceps and pectorals that had obviously done time in the weight-rooms. There were seven tubes snaking out of various parts of his body – a grim prognostic indicator. He lay utterly flaccid. According to the chart, he was unresponsive to even the most intense of stimuli.

'Twenty-four hours and not a twitch,' said the nurse. 'Plus, we're having trouble stabilizing his pressure. It goes haywire on us, shoots up, then bottoms out. I'm going crazy, juggling all these meds.'

Kat flipped through the chart, quickly deciphering the hurried notes of the ICU resident. The patient had been found unconscious in his car, parked outside his parents' apartment. He'd been sprawled on the front seat. Beside him on the floor had been his kit: a tourniquet, syringe and needle, spoon, and cigarette lighter. Somehow, during the frantic rush to stabilize the patient and transport him to the ER, the EMTs had lost track of the syringe. They thought the family might have it; the family claimed the EMTs had it. The police said they'd never even seen it. In any event, the blood toxicology screen would provide the answers.

At least, it should.

They'd found out a few things. A 0.13 ethanol level proved the man was legally drunk. Also, he'd been pumped full of steroids – something Kat could have guessed, judging from those bulging biceps. What the tests hadn't answered was the primary question: Which drug had put him into the coma?

All the usual medical steps had been taken. Despite a treatment of glucose, Narcan, and thiamine, he hadn't awakened. The only therapeutic strategy left was supportive: maintain his blood pressure, breathe for him, keep his heart beating. The rest was up to the patient.

'You have no history at all?' asked Kat. 'Nothing about what he shot up? Where he got it from?'

'Not a thing. His parents are in the dark. They had no idea their kid was a junkie. That's probably why he did it in the car. So they wouldn't know about it.'

'I've got two women in the morgue. Both with the same biphasic peak on gas chromatography. Like your man.'

Dietz sighed. 'Terrific. Another wonder drug hits our streets.'

'When will your final tox report be done?'

'I don't know. It's been twenty-four hours already. If this is something new, it may take weeks to identify. These pharmaceutical whizzes out there crank out drugs like new shoes. By the time we catch up with the latest fad, they're on to something else.'

'You agree, then? That it's something new?'

'Oh, yeah. I've seen it all come down the pike. PCP, tropical ice, fruit loops. This is something different. Something *bad*. I think the only reason this guy's still alive, and your two women aren't, is that he's a big dude. All that muscle mass. Takes a bigger dose to kill him.'

*It still might kill him*, thought Kat, gazing at the comatose patient.

'If this goes to the media, can I use you as a source?' she asked.

'What do you mean?'

'I think a warning ought to go out on the streets. That there's bad stuff making the rounds.'

Dietz didn't answer right away. He just kept looking at Nicos Biagi. 'I don't know,' he said at last.

'What do you mean, you don't know? It'd just be to voice your opinion. To confirm my statement.'

'I don't know,' he said again. He was gripping the IV pole. 'It's not as if you need me. You've got the authority.'

'I could use the backup.'

'It's just . . . the press. I'm not crazy about talking to them.'

'Okay, then just let me cite you by name. Would that be okay?'

He sighed. 'I guess so. But I'd rather you didn't.' Abruptly, he straightened and glanced at his watch. 'Look, I have to get going. I'll catch you later.'

Kat watched him walk out of the ICU, his shoulders hunched forward as though his whole body was straining to break into a sprint. What was he afraid of? she wondered. Why wouldn't he talk to the press?

She was on her way out of the ICU when she spotted the Biagis, coming in to visit their son. She guessed at once who they were, just by the grief in their faces. Mrs. Biagi was dark-haired, dark-eyed, and her face was seamed with worry. Mr. Biagi was much older and bald;

he looked too numb to be feeling much of anything at the moment. They went to Nicos's bedside, where they stood for a moment in silence. Mrs. Biagi stroked her son's hair and began to sing softly, something in Italian. A lullaby, perhaps. Then she faltered, dropped her head to her son's chest, and began to cry.

Mr. Biagi didn't say a word.

Kat walked out of the ICU.

In her haste to leave behind that scene, she took a wrong turn in the hallway. Instead of heading to the elevators, she found herself in a different wing, a part of the hospital she hadn't seen before. White walls and gleaming linoleum told her this was a new addition, constructed only recently. Behind a glass case on the wall were displayed various mementoes of the wing's opening: photographs of hospital officials at the ribbon cutting. Shots of a celebrity black-tie dinner. A bronze plaque, engraved with *The Georgina Quantrell Wing*. And a newspaper article with the headline: *Cygnus president dedicates multimillion-dollar drug rehab addition.* The accompanying photograph showed a sober-faced Adam Quantrell, posing beside the plaque.

For a long time, Kat stood by that case, studying the photos, the news articles. Drug rehab? A surprising crusade for a man who made his fortune from drugs. Her gaze traveled the length of the case, paused at a teaching display of commonly abused drugs. Mounted on the board was a multicolored variety of capsules. And below it was the label: *Display courtesy of the Cygnus Company.*

Something clicked in Kat's head. Dead junkies. A new drug on the street. Cygnus Pharmaceuticals.

And a matchbook with Adam Quantrell's phone number.

She reached for her cell phone, and called Sykes in Homicide.

He was just leaving for home and did not seem particularly eager to prolong his work day.

'Let me put it this way, Novak,' he said. 'In the grand scheme of things, drug ODs are not high on my list of priorities.'

'Think about it, Lou. What's an addict doing with Quantrell's personal phone number? Why was Quantrell so eager to look at the body? He's hiding something.'

'No, he's not.'

'I think he is.'

'They were junkies, Novak. They lived on the edge, they fell off. It's not homicide. It's not suicide. It's stupidity. Social Darwinism, survival of the smartest.'

'Maybe that's what you think. Maybe that's what Quantrell thinks. But I've still got two dead women.'

'Forget Quantrell. The man's into drug rehab, not drug pushing.'

'Lou, this is a new drug. I spoke to an ER doctor here who says he's never seen it before. To cook up a brand new drug, you need a biochemist. And a lab. And a factory. Cygnus has it all.'

'It's a legitimate company.'

'With maybe an illegitimate branch?'

'Christ, Novak. I'm not going to hassle Quantrell.'

'I heard you did a favor for him. On the side.'

There was a pause. 'Yeah. So what?'

'So what were you doing for him out in South Lexington?'

'Look, you want to hear the details?' Sykes snapped. 'Then you talk to *him*.' He hung up.

Kat stared at the phone. Well, maybe she *had* pushed Lou too far on this one. *My big mouth*, she thought. *One of these days it's going to get me into trouble.*

Slipping her cell phone into her pocket, she saw Mr. and Mrs. Biagi coming out of the ICU. They were leaning on each other, holding each other up, as though grief had sapped all their strength.

Kat thought of their son Nicos, with the seven tubes in his body. She thought of Jane Doe and Xenia Vargas, both relegated to the approximate level of primordial muck in Sykes' scale of social Darwinism. Something was killing these people, something that had sunk its evil roots into the Projects.

Her old neighborhood.

On her way back to the freeway, she drove up South Lexington. In the last few years, nothing had changed. The seven Project buildings still looked like prison towers, the playground still had a bent basketball hoop, and teenagers still hung out on the corner of Franklin and South Lexington. But the faces were different. It wasn't just that these were different people. There was a new hardness to their gazes, a wariness, as they watched her drive by. Only then did the thought strike her.

To them she was an outsider. Someone to be watched,

someone to be guarded against. Someone not to be trusted.

*They don't know I'm one of them. Or I was.*

She continued up South Lexington and took the freeway on-ramp.

Traffic was still heavy moving north. It was the evening exodus to the suburbs, a daily hemorrhage of white-collar types to Bellemeade, Parris, Clarendon, and Surry Heights. Those who could afford to flee, fled. Even Kat, a city girl born and bred, now called the suburbs home. Just last year, she'd bought a house in Bellemeade. It seemed a logical move, financially speaking, and she'd reached the point in life when she had to make a commitment – any commitment, even if it was only to a three-bedroom cape. Bellemeade was a hybrid neighborhood, close enough to town to make it feel like part of the city, yet far enough away to put it squarely in the safety of the suburbs.

On impulse, she bypassed the Bellemeade turnoff and stayed on the freeway. It took her a half hour to drive to Surry Heights.

Along the way, the traffic thinned out, the scenery changed. Cookie-cutter houses gave way to trees and rolling hills, newly green from those proverbial April showers. White fences and horses appeared – a sure harbinger of old money. She took the Surry Heights exit onto Fair Wind Lane.

Two miles down the road she came to the Quantrell residence. There was no mistaking the place. Two stone pillars flanked the driveway entrance; the name *Quantrell* was spelled out in wrought iron lettering mounted on one

of the pillars. The gate hung open to visitors. Kat drove
through, and followed the curving driveway to the house.

There were three cars parked out front, a Jaguar and
two Mercedes. She parked her five-year-old Subaru next
to the Jag and climbed out. *Nice paint job*, she thought,
eyeing the Jag's burgundy finish. The interior was spot-
less, with not a clue to its owner's personality in sight. No
bumper stickers, either, though one that said *Let them eat
cake* would have been appropriate.

She went to the front door and rang the bell. It pealed
like a church chime in a cavern.

The door opened, and a man wearing a butler-type
uniform gazed down at her. 'Yes?' he said.

Kat cleared her throat. 'I'm Dr. Novak. Medical
examiner's office. I wonder if I could speak to Mr. Adam
Quantrell.'

'Is Mr. Quantrell expecting you?'

'No. But I'm here on official business.'

For a moment the man seemed to consider her request.
Then he opened the door wider. 'Come in.'

Surprised at how easy that was, she stepped inside. In
wonder, she gazed up at a crystal chandelier. It was just a
modest little entry hall, she thought. Nothing you
wouldn't find in a typical castle. The floor was gleaming
terrazzo, and a massive banister traced a staircase to a
second-floor gallery. Paintings – mostly modern, vaguely
disturbing, wild blots of color – hung in various places of
honor.

'If you'll wait here,' said the butler.

He disappeared through a side door. She heard the

distant sound of a woman's laughter, the strains of classical music. *Oh, great. He's got a party going*, she thought. *Terrific timing, Novak.*

She turned as she heard footsteps. Adam Quantrell emerged from a side room, quietly shutting the door behind him. He was dressed formally, black tie, ruffled white shirt. He did not look pleased to see her.

'Dr. Novak,' he said. 'Is this urgent? Or can it wait till some other time?'

'I think it's urgent.'

'More questions?' he asked.

'And another body.'

She watched for his reaction and was not at all surprised to see his face flinch. After a pause he said, 'Whose?'

'A woman. They found her not too far from where they found the first one. In a stairwell off South Lexington. It looks like another drug OD.'

He still looked stunned. 'Do you . . . want me to come down and look at her?'

'Not necessarily. But maybe you'll know the name. She had her purse with her. The driver's license said Xenia Vargas. I assume it's hers because the photo matched the corpse. Does that name ring a bell?'

He let out a breath. She wondered if it was a sigh of relief.

'No,' he said. 'I don't know that name.'

'What about the name Nicos Biagi?'

'I don't know that name either. Why?'

'Just curious.'

Adam reacted with a snort of disbelief. 'You show up at my door and assault me with the names of corpses, just to see how I react. And all because you're curious?'

'Who said Nicos Biagi was a corpse?'.

'I don't know who the hell he is! I just assumed. Every-one else you mention seems to be a corpse!' His voice seemed to echo off the terrazzo floor and bounce around the far reaches of the vast entrance hall. At once he re-gained his composure, his face settling into an expression of cool unreadability. 'So,' he said. 'Who *is* Nicos Biagi? And is he or is he not a corpse?'

'Nicos happens to be alive – barely,' she said. 'He's a patient at Hancock General. A drug OD. We're worried about the drug. It seems to be something new, and it's already killed Jane Doe and Xenia Vargas. It's left Nicos Biagi critically ill. I wondered if you knew something about it.'

'Why would I?'

'A hunch.'

To her annoyance, he laughed. 'I hope this isn't the way the ME's office usually conducts business. Because if it is, our criminal justice system is in big trouble.'

The side door opened again. A woman appeared, look-ing quizzical. And gorgeous. Her evening dress, shot through with gold thread, seemed to glitter in the chandelier light. Her hair, an equally brilliant gold, fell in ripples to her shoulders. She glanced at Adam's visitor, a look that Kat recognized at once for what it was – a feminine sizing-up, then a curt dismissal. 'Adam?' she asked. 'Is something wrong?'

'No,' he said, his gaze still fixed on Kat. 'It's just – business.'

'Oh.' The woman smiled sweetly. 'Pearl just brought out the soup. And we didn't want to start without you.'

'Sorry, Isabel. Why don't you all just go ahead with supper? Dr. Novak and I aren't finished yet.'

Again, her gaze shifted to Kat. 'We can set another place, if you'd like. For your visitor.'

There was an awkward silence, as though Adam were hunting for a graceful way to avoid inviting this unwelcome guest.

'That won't be necessary,' said Kat, and thought she saw a look of relief cross Adam's face. 'I'll be leaving, as soon as we're done with our . . . business.'

Isabel smiled again, as though equally relieved. 'Join us when you can, Adam,' she said, and withdrew into the side room.

Adam and Kat regarded each other for a moment.

'Let's talk in the study,' he said, and abruptly turned and opened another door. She followed him inside.

It was a characteristically masculine space, dark and clubby, with a fireplace and wood paneling, the sort of room in which one smoked pipes and drank cognac. She sat on the leather couch. He didn't sit at all, but paced in front of the fireplace. The longer she watched him, the more annoyed she felt. It was irrational, of course, but she was insulted that *he* hadn't offered her a place at the supper table. She would have turned it down, of course; you didn't just drop into a formal supper, and judging from Isabel's evening gown, this was no potluck they were serving. But at least she would have had the pleasure of turning him down. It was a matter of pride.

'So what's the basis for this hunch of yours?' he demanded. 'Why do you think I would know anything about it?'

'Because of that matchbook.'

'Not much of a reason.'

'Because this is a new drug, never seen before.'

He shrugged. 'So?'

'And because you're president of Cygnus Pharmaceuticals. A company known for its R and D in painkillers. A company that just released a new class of opiates.'

'We also make drugs for athlete's foot.'

'Oh, and one more thing.'

'Yes?' When he tilted his head his blond hair caught the glow of the table lamp.

'Until you saw the body, you thought Jane Doe was someone you might know.'

At once he fell silent, all trace of mockery gone from his face. He sat down, his gaze avoiding hers.

'Who did you think she was, Mr. Quantrell?'

'Someone . . . close to me.'

'What's the secret here? Why can't you just say who you thought she was?'

'These are things I don't wish to discuss. Not with a stranger.'

'Then can you discuss the drug? It's something new. A narcotic with a biphasic peak on gas chromatography. Could it be something that leaked out of Cygnus? Something you're developing?'

51

'I wouldn't want to speculate.'

Of course he wouldn't. Because then he'd be vulnerable to all sorts of accusations. The manufacture of lethal drugs. The slaughter of junkies.

Slowly he looked up. 'You said you had another body in the morgue. A woman.'

'Xenia Vargas.'

'Is she . . . young?'

'About twenty.'

'Describe her for me.'

'You think you might know her?'

'Please. Just tell me what she looks like.'

Something about the tone of his voice, the stifled note of anxiety, made her feel sorry for him. 'She's about five foot four, on the thin side. Dark brown hair—'

'Could it be dyed?'

Kat paused. 'It's possible, I guess.'

'What about her eyes? What color?'

'Hazel.'

Another silence. Then, with sudden agitation, he rose to his feet. 'I think I'd better see her,' he said.

'You mean – now?'

'If we could.' He met her gaze. 'If you'd be so kind.'

She too stood up and followed him into the main hall. 'What about your dinner guests?'

'They can feed themselves. Would you excuse me a moment, while I gracefully duck out?'

He went through the side door, but this time he left it open. Kat caught a glimpse of a formal dining room and a half-dozen guests seated around the table. Some of them glanced curiously in Kat's direction. She heard Isabel ask, 'Should I wait for you, Adam?'

'Please don't,' he said. 'I don't know how long I'll be.'

'This is really quite naughty of you, you know.'

'It can't be helped. Good night, everyone! You're free to have a go at my wine cellar, but leave me a few bottles, will you?' He clapped one of the men on the shoulder, waved farewell, and came back into the hall, shutting the door behind him.

'That's done,' he said to Kat. 'Now. Let's go.'

# 4

The morgue elevator slid open. *Here we go again*, she thought.

The basement seemed calm tonight. The only noise was the morgue attendant's radio, playing in a side office. Something mean and gritty and tuneless. She and Adam passed the open door, where they could see the attendant sitting with his feet propped up on the desk, his gaze focused on a girly magazine.

'Hey, Willie,' said Kat.

'Hey, Doc,' he said, grinning at her over the cover. 'Not much action coming down tonight.'

'I can tell.'

'You mean this?' He waved the magazine and laughed. 'Man, I get tired of looking at *dead* chicks. I like mine live and sassy.'

'We're going into the cold room, okay?'

'Need any help?'

'No. You just stay with your sassy chicks.'

She and Adam walked on down the hall, beneath the bank of fluorescent lights. The bulb that had been flickering earlier that day was now dead; it left a patch of shadow on the linoleum floor.

They entered the storage room. She flicked on the wall switch and blinked at the painful blast of light on her retinas. The refrigerated drawers faced them from the opposite wall.

She moved to the drawer labeled *Vargas, Xenia,* and slid it open. Covered by the shroud, the body seemed shapeless, like a lump of clay still to be molded. She glanced up at Adam in silent inquiry.

He nodded.

She removed the shroud.

The corpse looked like a mannequin, not real at all, but plastic. Adam took one good look at Xenia Vargas, and all the tension seemed to escape his body in a single sigh.

'You don't know her?' said Kat.

'No.' He swallowed. 'I've never seen her.'

She replaced the shroud and slid the drawer shut. Then she turned and looked at him. 'Okay, Mr. Quantrell, I think it's time for you to fess up. Who, exactly, are you looking for?'

He paused. 'A woman.'

'I know that. I also know she's got hazel eyes. And the chances are, she's either a blond or a redhead. Now I want to know her name.'

'Maeve,' he said softly.

'Now we're getting somewhere. Maeve who?'

'Quantrell.'

She frowned. 'Wife? Sister?'

'Daughter. I mean, stepdaughter. She's twenty-three. And you're right. She's blond. Hazel eyes. Five foot five, a hundred fifteen pounds. At least, that's what she was when I saw her last.'

'And when was that?'

'Six months ago.'

'She's missing?'

He shrugged one tuxedoed shoulder. 'Missing, hiding. Whatever you want to call it. She drops out of sight whenever she feels like it. Whenever she can't face up to life. It's her way of coping.'

'Coping with what?'

'Everything. Bad grades. Love affairs. Her mother's death. Her lousy stepfather.'

'So you two didn't get along.'

'No.' Wearily he raked his fingers through his hair. 'I couldn't handle her. I thought I could shape her up. You know, a firm hand, some good old-fashioned discipline. The way my father raised me. I even got her a job, thinking that all she needed was some responsibility. That at a minimum she could show up on time, do the job right, and pay for her own damn groceries.' He shook his head. 'She went to work one day, two hours late, her hair dyed purple. She had a screaming match with her supervisor. Then she walked off the job.' He let out a breath. 'She was fired.'

'And that was the last time she was seen?'

'No. I took her out to lunch. To try to patch things up. Instead, we had an argument. Naturally.'

'Let me guess,' said Kat. 'You took her to L'Etoile, on Hilton Avenue.'

He nodded. 'Maeve showed up in black leather and green hair. She insulted the maître d'. Lit up a joint in the nonsmoking section. And proceeded to tell me I had sick values. I told her she was sick, period. I also told her I was withdrawing all financial support. That if she shaped up, behaved like a responsible human being, she was welcome to come back to the house. I'd just changed my phone number – I was getting crank calls – so I wrote my new number in a matchbook and gave it to her. Just in case she wanted to get in touch with me. She never did.'

'And the matchbook?'

He shrugged. 'Maybe she passed it around to a friend, and somehow Jane Doe got it. I don't know.'

'You haven't seen her since the restaurant?'

'No.'

She paused. 'Where does Lou Sykes come in?'

'A private detective I hired told me Maeve was hanging around South Lexington. That's Lieutenant Sykes' beat. I simply asked him to keep an eye out for her. As a favor to me. He thought he spotted her once, but that was it.'

It sounded believable enough, Kat thought, studying his pose, the elegant cut of his tuxedo. *So why do I get the feeling he's still hiding something?*

His gaze was focused elsewhere, as though he was afraid to let her see his eyes.

'What you're telling me, Mr. Quantrell, isn't exactly earth-shattering. Lots of families have problems with their kids. Why were you afraid to tell me about her? Why hide it from me?'

'It's a rather . . . embarrassing state of affairs.'

'Is that all?'

'Isn't that enough?' He swung around to look at her, the challenge plain in his aristocratic face. She felt trapped by the spell of that gaze. What was it about this guy?

She gave her head a shake, as though to clear it. 'No,' she said. 'It's not enough. So what if you had told me the truth this morning? I'm just a public servant. You don't get embarrassed in front of your servants, do you?'

He gave her a tight smile. 'You, Dr. Novak, I hardly consider a servant.'

'Is there something else about Maeve you don't want to tell me? Some minor detail you haven't mentioned?'

'Nothing of any relevance to your job.' He turned away, a sure sign that he wasn't telling the whole truth. His gaze focused on one of the body drawers.

'Then I'd say our business here is finished,' she said. 'Go on home to your guests. If you hurry, you might be able to make it back in time for brandy.'

'Who is this?' he asked sharply.

'What?'

'This drawer here. It says Jane Doe.'

Kat took a closer look at the label: #372-3-27-B. 'Another one. Dated seven days ago. Clark must have processed this one.'

'Who's Clark?'

'The other Assistant ME. He's on vacation right now.'

Adam took a breath. 'May I . . .' He looked up mutely at Kat.

She nodded. Without a word, she pulled open the drawer.

Wisps of cold vapor swirled out. Kat felt her old reluctance to lift the shroud, to reveal the body. This Jane Doe she hadn't laid eyes on. She steeled herself against the worst and slid off the shroud.

The woman was beautiful. Seven days of stainless-steel imprisonment couldn't dull the glow of her hair. It was a rich red, thick and tumbling about her shoulders. Her skin had the luster of white marble, and in life must have seemed flawless. Her eyes, revealed by partly opened, heavily lashed lids, were gray. Her torso was marred by a sutured Y-incision, the ugly aftermath of an autopsy.

Kat looked across at Adam.

He shook his head. 'You can close the drawer,' he murmured. 'It's not her.'

'I wonder who she is?' said Kat, sliding the drawer shut. 'She looks like the kind of woman who'd be missed. Not our usual Jane Doe type.'

'Would you know how she died?' The question was asked softly, but its significance at once struck Kat.

'Let's pull the file,' she said.

They found it in Clark's office. It was buried in a stack on his desk, waiting to be completed. On top were clipped a few loose pages, recent correspondence from the central identification lab.

'Looks like she's no longer a Jane Doe,' said Kat. 'They found a fingerprint match. Her name's Mandy Barnett. I guess Clark never got around to relabeling the drawer.'

'Why does she have fingerprints on file?'

Kat flipped to the next page. 'Because she has a police record. Shoplifting. Prostitution. Public drunkenness.' Kat glanced up at Adam. 'Guess she wasn't as sweet as she looked.'

'What was the cause of death?'

Kat opened the folder and squinted at Clark's notes. He must have been in a rush when he wrote them; it was a typical doctor's scrawl, the *i*s undotted, the *t*s uncrossed. 'Subject found 3/27 at 02:35 in public restroom at Gilly's bar, off Flashner Avenue.' Kat looked up. 'That's in Bellemeade. I live there.' She turned to the next page. 'No injuries noted . . . tox screens pending. Police report empty bottle of Fiorinal pills found near body. Conclusion: cardiopulmonary arrest, most likely due to barbiturate overdose. Awaiting tox screen from state lab.'

'Is the report back yet?'

Kat went to the courier box and riffled through the stack of pages. 'I don't see it here. It's probably still pending.' She closed the file. 'This case doesn't really fit with the others. Bellemeade's a different neighborhood, with a different class of drug users. Higher priced.'

'The others were all in South Lexington?'

'Within blocks of each other. Jane Doe was smack in the Projects. So was Xenia Vargas. Nicos Biagi was a little further out, on Richmond Street. Let's see, that'd make it somewhere near the old railroad tracks. But it's still the same neighborhood.'

'You seem to know the area well.'

'Too well.' She tossed Mandy Barnett's file on Clark's desk. 'I grew up there.'

He looked at her in surprise. 'You?'

'Me.'

'How did you . . .' He paused, as though not certain how to phrase the question with any delicacy.

'How did I happen to grow up there? Simple. That's where my mom lived. Right up until she died.'

'So you would know the people there.'

'Some of them. But the neighborhood's always changing. People who can get out, get out. It's like this giant pond. Either you float up and crawl out or you sink deeper into the mud.'

'And you floated.'

She shrugged. 'I got lucky.'

He studied her with new appreciation, as though he was really seeing her for the first time. 'In your case, Dr. Novak,' he said, 'I think luck had nothing to do with it.'

'Not like some of us,' she said, looking at his tuxedo and his immaculate shirt.

He laughed. 'Yes, some of us *do* seem to be rolling in it.'

They rode back up in the elevator and walked out of the building. It was chilly outside. The wind blew an empty can down the street; they could trace its progress by the tinny echoes in the darkness.

He had driven in his car, and she in hers. Now they paused beside their respective vehicles, as though reluctant to part.

He turned to her. 'What I was trying to say earlier – about your knowing people in South Lexington . . .' He paused. She waited, feeling strangely breathless. Eager. 'I was trying to ask for your help,' he finished.

'My help?'

'I want to find Maeve.'

*So it's my help he wants*, she thought. *Not me in particular.* She wondered why that fact should leave her feeling so disappointed. She said, 'Lou Sykes is a good cop. If he can't find her—'

'That's just it. He's a *cop*. No one out there trusts cops. Certainly Maeve wouldn't trust him. She'd think he was out to arrest her. Or reel her in for me.'

'Is that what you're trying to do?'

'I just want to know she's alive and well.'

'She's an adult, Adam. She can make her own choices.'

'What if her choices are insane?'

'Then she lives with them.'

'You don't understand. I made a promise to her mother. I promised that Maeve would be taken care of. So far I've done a pretty deplorable job.' He sighed. 'At the very least, I should look for her.'

'What if she doesn't want to be found?'

'Then she should *tell* me that, face to face. But I have to find her first. And you're the only one I know who's familiar with South Lexington.'

Kat laughed. 'Yeah, I guess it's not the sort of neighborhood your dinner guests would frequent.'

'I would appreciate it. I really would. Just show me the place. Put me in touch with some of the people. I'd reimburse you for your time, of course. You only have to say how much—'

'Wait a minute.' She moved closer to him, her chin tilted up in astonishment. 'You were going to *pay* me?'

'I mean, it's only appropriate—'

'Forget it. *Forget it.* I'm a doctor, Quantrell, okay? I'm not the butler. I'm not the cook. I'm a doctor, and I already get paid for what I do.'

'So?'

'Which means I *don't* need a moonlighting job. When I do a favor for a friend – and I'm not necessarily putting you in the category – I do it *as* a friend. Gratis.'

'You want to do it out of the kindness of your heart. You want me to feel grateful. And I do, I really do.' He paused, then added softly: 'I also really need your help.'

Kat wasn't philosophically opposed to helping her fellow man. And a devoted dad in search of his daughter, well, that was an appeal she could hardly refuse. But this particular dad was no charity case.

Still . . .

She walked over to her car and flung open the door. 'Get in, Quantrell.'

'Excuse me?'

'We're not taking your car, because a nice new Volvo's an invitation to a chop job. So let's go in mine.'

'To South Lexington?'

'You want an intro to the place, I know some people you can talk to. People who'd know what's going on in the neighborhood.'

Adam hesitated.

'Listen,' she said. 'You want to live dangerously or not?'

He regarded her battered Subaru. Then he shrugged. 'Why not?' he said, and climbed into her car.

South Lexington was a different place at night. What by day had seemed merely drab and depressing had, by night, assumed new menace. Alleys seemed to snake away into nowhere, and in that darkness lurked all the terrible unknowns a mind could conjure.

Kat parked beneath a streetlamp, and for a moment she studied the sidewalk, the buildings. A block away, a dozen or so teenagers had gathered on the corner. They looked harmless enough, just a bunch of kids engaged in the adolescent rites of spring.

'It looks okay,' she said. 'Let's go.'

'I hope you know what you're doing.'

They got out of the car and walked up the sidewalk, toward Building Five. The teenagers, at once alerted to intruders in their territory, turned and stared. Automatically, Adam moved close beside Kat and tightly grasped her arm.

The building was unlocked, so they went inside. The lobby was as she'd remembered it: dingy walls, nutmeg-colored carpet to hide the stains, half the hall lights burned out. The graffiti was a little more graphic, and less poetic than she remembered; the artwork had definitely taken a slide for the worse.

The elevator, as always, was out of commission.

'I don't think it *ever* worked,' she muttered, noting the faded *Out of Order* sign. 'It's four flights up. We'll have to walk.'

They went up the stairs, stepping over broken toys and

cigarette butts. The handrail, once smoothly burnished, was now scarred by a series of initials carved in the wood. Noises filtered out from the various apartments: crying babies, blaring TV sets and radios, a woman yelling at her kids. Floating above it all were the pure and crystalline tones of a girl singing 'Amazing Grace.' The sound soared like a cathedral above the ruins. As they ascended the stairs to the fourth floor, the girl's voice grew louder, until they knew it was coming from behind the very door where they stopped.

Kat knocked.

The singing stopped. Footsteps approached, and the door opened a crack. A girl with a silky face the color of mocha gazed out over the security chain with doe eyes.

'Bella?' said Kat.

The smile that appeared on the girl's face was like a brilliant wash of sunshine. 'Kat!' she cried, unlatching the door chain. She turned and called out: 'Papa Earl! It's Kat!'

'Don't rush me,' grumbled a voice from the next room. 'I don't go runnin' for no one.'

Bella gave Kat an embarrassed look as they stepped into the apartment. 'Those bones of his,' she murmured. 'Ache him real bad in this weather. He's in a foul mood . . .'

'*Who's* in a foul mood?' snapped Papa Earl, shuffling into the room. He moved slowly, his head tipped forward, his once jet-black hair now a grizzled white. How old he had gotten, thought Kat sadly. Somehow, she had never thought this man would be touched by the years.

Kat went forward to give him a hug. It was almost like hugging a stranger; he seemed so small, so frail, shrunken by time. 'Hi, Papa Earl,' she said.

'You got your nerve, girl,' he grumbled. 'Go two years, three, not even droppin' by.'

'Papa Earl!' Bella said. 'She's here now, isn't she?'

'Yeah, got good 'n' guilty, did she?'

Kat laughed and took his hand. It felt like bones wrapped in parchment. 'How you been, Papa Earl? Did you get the coat I sent?'

'What coat?'

'You know,' sighed Bella. 'The down jacket, Papa Earl. You wore it *all* winter.'

'Oh. *That* coat.'

Bella gave Kat a weary *you know how he is* look and said, 'He *loves* that coat.'

'Papa Earl,' said Kat. 'I brought someone with me.'

'Who?'

'His name is Adam. He's standing right over here.'

Gently she turned the old man to face Adam. Papa Earl extended his arm, held it out in midair for the expected handshake. Only then, as the two men faced each other, did Adam notice the snowy cataracts clouding the old man's eyes.

Adam took the offered hand and grasped it firmly. 'Hello . . . Papa Earl,' he said.

Papa Earl let out a hoot. 'Makes you feel dumb, don't it? Big fella like you callin' a shrimp like me Papa.'

'Not at all, sir.'

'So what you got going with our Katrina here?'

'He's just a friend, Papa Earl,' said Kat.

There was a pause. 'Oh,' the old man said. 'It's like that.'

'I wanted you to meet him, talk to him. See, he's looking for someone. A woman.'

Papa Earl's grizzled head lifted with sudden interest. The blind eyes seemed to focus on her. 'What do I know?'

'You know everything that goes on in the Projects.'

'Let's sit down,' the old man said. 'My bones are killing me.'

They went into the kitchen. Like the rest of the apartment, the room was on the far side of used. Linoleum tiles had worked loose below the sink. The formica counters were chipped. The stove and refrigerator were straight from the *Leave It to Beaver* era. Papa Earl's other grandchild, Anthony, sat hunched at the table, shoveling spaghetti hoops into his mouth. He scarcely looked up as the others came in.

'Hey, Anthony!' barked Papa Earl. 'Ain't you gonna say hello to your old babysitter?'

'Hello.' Anthony grunted and stuffed in another spoonful of spaghetti hoops.

Their personalities hadn't changed a bit, Kat realized, watching Anthony and Bella, remembering all those evenings she had looked after them while Papa Earl worked. Back in the days when the old man still had his vision. These two might be twins, they might have the same mocha coloring, the same high, sculpted cheekbones, but their personalities were like darkness and light.

Bella could warm a room with her smile; Anthony could chill it with a single glance.

Papa Earl shuffled about the familiar kitchen with all the sureness of a sighted man. 'You hungry?' he asked. 'You want something to eat?'

Kat and Adam watched Anthony noisily lap tomato sauce and they said, in the same breath, 'Nothing, thanks.'

They all sat down at the table, Papa Earl across from them, his cataracts staring at them eerily. 'So who's this woman you looking for?' he asked.

'Her name is Maeve Quantrell,' said Kat. 'We think she's living in the Projects.'

'You have a picture?'

Kat glanced at Adam.

'Yes. As a matter of fact, I do,' he said, and reached for his wallet. He placed a snapshot on the table.

Kat had been expecting to see a version of what he'd described to her, a hellion in black leather with Technicolor hair. What she saw instead was a fragile blond girl, the sort you'd find shrinking in the corner at a school dance.

'Bella?' said Papa Earl.

Bella reached for the photo. 'Oh, she's real pretty. Blond hair. Sort of shy looking.'

'How old?'

'She's twenty-three,' said Adam. 'She looks different now. Probably dyed her hair some crazy color. Wears more makeup.'

'Anthony? You seen this girl around?' asked Papa Earl.

Anthony glanced at the photo and shrugged. Then he rose, tossed his empty bowl in the sink, and stalked out of the kitchen. A moment later, they heard the apartment door slam shut.

'Like a wild animal, that boy,' Papa Earl said with a sigh. 'Comes and goes when he wants. Don't know what to do 'bout him.'

Bella was still studying Maeve's photo. Softly she asked, 'Who is she?'

'My daughter,' said Adam.

Papa Earl sat back, nodding with instant understanding. 'So you lookin' for your girl.'

'Yes.'

'Why?'

Adam shook his head, puzzled by the question. 'Because she's my daughter.'

'But she run away. She don't want to be found. Girl like that, you ain't never gonna find her 'less she comes to *you*.'

'Then I suppose . . .' Adam looked down wearily. 'I suppose I'd settle for just knowing she's all right.'

Papa Earl was silent a moment. It was hard to tell what thoughts were going on behind those clouded eyes of his. At last he said, 'You'll want to talk to Jonah.'

'Jonah?' asked Kat.

'He's the big man now.'

'Since when?'

'Year ago. Took over when Berto went down. Anything you want round here, gotta go through Jonah.'

'Thanks,' said Kat. 'We'll follow up on that.' She was

about to stand up when another question occurred to her. 'Papa Earl,' she said, 'did you know a boy named Nicos Biagi?'

The old man paused. 'I heard of him, yeah.'

'Xenia Vargas?'

'Maybe.'

'Did you hear she died?'

He sighed. 'Lotta people die 'round here. Don't stick in your mind much anymore, people dying.'

'They both took the same drug, Papa Earl. This drug, it's moved into the Projects and it's killing people.'

He said nothing. He just sat there, his sightless eyes staring at her.

'If you hear anything, anything at all about it, will you call me?' She took out her business card and laid it on the table. 'I need help on this.'

He touched the card, his bony fingers moving across 'Kat Novak, M.D.' printed in black. 'You still workin' for the city?' he asked.

'Yes. The medical examiner.'

'Don't understand you, Katrina. You a doctor now, and you takin' care of dead people.'

'I find out why they die.'

'But then it's too late. Don't do 'em no good. You should be in a hospital. Or open your own place out here. It's what your mama wanted.'

Kat was suddenly aware of Adam's gaze on her. *Damn it, Papa Earl,* she thought. *Save the lecture for another time.*

'I like my job,' she said. 'I couldn't stand it in a hospital.'

Papa Earl gazed at her with sad understanding. 'Those

were bad times for you, weren't they? All those months with your mama . . .'

Kat rose to her feet. 'Thanks for your help, Papa Earl. But we have to leave.'

Bella and her grandfather escorted them through the living room. It never changed, this room. The chairs were set in precisely the same places they'd always been, and Papa Earl navigated past them like a bat with sonar.

'Next time,' he grumbled as Adam and Kat left the apartment, 'don't you wait so long before visits.'

'I won't,' said Kat. But it sounded hollow, that promise. *I don't believe it myself*, she thought. *Why should he?*

She and Adam headed back down the four flights of stairs, stepping over the same broken toys, the same cigarette butts. The smells of the building, the echoes of TV sets and babies' squalls, funneled up the stairwell and unleashed a barrage of memories. Of how she used to play on these steps, used to sit outside her apartment door, her knees bunched up against her chest. Waiting, waiting for her mother to calm down. Listening to the crying inside the apartment, the sounds of her mother's anguish, her mother's despair. The memories all rushed at her as she walked down the stairwell, and she knew exactly why she'd waited three long years to come back.

On the third floor landing, she paused outside apartment 3H. The door was a different color than she'd remembered, no longer green. Now it was a weirdly bright orange, and it had a built-in peephole. It would be different inside as well, she realized. Different people. A different world.

She felt Adam's hand gently touch her arm. 'What is it?' he asked.

'It's just—' She gave a tired little laugh. 'Nothing stays the same, does it? Thank God.' She turned and continued down the stairs.

He was close beside her. *Too close*, she thought. *Too personal. Threatening to invade my space, my life.*

'So your name's Katrina?'

'I go by Kat.'

'Katrina's lovely. But it doesn't quite fit with Novak.'

'Novak's my married name.'

'Oh. I didn't know you were married.'

'Was. My divorce became final six months ago.'

'And you kept your ex-husband's name?' He looked surprised.

'Not out of affection, believe me. It just felt like a better fit than Ortiz. See, I don't *look* like an Ortiz.'

'Are you referring to your green eyes? Or the freckles on your nose?'

Again, Kat paused on the steps and looked at him. 'Do you always notice the color of women's eyes?'

'No.' He smiled. *What a lot of practice that smile must have had*, she thought. 'But I did notice yours.'

'Lucky me,' she said, and continued down the stairs to the ground floor.

'Could you explain something?' he asked. 'Who is this Jonah person you were talking about in there? And what's a "big man"?'

'The big man,' said Kat, 'is like a – a head honcho. The guy in charge of this territory. For years it was Berto, but I guess he's gone. So now it's a guy named Jonah. He watches over things, keeps out rival gangs. If you want any favors, have any questions to ask, you have to go through the big man.'

'Oh. A sort of unofficial mayor of the neighborhood.'

'You got it.'

They went outside, into a night that smelled of wind and rain. She glanced up at the sky, saw clouds hurtling past the moon. 'It's getting late,' she said. 'Let's get out of here.'

They hurried down the steps. Two paces was all they managed to take before they both halted, staring in shock at the empty stretch of road beneath the streetlamp.

Kat let fly an oath that would have made a sailor cringe.

Her car had vanished.

# 5

Laughter drifted down the dark street, carried by the wind.

Kat spun around and saw the teenagers, still standing at the far corner. They were looking her way and grinning. *Damn punks*, she thought. *They think this is hilarious.* In fury she stalked toward them. 'Hey!' she yelled. '*Hey!*'

Adam grabbed her arm and dragged her to a halt. 'I think this is a bad idea,' he whispered.

'Let me go.'

'On further thought, it's a *terrible* idea.'

'I want my car back!' she said, and yanked her arm free. Rage was all the fuel she needed to propel her to the corner. The kids stood watching her, but they made no move. 'Okay,' she snapped. 'Where is it?'

'Where's what, lady?'

'My car, asshole.'

'You had a car?' a boy asked with mock innocence.

74

Kat ignored him. 'It's not worth a hell of a lot, that car. And it's sure not worth going to jail for. So just give it back to me. And maybe I won't call the cops.'

Some of the kids retreated and faded into the background. The rest – a half-dozen of them – began to fan out into a semicircle. Suddenly she realized that Adam was standing right beside her, shoulder to shoulder. *Amazing. He didn't turn tuxedo and run*, she thought. Maybe she had underestimated him.

The kids were watching her, waiting for signs of fear. She knew how their minds worked; she'd grown up with kids just like these. Turn your back, show a flicker of anxiety, and you were theirs.

She said, slowly, deliberately, '*I want my car.*'

'Or what?' one of the boys said.

'Or my friend here' – she nodded at Adam – 'gets nasty.'

All gazes turned to Adam. *Just a bluff, Quantrell*, she thought. *Don't fold on me.*

He stayed right where he was, solid as a wall.

Now two more of the boys backed down and slid away into the darkness. Only four were left, and they were getting edgy.

'No way you gonna get your wheels back,' one of them said.

'Why not?'

'Man, she's long gone. Wasn't us.'

'Who was it?'

'Repo dude. He's in and outta here. Your car, lady, she's chop.'

*Damn.* They were probably telling the truth, she thought.

'This is hopeless,' she muttered to Adam. 'Let's go.'

'I thought you'd never ask,' he hissed between his teeth.

Cautiously they eased away from the gang and quickly headed back toward Building Five. She would make her call to the police from Papa Earl's apartment. As for her Subaru, well, at least it was insured.

Kat was so worried about whether the boys were pursuing them that she scarcely noted the footsteps moving in the darkness ahead. Just as they reached the front steps of Building Five, two figures emerged from the darkness and barred their way.

'Let us through,' said Kat.

The boys didn't move.

'Just move aside,' said Adam calmly. 'And there won't be any trouble.'

They laughed, and Kat saw them glance past her, behind her.

She whirled around, just in time to spot the rear attack.

A figure flew at Adam's back, thudding into him so hard he staggered forward to his knees.

Now the two in front launched their assault. A fist slammed into Adam's jaw. Grunting, he brought his arm up to fend off the second blow.

Kat leaped into the fight. With a cry of rage she threw a left hook at the nearest attacker. Her knuckles connected with cheekbone. Pain exploded in her hand, but the triumph of watching the punk stagger away was worth it.

By now Adam had hauled off and landed a blow on his forward attacker. The rear attacker was still pummeling him on the back. Adam flung him loose. The kid rolled a few feet, then leaped to a crouch. Something clicked in his hand – a switchblade.

'He's got a knife!' yelled Kat.

Adam's gaze instantly focused on the silvery blade. He was unprepared for the sideways tackle by the other punk. They both landed on the ground, the punk on top.

The boy with the switchblade moved in toward the struggling pair.

Kat let fly a kick, felt an instant thump of satisfaction as her shoe connected with the back of Mr. Knife's knee. He groaned and fell forward, but didn't drop the knife.

Something thudded into her from behind, made her stumble to her knees. *A fourth?* she thought in confusion as hands gripped her arms. How many were there?

Her hair was jerked back, her throat lay bare.

The boy with the knife crouched beside her.

'No!' yelled Adam. 'Don't hurt her!'

The blade touched her throat, lingered there a moment. She caught a peripheral view of Adam struggling to reach her, panic stamped plainly on his face. Two boys had him by the arms. A third kicked him soundly in the ribs. Adam doubled over, groaning. 'Leave her alone,' he gasped.

'We won't cut you,' whispered a voice in Kat's ear. 'Not now. But you stay away, you hear, lady cop? 'Cause she don't want to be found.'

'I'm not a cop,' rasped Kat.

The knife bit sharply into her flesh; she felt a drop of blood trickle down her neck. Then, suddenly, the knife was lifted away and her hair was released. Kat knelt on the ground, her heart thudding, her throat closed down by terror. She touched her neck, then stared at the blood on her fingers. 'I thought,' she said hoarsely, 'that you weren't going to cut me.'

'That?' the kid with the knife laughed. 'That's not a cut. That's just a little *kiss*.' He signaled to his buddies that it was time to leave. With startling efficiency, they picked Adam's wallet, stripped off his overcoat, relieved Kat of her purse.

'This time,' said the kid, 'you get off easy.' He gave Kat a kick in the shoulder, which sent her sprawling onto the glass-littered sidewalk.

'No goddamn car is worth it,' said Adam, gingerly holding an ice pack to his cheek. The left side of his face was swollen, and dried blood had caked in his eyebrow. His tuxedo, which had started the evening crisply im- maculate, was now in tatters.

He fit right in with the other down-and-outers sitting in the Hancock Emergency Room waiting area. The benches were filled with a tired collection of the bruised and sick, coughing kids, wailing babies, all of them resigned to the long wait for a doctor.

'Anyone with a modicum of sense knows when to fight, and when to turn tail and run,' said Adam. 'You should've run.'

'I didn't see *you* running,' she shot back.

'How could I? I wasn't going to let you take them on by yourself.'

'Well, I do appreciate the gesture.'

'Let me tell you, I wasn't the least bit happy about getting killed over some old Subaru.'

'I liked that car,' muttered Kat. 'It was the first car I ever bought brand-new.'

'It could've been the *only* car you ever bought brand-new.'

A man staggered into the waiting room, rolled his eyes back, and fainted. He was quickly scooped up by two orderlies and wheeled into the inner sanctum. Everyone in the room gave a collective sigh of unhappiness. The wait would be that much longer.

'I tell you what,' said Adam. 'Next time this happens, I'll *buy* you a new car.'

'I can buy my own car,' said Kat. 'I just don't like getting ripped off.' She – as well as everyone else – looked up hopefully as the ER nurse came into the waiting area.

'Ripped off,' said Adam, 'is better than beaten to a pulp. I can't believe they did that to us. And all over something so trivial.'

'But it wasn't over the car,' said Kat. 'Don't you get it? My car had nothing to do with it.'

The nurse called out: 'Novak!'

Kat shot to her feet. 'Here.'

'Follow me.'

'Wait,' said Adam, tossing aside the ice pack. 'What do you mean, your car had nothing to do with it? Then what was that fight all about?'

'Your daughter,' Kat replied, following the nurse out of the waiting area.

Adam was right behind her as she went into the treatment room.

'You'll have to wait outside, sir,' said the nurse.

'He's with me,' said Kat.

The nurse looked at Adam's battered face, then at Kat's black eye. 'I think I can tell,' she said, and shook out a paper drape. 'Lie down and put this over your blouse. So it doesn't get blood on it.'

'It's already got blood on it,' said Kat as she settled back on the treatment table. The nurse began to clean the knife slash; the sting of Betadine was almost worse than the blade itself.

'What makes you think Maeve had anything to do with this?' said Adam.

'Something our friend with the knife whispered in my ear.'

'Hold still,' snapped the nurse.

'He said, "Stay away, lady cop. Because she doesn't want to be found." Now, that tells me a couple of things. First, he's stupid. He can't tell a cop from a civilian. Second, he's warning us that *she* doesn't want to be found. Who do you suppose *she* is?'

'Maeve,' he said, looking stunned.

The ER doctor came in, a shaggy version of Dr. Michael Dietz, with the same look of battle fatigue. Kat wondered how many hours he'd been working, how many bodies he'd laid hands on. He glanced at her neck wound. His name tag said *Dr. Volcker*.

'How'd you get it?' he asked.

'Switchblade.'

'Someone try to kill you?'

'No, it was an accident.'

'Okay' The doctor sighed. 'I'll skip the dumb questions.' He turned to the nurse. 'Suture set. She'll need about three stitches. And hand me the Xylocaine.'

Kat winced as the needle with local anesthetic pierced her skin. Then there was the moment's wait for the drug to take effect.

'I can't believe she'd do it,' said Adam. 'I mean, we've had our differences. But for Maeve to have her friends assault us . . .'

'She wasn't attacking you, specifically. She probably didn't know who the hell was asking about her. We might've avoided the whole scene if we'd just told Anthony right off that you were her father.'

'You're saying *Anthony* warned her?'

'He left the apartment while we were still there, remember? Before you said anything about her being your daughter. Probably went straight to Maeve.'

'And she had her friends jump us.'

'Well,' said the doctor, tying off the first stitch. 'You two lead exciting lives.'

They ignored him. 'Maeve must be scared of something,' said Kat. 'Why send the troops to attack at the first sign of strangers?' She glanced at Adam and saw his troubled look. 'What's she afraid of? What did you forget to tell me?'

He shook his head. 'She's in trouble.'

'What kind of trouble?'

He sank into a nearby chair and wearily ran his hands across his battered face.

'Does it have to do with Jane Doe?' asked Kat. 'With Xenia Vargas and Nicos?'

'Maybe.' His answer came out muffled, as though he wanted to bury the words in his throat.

'Or does it have to do with Cygnus? Some miracle drug you've got in development?'

He looked up in anger. 'Why blame it on Cygnus? None of your tests are back! You don't know what the hell those junkies were shooting up.'

'Do *you* know?'

He started to speak, then saw that both the doctor and nurse were watching them in fascination.

'Are you going to sew her up or what?' Adam snapped.

'I was hoping I could hear the end of the story,' said the doctor. He tied off the last stitch and snipped the thread. 'All done. Come back for suture removal in five days.'

'I can pull them myself, thanks,' said Kat. She sat up. The room seemed to sway around her like a boat. She waited for a moment for everything to stop moving.

'Last tetanus shot?' the doctor asked.

'Two years ago. I'm current.'

'Keep the wound dry for twenty-four hours. Clean it twice a day with peroxide. And call if it gets red or warm.' He gave her the ER sheet to sign, then he headed for the door. 'Come back any time,' he said over his shoulder. 'I can't wait for the next installment.'

Back in the hospital lobby, Kat waited for Adam to call his house. Collect, of course; the punks had done a thorough job of emptying their pockets. It was a helpless feeling, being penniless. When Kat had told the ER billing clerk she'd mail in her payment, the clerk had given her a *yeah, sure* look. No respect at all.

'Thomas is on his way,' said Adam, hanging up. 'We'll give you a ride home.'

'Who's Thomas?'

'Sort of my man Friday.' Adam glanced down at his soiled shirt. 'And he's not going to be pleased when he sees what I've done to his ironing job.'

Kat looked down at her own wrinkled shirt. 'Maybe I should borrow him sometime,' she said. 'Along with his iron.'

They sat down in the waiting area. A nurse walked by, carrying a cup of coffee from the vending machine. Kat would have loved a cup of coffee, but her pockets were empty. *Broke and in purgatory*, she thought.

A half hour passed, forty-five minutes. It was almost midnight, and things were still hopping at Hancock General. The next shift of nurses dribbled in from the parking lot, lugging umbrellas and lunch sacks. At the front door, an armed guard eyed everyone who entered. This was frontline medicine, and Hancock General was the equivalent of trench warfare. Every stabbing, every shooting that took place within a three-mile radius, anything on South Lexington, would roll in these ER doors. So would the drug ODs. Kat wondered if another Nicos Biagi or Jane Doe had been found.

'He's upstairs, you know,' she said. 'In the ICU.'

'Who?'

'Nicos Biagi. I came by to see him, earlier today.' She

shook her head. 'He didn't look good. Whatever it was he shot up, it's fried his brains. And kidneys.'

Adam was silent. Coldly so.

'The ER doc says it's something new. Something he's never seen before . . .' She paused, as a chilling thought suddenly came to mind. She looked at Adam and saw that he was avoiding her gaze. 'You said you gave Maeve a job. Was it at Cygnus?'

He sighed. 'Yes.'

'Which department?'

'Really, this has nothing to do with Maeve—'

'Which department, Adam?'

He let out another breath, a sound of profound weariness. 'Research and Development,' he said. 'She was doing cleanup in the lab. Running the autoclave. Nothing vital.'

'What was the lab working on?'

'Various projects. Everything from antibiotics to hair restorers.'

'Morphine analogues?'

'Look,' he snapped. 'We're a pharmaceutical company. And pain relief is a big market—'

'You're cooking up something new in that lab, aren't you? Something no one else has developed yet.'

A pause. Then, reluctantly, he nodded. 'It's . . . a breakthrough. Or it will be, if we can iron out the kinks. It's a close relative to natural endorphins. Latches onto the same enzyme receptors as morphine does, holds onto those receptors like Krazy Glue. So it's very long-lasting. Which makes it perfect for terminal cancer patients.'

'Long-lasting? How long?'

'A dose will give pain relief for seventy-two hours, maybe longer. That's its advantage. And its disadvantage. If you overdose an animal, you'll put it in a long-term coma.' He looked up at her; what she saw in his eyes was worry, maybe guilt. And absolute honesty.

She rose suddenly to her feet. 'Come upstairs with me.'

'The ICU?'

'Nicos Biagi's tox screen might be back. I want you to look at it, tell me if it matches your miracle drug.'

'But I'm not a biochemist. I'd need confirmation from my staff—'

'Then take the report back to them. Have them confirm it.'

He shook his head. 'Hospital tox screens aren't specific enough.'

'Why are you so reluctant? Afraid to hear the truth? That it could be a Cygnus drug that's killing people?'

Slowly he rose to his feet. His height put her at a disadvantage. Now she was looking up at *him*, confronting the chilly silence of his eyes.

Up till now, she hadn't felt in the least bit intimidated by Adam Quantrell, not by his wealth or his power or his good looks. But his anger – this was something else. This she couldn't brush off, couldn't turn her back on. Their gazes held and all at once something new flared inside her, so unexpected she was stunned by its intensity. Suddenly she was unable, unwilling, to take note of anything else in the room.

It was a woman's voice, calling Adam's name, that finally broke the spell.

'Adam! What on earth did you *do* to yourself?'

Kat turned and saw Isabel, still in full evening dress. She'd just come through the ER doors and now was staring at Adam in dismay.

'Look at your clothes! And your face! What happened?' Isabel reached up and touched the bruise on his cheek.

He winced. 'We got into a little . . . trouble,' he said. 'What are you doing here, Isabel?'

'I heard Thomas say he was coming to fetch you. I told him I'd do it instead.'

'I'll have to talk to him about this—'

'No, I insisted. I thought you'd be glad to have me rescue you.' She flashed him a smile. '*Aren't* you glad?'

'You shouldn't be down here,' he said. 'Not at this time of night. It's not safe.'

'Oh, well.' Isabel glanced around in disbelief at the tired army of people waiting on the benches and she clutched her wrap more tightly around her shoulders. 'I can't imagine what you're doing in this part of town.' She looked at Kat's equally bruised face. 'It appears you both got into a little trouble.'

'Dr. Novak needs a ride home, too,' said Adam. 'Her car got stolen. And at the moment, we're penniless.'

There was a brief silence, then Isabel shrugged. 'Why not? The more the merrier, I say.' She turned toward the exit. 'Come on. Let's get out of here before *my* car gets stolen.'

'Wait.' Adam looked at Kat. 'There's something we need to do first.'

'What's that?' asked Isabel.

'We have to go upstairs. There's a patient we have to see. In the ICU.'

Kat gave him a nod of approval. So he was finally ready to hear the truth.

'I'll just come along,' said Isabel. 'You wouldn't leave me down here all by myself, would you?'

With Adam and Isabel in tow, Kat retraced the steps she'd taken earlier that day. Down the hallway with the tired aqua walls. Up the elevator. Down another hall. Isabel's high heels clacked across the floor.

The ICU was a hive of activity, nurses scurrying about, monitors beeping, ventilators whooshing. At the central nursing desk, two dozen heart tracings zigzagged across a bank of oscilloscopes.

The ward clerk glanced up in surprise at the trio of visitors. 'Are you visiting someone?' he asked.

'I'm Dr. Novak, ME's office,' said Kat. 'I was here earlier with Dr. Dietz, looking over Nicos Biagi's chart. Would you know if his tox screen came back?'

'I just came on duty. Let me check the reports.' The clerk turned to the in-box, riffled through the stack of newly delivered lab slips. 'There's no tox screen here for a Biagi.'

'How is he doing?'

'You'll have to talk to one of the nurses. Which bed is he in?'

'Bed thirteen.'

'Thirteen?' The clerk looked at the Cardex file and frowned. 'There's no one in bed thirteen.'

'That's his bed number, I'm sure of it.' Kat glanced at

the oscilloscope, where every patient's heart rhythm wriggled across the screen. Number thirteen was blank.

A nurse walked past the desk, carrying an armful of charts. 'Excuse me, Lori?' called the ward clerk. 'There was a Mr. Biagi in bed thirteen. Do you know if he's been moved?'

Lori stopped, turned to look at the trio of visitors. 'Are you friends or relatives?'

'Neither,' said Kat. 'I'm from the ME's office.'

'Oh.' The look of caution eased from the nurse's face. 'Then I guess it's okay to tell you.'

'Tell me what?'

'Mr. Biagi died. Two hours ago.'

# 6

Jane Doe. Xenia Vargas. Nicos Biagi. They were all dead.

How many more would die?

Kat sat in the back seat of Isabel's Mercedes and stared out at the midnight scenery of South Lexington. She'd forgotten about her bruises, her empty stomach, the throbbing of her freshly sutured neck. She was numb now, shaken by the new addition to the death toll. Three in two days. It was lethal, this drug. It sucked the life out of its victims as surely as a dose of strychnine. Unless the word got out on the streets, there'd be more Jane Does checking into private drawers in the morgue. She only hoped Wheelock had stressed the urgency in his press conference. *Had* there been a press conference? She'd missed the evening news . . .

Exhausted, she sank back into the luxury of soft, buttery leather. She'd never been in such a clean car. She'd never been in the back seat of a Mercedes, either.

This she could learn to like. She could also learn to like the smooth ride, the sense of insulated safety. Maybe there was something to be said for money.

Isabel had stopped at a red light, and she brushed back Adam's hair with her manicured fingers. 'You poor thing! Look at those bruises! I'll have to get you all cleaned up when we get home.'

'I'm perfectly fine, Isabel,' Adam said with a sigh.

'What happened to your overcoat?'

'They took it. Along with my wallet.'

'Oh! And you got hurt trying to fight them off?'

'No, as a matter of fact, I got hurt trying to get away.'

'Don't say things like that, Adam. I know perfectly well you're not a coward.'

*So do I*, thought Kat.

Adam merely shrugged. 'Keep your illusions, then. I'll try not to shatter them.'

The red light changed to green. Isabel drove up the freeway on-ramp. 'We missed you at dinner, you know,' she said.

Adam looked out the window. 'Hope you left some wine in my cellar.'

'Enough for a nightcap.'

'I'm really pretty tired. I think I'll probably go straight to sleep.'

There was a silence. 'Oh,' said Isabel. 'Well, there's still tomorrow night. You *are* up for that, aren't you?'

'What's tomorrow night?'

'The mayor's dinner. Adam, how *could* you forget?'

'I just did.'

Isabel gave a laugh. 'You'll be a hit, you know. All those lovely bruises. Like some macho badge of honor.'

'More like a badge of stupidity,' said Adam.

'What is the matter with you?'

'Get off here,' said Adam. 'Bellemeade exit.'

'Why would I want to go to Bellemeade?'

'It's where I live,' said Kat from the back seat. Had Isabel forgotten she was there?

'Oh, of course.' Isabel took the exit. 'Bellemeade. That's a nice neighborhood.'

'It's close to town,' said Kat, a neutral response that could be taken in many different ways.

After a few blocks and a few turns, they pulled up in front of Kat's house. She was proud of that house. It had three bedrooms, a charming front porch, and a lawn that wasn't loaded with chemicals. It wasn't Surry Heights, but she was happy here. So why did she feel the sudden urge to apologize?

Adam got out and opened her door. To her surprise, he also offered his hand. She stepped out onto the sidewalk beside him. The streetlamp spilled light across his golden hair.

'Can you get into the house?' he asked.

'I keep an extra key under the flowerpot.'

'You don't have a car.'

'I'll catch the bus to work.'

'That's crazy. I'll arrange something.'

'I'm really okay, Adam. I've gone without wheels before.'

'Still, I feel responsible. You got into this mess because

of me. So let me take care of it. A taxi to work, at least.'

She looked up at him, sensed how very much he wanted her to accept his help. 'Okay,' she said. 'Just for a day or two. Until I come up with a new car.'

She headed up the walkway to her front porch. Then she glanced back.

He was still watching, waiting for her to go inside.

Only when she'd entered the house and turned on the hallway light did he get back in the car. She looked out the front window and saw the Mercedes drive away.

*Back to Surry Heights*, she thought. *Back to his world.*

And Isabel's.

She locked the front door and wearily climbed the stairs to bed.

After he'd sent Isabel home, Adam holed up in his study and nursed a much-needed glass of brandy. His head ached, his eyes were bleary, and his ribs hurt like hell when he took a deep breath, but he couldn't quite drag himself off to bed yet.

He kept playing and replaying that terrifying image from tonight: Kat Novak, down on her knees, her hair yanked back, her throat bared. And the switchblade, pressing against her flesh. He closed his eyes and tried to shut it out, but couldn't. At the instant he'd seen it, he'd lost all fear for himself, had stopped caring what would happen to *him*. All he knew was that they were going to kill her, and there was nothing he could do to stop it, not a single damn thing.

He clutched the brandy glass and drained it in one

neat gulp. *She came through it better than I did*, he thought.

But then, Kat Novak was something extraordinary. A true survivor who would land on her feet every time. Considering her roots, she *had* to be a survivor. He wondered what she saw when she looked at him.

He wasn't sure he really wanted to know.

Finally he set down the brandy glass and hauled himself out of the chair. On the way out of the room, he passed the photo of Maeve. It sat on the end table, a quiet portrait of his smiling stepdaughter. Was Maeve smiling much these days?

He should have known. He should have seen it coming.

He had no excuses, except that he'd felt overwhelmed, by his work, by single fatherhood, by a daughter who was so traumatized by her mother's death that she slipped into an eternally sullen adolescence. He couldn't talk to her; after a while he'd given up trying and had resorted to a father's tactic of last resort: asserting his authority. That hadn't worked, either.

By the time he'd realized Maeve was in trouble, it was too late. She was on a constant high – booze, pills, every-thing, anything.

Like Georgina.

Maybe it was in their genes, some cruel twist in their DNA that preordained their addictions. Maybe it was simply that they couldn't cope with life or stress.

Or was it him?

He turned away from the photograph and climbed the stairs. Once again, alone to bed. It didn't have to be this way. It had been clear tonight that Isabel was ready and willing – and frustrated by his lack of interest. They'd known each other for years, had been seeing each other on a regular basis for months. Shouldn't he be making *some* kind of move?

But tonight, when she'd driven him to his door, he'd taken a good look at her. She was perfect, of course – her hair, her dress, her smile – perfect in every way. And yet he felt no interest whatsoever in taking her to bed. He'd looked at her, and all he could see was Kat Novak, her face as bruised as a prizefighter's, grinning at him by the light of that Bellemeade streetlamp.

*Wonderful*, he thought. *After all these years I finally admit to the possibility of romance, and look who inspires it. A woman who almost gets me killed over some beat-up Subaru.*

Not at all a promising match.

Kat woke up with every muscle in her body aching. It took a massive infusion of willpower just to roll out of bed. She went into the bathroom and saw, in the mirror, the evidence of last night's brawl: three neat stitches on her neck and the bruises and scrapes on her face. So it hadn't been a nightmare after all.

She managed to wash around that painful minefield of facial cuts and sweep her hair back in a ponytail. Forget the makeup; she'd wear her bruises to work instead.

Downstairs, fueled by a cup of extra-strength Yuban, she started in on the tasks at hand: canceling her credit cards and her bank card, replacing her driver's license. When the punks had grabbed her purse, they'd made off with most of her financial identity. At least she still had her checkbook – that she'd left safely at home last night. She made one last call, begging a locksmith to come change her locks ASAP. Then she got up and poured herself another cup of coffee. The caffeine was having its blessed effect – she was feeling human again. And feisty. Getting beaten up and robbed wasn't good for her disposition.

So when she heard the footsteps on her front porch, she was expecting the worst. Were the punks there already to try out her house keys?

She scurried into the living room, grabbed the baseball bat out of the front closet, and stood poised by the front door. When she heard the clink of keys, she raised the bat, expecting the door to swing open any second.

Instead, the mail slot squealed open, and a set of car keys slid through and clattered to the wood floor. Kat stared at them. What the hell?

Whoever had dropped them off was now walking away. She yanked open the door and saw Adam Quantrell's butler climb into a car driven by another man.

'Hey!' Kat yelled, waving the keys. 'What's this?'

The butler waved back and called, 'Compliments of Mr. Quantrell!'

Bewildered, Kat watched them drive off. Then her gaze shifted to her driveway.

A lemon yellow Mercedes was parked there.

She looked down at the keys she was holding. Then she went to the driveway and slowly circled the car. It was beautiful. Absolutely beautiful. *Regis Luxury Rentals*, said the license plate frame. She peered in the window –

leather seats. *Clean.* She opened the door, climbed in behind the wheel, and just sat there for a moment. There was a note taped to the dashboard, addressed to Dr. Novak. She unfolded the slip of paper and read it.

*Hope this will do. A.Q.*

She sat back. 'Well, I just don't know, Mr. Quantrell,' she said aloud. 'Lemon yellow isn't *quite* my color. But I suppose it will have to do.' Then she threw her head back and laughed.

At work, she stopped laughing.

Davis Wheelock told her the mayor had vetoed the idea of any press conference.

'You can't be serious,' said Kat.

Wheelock looked genuinely apologetic. 'I explained the situation to the mayor and his staff. I told them we'd had two deaths—'

'Three, Davis. Nicos Biagi died. I've had it classified an ME case.'

'All right, three. I told them the trend was not good. But they felt a press conference was premature.'

'At what point does this crisis become mature?'

Wheelock shook his head. 'It's not in my power to go around them. The line of authority's clear. When it comes to press releases, the mayor has final say.'

'Maybe you weren't persuasive enough.'

'Maybe we should ride this out a bit. See what develops.'

'I can tell you what'll develop. And it won't be good press.' She leaned across Wheelock's desk. 'Davis, we're going to come out of this looking incompetent. When all hell breaks loose, do you think the mayor's going to take the rap? We will. *You* will.'

Wheelock was looking more and more unhappy.

'Let me talk to them,' said Kat. 'I'll bring in Dr. Dietz from Hancock General as my authority. This news has to get out, and soon. Before South Lexington turns into a graveyard.'

For a moment, Wheelock said nothing. Then he nodded. 'All right. You take care of it. But don't be surprised if they slap you down.'

'Thanks, Davis.'

Back in her office, the first call she made was to the mayor's secretary. She learned that His Honor had a hole in his appointment book at one o'clock and she might be able to slip in then, but there were no guarantees.

The second call she made was to Hancock General. Unfortunately, Dr. Michael Dietz was not on duty in the ER.

'Is there any way I can reach him?' asked Kat. 'This is urgent. I've booked us into the mayor's office at one o'clock.'

'I'm afraid that's impossible,' said the ER clerk.

'Why?'

'Dr. Dietz has left town. He resigned from the staff. Effective yesterday evening.'

During his three and a half years in office, Mayor Sampson had presided over the worst economic slide in Albion's history. To be fair, it wasn't entirely his fault – across the country, cities were reeling from the recession.

But with three major plant closings, a host of business bankruptcies, and an inner city rotting at its core, Albion had suffered worse than most. So it struck Kat as more than a little ironic that the bicentennial poster displayed behind the receptionist's desk showed a slick couple in evening dress, dancing before a view of the night skyline.

*Albion – a city for all reasons.*
*Nolan Sampson, Mayor.*

It was, of course, just your typical election year hype. How convenient for His Honor that the celebration just happened to coincide with the kickoff for his reelection campaign.

She approached the receptionist. 'I'm Dr. Novak, ME's office. Is there a chance I could get in to see Mayor Sampson?'

'I'll check.' The receptionist pressed the intercom. 'Mayor Sampson? There's a doctor here from the ME's office. Are you free?'

'Uh, yeah. We just finished lunch. Send him in,' Kat heard from the speaker.

*Him? He must think I'm Wheelock,* she thought. She opened the door and masculine laughter spilled out. Just inside the office, she halted.

The mayor was behind his desk, puffing on a cigar. In a nearby chair sat the acting district attorney – Kat's ex-husband.

'Hello, Ed,' said Kat stiffly. 'Mayor Sampson.'

Both men looked surprised. 'It's you,' Ed said, for want

of anything else to say. She noticed he'd spiffed up his wardrobe since their divorce. He had a new suit, Italian shoes, a shirt that looked like a hundred percent linen. *Just think of all those wrinkles. I wonder who he's got ironing his shirts these days.*

'Is this . . . official business?' asked the mayor, looking bewildered.

'Yes,' said Kat. 'Davis Wheelock spoke to you yesterday. About that press conference.'

'What? Oh.' Sampson waved his hand in dismissal. 'You mean the junkies. Yeah, we talked about it.'

'I think it's time to go to the press, sir,' said Kat. 'We've had three deaths.'

'I thought it was two.'

'Another OD died last night. At Hancock General.'

'Have you confirmed it's the same drug?'

'Let's just say my suspicions are running high.'

'Ah.' Sampson sat back, suddenly at ease. 'So you don't have confirmation.'

'Toxicology screens take time. Especially when the drug's an unknown. By the time we get a positive ID, we could have a full-blown crisis in South Lexington.'

Ed laughed. 'South Lexington *is* a crisis.'

Kat ignored him. 'All I'm asking for is a statement to the press. Call in the local news stations. Tell them we've got some bad stuff on the streets. Junkies are dying.'

The mayor glanced at Ed with an amused look. 'Some would say that's progress.'

'Sir,' said Kat, trying to stay calm, 'you have to let people know.'

'Now therein lies our problem,' said Mayor Sampson, shifting forward in his chair. 'Dr. Novak, in case you're not aware of it, we have a bicentennial celebration coming up. Parade, marching bands, the whole nine yards. We have the heads of eight major corporations coming to town to join in the fun. And to look us over, see if they like us. We're talking jobs they could bring to Albion. But they won't bring a *thing* to town if they start seeing headlines like *Junkie epidemic* or *Grim reaper stalks city*. They'll just move their companies to Boston or Providence instead.'

'So what do you suggest?' asked Kat. 'We sweep it under the rug?'

'Not exactly. We just . . . wait a while.'

'How long?'

'Until you've got more information. Next week, say.'

'A lot of people can die in a week.'

'Lighten up, Kat,' Ed cut in. 'These aren't the pillars of society we're talking about. These are the same folks who mug old ladies and hold up gas stations. The same folks I'm already sticking in jail.' He paused. 'The same folks who ripped off your car.'

'How did you hear about that?' Kat snapped.

Ed grinned. 'We hear a lot of things at the office. Like who's been filing stolen car reports.'

'Forget my car. I want to know when we can see some action on this.'

'I think I answered that question, Dr. Novak,' said Mayor Sampson.

'You're making a mistake.'

'Christ,' Sampson said with a sigh. 'You can't even

prove to me these deaths are related. Why go and get the whole town panicked about it?'

Ed added, 'They're only junkies.'

She shook her head in disbelief. 'You know what, Ed?' she said with a laugh. 'It's a continuing source of wonder to me.'

'What is?'

'What the hell I ever saw in you.' She turned and walked out of the room.

Ed followed her, through the receptionist's office and into the hallway. 'Kat, wait up.'

'I'm going back to work.'

'Just love those stiffs, huh?'

'Compared to present company? Don't ask.' She got into the elevator, and he slipped in beside her.

'Looks like life's been rough since you left me,' he said, glancing at her bruised face with a grin.

'Not nearly as rough as it was *with* you. And you left *me*, remember?'

'You know, you really blew it in there with Sampson. Next time you should try a little honey, not so much vinegar. It'd be better for your career.'

'I see *your* career doesn't need any help,' she said, glancing at his tailored shirt.

He grinned. 'You heard that Sampson endorsed me? The campaign coffers are already loaded.'

'Be careful whose coattails you grab onto. Sampson's days are numbered.'

They stepped out of the elevator and left the building.

'It's just a stepping stone,' he said. 'Today, DA. Tomorrow – who knows? Are you coming to the campaign benefit? I could use you there. Show of support from the ME's office.'

'I've got better ways to spend my money.'

He reached in his pocket and produced an invitation. 'Here.' He dropped it in her purse. 'My compliments. Will you vote for me, at least?'

She laughed. 'What do *you* think?'

'I think you're gonna need a friend in high places. Especially with the rut your career seems to be—' He broke off and stared as Kat unlocked the door of the Mercedes. 'This is *your* car?' he asked.

'Nice, isn't she?' Kat slid into the driver's seat and slammed the door. She smiled sweetly out the window. 'Those of us in career ruts have to find *some* way to compensate.'

The look on his face was enough to keep her smiling for a block. Then the anger hit, anger at Ed and Sampson and Wheelock. And at herself, for acknowledging defeat. She could go around them all. Ignore the lines of authority, call up the news stations herself, and announce a crisis . . .

And promptly get herself fired.

She gripped the steering wheel, silently railing at herself, at election-year politics, at a system that made you park your conscience if you wanted to stay employed. She just didn't have the evidence to force the issue – not yet. What she needed was a pair of matching tox screens – just one pair, enough to link two of the deaths. Enough to go to the press and say, 'We have a trend here.'

The minute she got back to her office, she called the

state lab. 'This is Dr. Novak, Albion Assistant ME. Do you have results yet on Jane Doe number 373-4-3-A?'

'I'll check,' said the technician.

A moment later, the tech came back on the line. 'I have a blood, urine, and vitreous on Jane Doe number 372-3-27-B.'

'That's a different number.'

'It was ordered by a Dr. Clark, Albion ME. Is this the one you want?'

'No, that's the wrong Jane Doe. I want 373-4-3-A.'

'I have no record of any such request.'

'I sent it in April third. Name's Dr. Novak.'

'My log for April third doesn't show any Jane Doe specimens from Albion. Or anything from you, Dr. Novak.'

Kat tugged at a loose hair in frustration. 'Look, I know I sent it in. It was even marked *Expedite*.'

'It's not in the log or in my computer.'

'I can't believe this! Of all the lab requests, you have to lose this one? I *need* those results.'

'We can't run a test without specimens,' said the tech with undeniable logic.

'Okay.' Kat sighed. 'Then give me the results from another case. Xenia Vargas. I sent that in April fourth. You *do* have that one?'

'It was logged in. Let me check . . .' There was a brief silence, punctuated by the clicking of fingers on a keyboard. Then the tech said, 'It was shipped to an outside lab.'

'Why?'

'It says here, "Nonspecific opioids detected. Unable to

identify using available techniques. Specimen referred to independent lab for further tests." That's all.'

'So I *will* get an ID? Eventually?'

'Eventually.'

'Thank you.' Kat hung up. Then it was something new. Something even the state lab couldn't identify.

But it was only one case. To prove a trend, she needed a second case, at the very least.

She rose and pulled on her lab coat. Then she walked down the hall to the morgue. One of the day attendants was tidying up the room. He glanced at her.

'Hey, Doc,' he said. 'What's up?'

'Hal, you remember those specimens I sent off on Monday? For Jane Doe? I put them in the out-box. Did you see the courier pick them up?'

'Don't tell me they went and lost something again?'

'They say they never got it.'

Hal rolled his eyes. 'Yeah, I heard them give Doc Clark the same story. So what do you want me to do? Run another set over?'

'If you're willing.' She glanced at her watch. 'It's four. Take an hour of overtime. That'll cover the drive. And make sure they log it in.'

'Sure thing.'

Now there would be another long wait for results. Luckily, they'd retained several tubes of Jane Doe's blood and urine, for just this situation. While it was rare for specimens to be lost, it did happen.

Her head was starting to ache again, a reminder of last night's scuffle. She should go home early, put up her feet, and OD on the opiate of the masses – TV. But she'd accumulated too much paperwork.

Back at her desk, she shuffled through her in-box. There were dictations to sign, reports from ballistics, lab slips, pathology journals. She had just emptied her box when the mailroom clerk came in, whistling, and dumped another stack onto her desk.

'Forget this,' Kat muttered. 'I'm going home.'

Then she saw the envelope on the stack. *Dr. Novak* was scrawled on top. No address, no stamp; someone must have dropped it off at the front desk.

She opened the envelope and read the note.

Nicos Biagi results just back, MIT lab. Identified as new generation long-acting narcotic, levo-N-cyclobutylmethyl-6, 10 beta-dihydroxy class. Not FDA approved for use in humans. MIT says research patent application made six months ago. Trade name: Zestron-L. Applicant: Cygnus Corporation.

Sorry I'm cutting out on you, but I don't need the headache. Good luck, Novak. You'll need it.

Mike Dietz

*The Cygnus Corporation.* She stared at the name, stunned by the revelation. *Thanks, Dr. Dietz, you coward. You drop this can of worms on my desk, and then you turn and run.*

She grabbed the phone and called the state lab once again.

'About that tox screen, on Xenia Vargas,' she said to the technician. 'There's a specific drug I want you to test for. It's called Zestron-L.'

'You'll have to talk directly to the outside lab. They're handling it now.'

'Okay, I'll call them. Where did you send it to?'

'Cygnus Laboratories, in Albion. Do you want the number?'

Kat didn't answer. She kept staring at that note from Dietz, at the name: *Cygnus*. Pharmaceuticals. Diagnostic labs. How many tentacles did the corporation have?

'Dr. Novak?' asked the tech again. 'Do you want the Cygnus phone number?'

'No,' said Kat softly, and hung up.

It took her a few minutes to dredge up the courage to make the next phone call. It had to be done; Adam Quantrell had to be confronted.

The phone rang once, twice. A male voice answered: 'Quantrell residence. Thomas speaking.'

'This is Dr. Novak.'

'Ah, yes, Dr. Novak. I hope the new automobile is working out.'

'It's fine. Is Mr. Quantrell in?'

'I'm afraid he just left for the evening. The mayor's benefit, you know. Shall I give him a message?'

And what message could she leave? she thought. *That I know the truth? It's your company, your drug, that's killing people?*

'Dr. Novak?' asked Thomas when she said nothing.

She folded Dietz's note and stuffed it in her purse. 'No message, Thomas. Thanks,' she said. 'I'll catch him at the benefit.'

Then she hung up and walked out of the office.

# 7

It took Kat an hour and a half to drive home, change her clothes, and fight her way back through midtown traffic. By that time, a major jam had built up along Dorchester Avenue, leading to the Four Seasons Hotel. All the red lights gave her time to shake her hair loose, dab on lipstick, brush on mascara while looking in the visor mirror. Even with a ton of face powder the bruises were still obvious, but at least she'd found a silk scarf to wrap around her neck and conceal the stitches. It actually looked rather dashing, that slash of red and purple silk trailing across the black dress. Too bad the whole effect required high heels; before the night was over, her feet would be killing her.

The ballroom of the Four Seasons was packed. There were probably enough furs and jewels in the room to fund the city budget for a year. A buffet table held platters of shrimp and smoked salmon, pastries and caviar, all of it served on real china, of course. A balalaika troupe was playing Russian music – a tribute to Albion's equally depressed sister city on the Volga. Kat handed her invitation to the official at the door and headed into the thick of things.

She was reminded at once of why she hated going to affairs like this, especially on her own. Bring an escort and you were an instant social circle; go alone and you're invisible. Sipping at the requisite glass of white wine, she wandered through the crowd and searched for a familiar face – any familiar face. Mostly she saw a lot of tuxedoes, a lot of mink, a lot of orthodontically perfect teeth bared in perfect smiles.

She heard her name called. Turning, she saw her ex-husband. 'And I thought you weren't going to vote for us,' he said as he approached.

'I didn't say I would. I just can't pass up a free invite.'

'Hey, I want to get a photo taken. You and the mayor together.' He glanced around and spotted Sampson off in a corner, surrounded by admirers. 'There he is. Come on.'

'I don't do photo ops.'

'Just this time.'

'I told you, I'm not here to endorse him. I'm here to partake of a few free drinks and—' She stopped, her gaze suddenly focusing across the room, on a man's fair hair. Adam Quantrell didn't see her; he was facing sideways, engaged in conversation with another man. Next to Adam stood Isabel, her equally blond hair done up in an elaborate weave of faux pearls. *The perfect couple*, she thought. A stunning pair in tuxedo and evening dress.

The sort of couple you saw epitomized in *Cosmo* ads.

Adam must have sensed he was being watched. He glanced her way and froze when he saw her. To Kat's surprise, he abruptly broke off his conversation and began to move toward her, across the room. She caught a glimpse of Isabel's frown, of faces turning to look at Adam as his broad shoulders pushed past. And then all she could seem to focus on was *him*.

He was smiling at her, the relaxed greeting of an old friend. The bruise on his cheek was almost lost in the laugh lines around his eyes. 'Kat,' he said, 'I didn't know you were coming.' He reached out to her, and her hand felt lost in the warmth of his grip.

'*I* didn't know I was coming,' she said.

The sound of a throat being cleared caught her attention. She glanced sideways at Ed. 'I guess I should introduce you two,' she said. 'Ed, this is Adam Quantrell. Adam, this is Ed Novak. Our acting DA.'

'Novak?' said Adam as the two men automatically shook hands.

'I'm her ex-husband,' said Ed, grinning. 'We're still *very* close.'

'Speak for yourself,' said Kat.

'So you're both campaigning for Sampson?' asked Adam.

'Ed is,' said Kat. 'I'm not.'

Ed laughed. 'And I'm going to change her mind.'

'I came for the free meal,' said Kat. She took a sip of wine, then she looked directly at Adam, a cool, hard gaze that no one could mistake as flirtatious. 'And to see you.'

'Well,' said Ed. 'She always *did* favor the direct approach.'

'I'd like to say I'm flattered,' said Adam, frowning as he studied her face. 'But I get the feeling this isn't a social chat we're about to have.'

'It's not,' said Kat. 'It's about Nicos Biagi.'

'I see.' Suddenly he seemed stiff and guarded – as well he should be. 'Then perhaps we should talk in private. If you'll excuse us, Mr. Novak.' He placed a hand on Kat's shoulder.

'Adam!' called Isabel, moving swiftly toward them. 'I want you to meet someone. Oh, hello, Dr. Novak! Have you recovered from last night?'

Kat nodded. 'A few sore muscles, that's all.'

'You're amazingly resilient. I would have been terrified, having my life threatened that way.'

'Oh, I was terrified all right,' admitted Kat.

'And then to have your car stolen. How fortunate it was only a Subaru—'

'Will you excuse us?' said Adam, continuing to guide Kat toward the exit. 'I'll join you later, Isabel.'

'How much later?'

'Just later.' With a firm hand, he hustled Kat out to the lobby, where it was every bit as crowded. 'Let's go outside,' he suggested. 'At least we can get out of this madhouse.'

They found a spot near the hotel fountain, its trickling waters aglow in a rainbow of colored lights. The sounds of the gathering spilled out even here, in the darkness. From the ballroom came the faint strumming of balalaikas.

He turned to face her, his hair glittering in the reflected lights of the fountain. 'What's going on?' he asked.

'I could ask you the same question.'

'Are you angry at me for some reason?'

'Zestron-L,' she said, looking at him intently. 'You *have* heard of it, haven't you?'

She could see at once that he had. She caught a glimpse of shock in his eyes, and then his expression smoothed into unreadability. So he knew. All this time he knew which drug might be killing these people.

'Let me refresh your memory, in case you've forgotten,' she went on. 'Zestron-L is a long-acting narcotic, new generation, of the class levo-N-cyclobutyl—'

'I know what it is.'

'Then you also know Cygnus holds the patent.'

'Yes.'

'Did you also know your drug was out on the streets?'

'It's not possible. We're still in the research stage – primate trials. It hasn't gone to human trials yet.'

'I'm afraid human trials have already started. The lab is South Lexington. And the results aren't too encouraging. Bad side effects. Mainly, death.'

'But it hasn't been released yet!'

'Nicos Biagi got his hands on it.'

'How do you know?'

'The hospital couldn't ID it, so they sent the blood sample to a university lab. A lucky break, too. They were able to identify it.'

'There are two other victims—'

'Yes, and a funny thing happened to their blood

samples. Jane Doe's got lost in transit. And as for Xenia Vargas, I won't trust any results I get back on hers. In fact, I half expect that *her* blood sample will get lost as well.'

'Don't you think you sound just the slightest bit paranoid?'

'Paranoid? No, I'm afraid I've never had much of an imagination. It's one of my faults.'

He moved closer to her, so threateningly close she had to fight the impulse to retreat a step. 'Whatever your faults, Dr. Novak, a lack of imagination isn't one of them.'

'Let me lay out the facts, disturbing but true. First, Jane Doe's specimens were lost. I know I labeled them properly, I filled out all the right forms, and put them in the right box.'

'The carrier could have lost it. Or it could've been stolen from his vehicle. There are dozens of possibilities.'

'Then there's the matter of Xenia Vargas. Her specimens *did* make it to the state lab, but they can't ID the drug. So they send it to an outside lab for further testing. Guess which lab?' She looked him in the eye. 'Cygnus.'

He didn't even flinch. Calmly he said, 'We routinely handle requests from the state. We're only thirty miles away and we're better equipped.'

'*Third*, there's the matter of Dr. Michael Dietz, Nicos Biagi's doctor. He identifies the drug as Zestron-L. Then he resigns from Hancock General and skips town. I think he was forced out by the hospital. Because Cygnus just *happens* to be a major donor to Hancock General.'

'Cygnus had nothing to do with Dietz's resignation. He was already on his way out.'

'How would you know that?'

'I'm on the hospital board. Three malpractice suits were more than we'd tolerate. Dietz was a disaster waiting to happen. His license was already in jeopardy.'

Kat paused. That *would* account for Dietz's reluctance to face the press. He didn't need the publicity.

'But Zestron-L *is* your drug. And someone's trying to keep its identity from the ME. Someone's protecting Cygnus.'

He began to pace back and forth by the fountain. 'This is bizarre,' he muttered. 'I don't see how that ID could be right.'

'You can't argue with a lab result.'

He stopped and looked at her, the gaudy lights from the fountain washing him in their watery glow. 'No,' he said at last. 'You're right. I can't.'

The absolute steadiness of his gaze made her want to believe that there were no lies between them, no hidden agendas, that his bewilderment was real. *I must be getting soft*, she thought. *A pair of blue-gray eyes, a tuxedo, a man too gorgeous for words, and my horse sense bites the dust. What is wrong with me?*

'Come with me,' he said, and held out his hand.

She didn't move, feeling shaken by the sudden temptation to take his hand, to feel her whole body swallowed in his warmth. This was what she'd fought against, from the first time they'd met, this quickening of desire.

He was still holding out his hand, still trapping her in a gaze she couldn't seem to escape. 'Come on, Kat,' he said.

'Where?'

'To Cygnus. The lab. Tonight, I'm going to root out the answers. And I want you there with me, as a witness.'

She shook her head. 'I'm not so sure that you'll like the answers.'

'You may be right. But it's clear to me that you're not going to let up. One way or another, you're going to dig up the truth. So I might as well work with you. Not against you.'

The logic of the devil. How could she argue with it?

She said, at last, 'All right. I'll go with you.'

'First let me smooth things over with Isabel.'

Back in the ballroom, she watched him approach Isabel, saw the hurried excuses, the apologetic head-shaking. Isabel glanced in Kat's direction with a poorly disguised look of annoyance.

Kat spotted Ed by the buffet table. She sidled up to him. 'Ed,' she said.

He grinned. 'Did the direct approach work?'

'Quantrell's taking me to his lab tonight.'

'Lucky you.'

'I want you to let Sykes and Ratchet know. Just in case.'

'In case what?'

Instantly she fell silent as Adam came towards her. 'Just keep it in mind,' she muttered to Ed. Then, with an automatic smile pasted in place, she followed Adam out the door.

They went into the hotel garage. 'We'll take your car,' he said. 'Isabel's going home in mine.'

'She didn't look too happy about it.'

'She hasn't much of a choice.'

Kat shook her head in disbelief. 'Are you always this thoughtful with your lady friends?'

'Isabel,' he sighed, 'is a lovely woman with a cozy inheritance. And a whole stable of suitors. She hardly needs me to keep her warm at night.'

'Do you?'

'Do you keep Ed Novak warm at night?'

'None of your business.'

He cocked his head. 'Ditto.'

They got into the rented Mercedes. The smell of leather upholstery mingled with the scent of his after-shave. It left her feeling a little light-headed.

Kat started the car, and they swung into evening traffic.

'How do you like the car?' he asked.

'It's okay.'

'Okay?' he said, obviously waiting for her to elaborate.

'Yeah. It's okay.'

He looked out the window. 'Next time, I'll have to choose something that'll *really* impress you.'

Kat put her foot on the gas pedal.

'A horse-drawn chariot,' Adam mused. 'Or maybe a team of sled-dogs.' He turned to her. 'How does that sound?'

'I'm allergic,' she replied, as they sailed onto the highway.

'To horses or dogs?'

'To chariots and sleds.'

'Ah.' He nodded solemnly. 'A unicycle it'll have to be, then.'

Kat felt a smile tug at the corner of her lips.

'There,' he said. 'Take the next turnoff. It's eight miles north.'

The road took them out of midtown Albion, into a district of industrial parks and corporate headquarters. In the last ten years, many of the buildings had become vacant; dark windows and *For Lease* signs had sprung up everywhere. Albion, like the rest of the country, was struggling.

The Cygnus complex was one of the few that appeared to house a thriving corporation. Even at eight o'clock at night, some of the windows were still lit, and there were a dozen cars in the parking lot. They drove past the security booth and pulled into a stall marked *Quantrell*.

'Your people work late,' said Kat, glancing at the parked cars.

'The evening shift,' said Adam. 'We run a twenty-four-hour diagnostic lab. Plus, some of our research people like to keep odd hours. You know how it is with eggheads. They have their own schedules.'

'A flexible company.'

'We have to be, if we want to keep good minds around.'

They walked to the front door, where Adam pressed a few numbers on a wall keypad and the lock snapped open. Inside, they headed down a brightly lit hallway. No smudged walls, no flickering fluorescent bulbs here; only the best for corporate America.

'Where are we going?' she asked.

'Diagnostics. I'm going to prove to you we're not engaged in a cover-up.'

'Just how are you going to do that?'

'I'm going to personally hand over to you Xenia Vargas's toxicology screen.'

The diagnostics lab was a vast chamber of space-age equipment, manned by a half-dozen technicians. The evening supervisor, a grandmotherly type in a lab coat, immediately came to greet them.

'Don't worry, Grace,' said Adam. 'This isn't a surprise inspection.'

'Thank God,' said Grace with a laugh. 'We just hid the beer keg and the dancing girls. So what can I do for you, Mr. Q.?'

'This is Dr. Novak, ME's office. She wants to check on a tox screen sent here from the state.'

'What's the name?'

'Xenia Vargas,' said Kat.

Grace sat down at a computer terminal and typed in the name. 'Here it is. Logged in just this afternoon. It's not checked priority, so we haven't run it yet.'

'Could you run it now?' asked Adam.

'It'll take some time.'

Adam glanced at Kat. She nodded. 'We'll wait,' he said.

Grace called to another tech: 'Val, can you check that box of requests from the state? We're going to run a STAT on Xenia Vargas.' She looked at Adam. 'Are you sure you want to hang around, Mr. Q.? This is going to be boring.'

'We'll be up in my office,' said Adam. 'Call us there.'

'Okay. But if I was dressed like *that*—' she nodded at their evening clothes, 'I'd be out dancing.'

Adam smiled. 'We'll keep it in mind.'

By the time they reached Adam's office, which was

upstairs and down a long corridor, Kat's feet were staging a protest against her high heels and she was silently cursing every cobbler in Italy. The minute she hobbled through the office door, she pulled off her shoes, and her stockinged feet sank into velvety carpet. *Nice. Plush.* Slowly she gazed around the room, impressed by her surroundings. It wasn't just an office; it was more like a second home, with a couch and chairs, bookshelves, a small refrigerator.

'I was wondering how long you'd last in those shoes,' Adam said with a laugh.

'When Grace mentioned dancing, I felt like crying.' She sat down gratefully on the couch. 'I confess, I'm the socks and sneakers type.'

'What a shame. You look good in heels.'

'My feet would beg to differ.' Groaning, she reached down and began to massage her instep.

'What your feet need,' he said, 'is a little pampering.' He sat down beside her on the couch and patted his lap in invitation. 'Allow me.'

'Allow you to what?'

'Make up for that long walk down that long hallway.'

Laughing, she rose from the couch. 'It won't work, Quantrell. It takes more than a foot rub to soften up my brain.'

He gave a sigh of disappointment. 'She doesn't trust me.'

'Don't take it personally. When it comes to men, I'm just an old skeptic.'

'Ah. Deep-rooted fears. An unreliable father?'

'I didn't have a father.' She wandered over to the book-case, made a slow survey of the spines. An eclectic collection, she noted, arranged in no particular order. Philosophy and physics. Fiction and pharmacology. Over the bookcase hung several framed diplomas, strictly Ivy League.

'So what happened to your father?' he asked.

'I wouldn't know.' She turned and looked at him. 'I don't even know his last name.'

Adam's eyebrow twitched up in surprise. That was his only reaction, but it was a telling one.

'I know he had light brown hair. Green eyes,' said Kat. 'I know he drove a nice car. And he had money, which was what my mother desperately needed at the time. So . . .' She smiled. 'Here I am. Green eyes and all.'

She expected to see shock, perhaps pity in his gaze, but there was neither. The look he gave her was one of utter neutrality.

'So you see,' she said, 'I'm not exactly to the manner born. Though my mother used to claim she had noble Spanish blood. But then, Mama said a lot of crazy things toward the end.'

'Then she's . . .' He paused delicately.

'Dead. Seven years.'

He tilted up his head, the next question plain in his eyes.

'Mama would say these really bizarre things,' explained Kat. 'And she'd get headaches every morning. I was in my last year of medical school. I was the one who diagnosed the brain tumor.'

Adam shook his head. 'That must have been terrible.'

119

'It wasn't the diagnosis that was so wrenching. It was the part afterwards. Waiting for the end. I spent a lot of time at Hancock General. Learned to royally despise the place. Found out I couldn't stand being around sick people.' She shook her head and laughed. 'Imagine that.'

'So you chose the morgue.'

'It's quiet. It's contained.'

'A hiding place.'

Anger darted through her, but she suppressed it. After all, what he'd said was true. The morgue *was* a hiding place, from all those painfully sloppy emotions one found in a hospital ward.

She said, simply, 'It suits me,' and turned away. Her gaze settled on the refrigerator. 'You wouldn't happen to have anything edible in there, would you?' she asked. 'The wine's going straight to my head.'

He rose from the couch and went to the refrigerator. 'I usually stock a sandwich or two, for those impromptu lunch meetings. Here we are.' He produced two plastic-wrapped luncheon plates. 'Let's see. Roast beef or . . . roast beef. What a choice.' Apologetically he handed her a plate. 'Afraid it's not quite the mayor's benefit dinner.'

'That's all right. I didn't pay for my ticket anyway.'

He smiled. 'Neither did I.'

'Oh?'

'It was Isabel's ticket. She's a big fan of Mayor Sampson.'

'I can't imagine why.' Kat unwrapped the sandwich and took a bite. 'I think he's Albion's *Titanic*.'

'How so?'

'Just look at South Lexington. Sampson would like to pretend it doesn't exist. He caters entirely to the more suburban areas. Bellemeade and beyond. The inner city? Forget it. He doesn't want to hear about the Jane Does and Nicos Biagis.' She went back to the couch and sat down, tucking her stockinged feet beneath her.

He sat down as well. Not too close, she noted with a mingling of both relief and disappointment, but sedately apart, like any courteous host.

'To be honest,' he admitted, 'I'm not a fan of Sampson's either. But Isabel needed an escort.'

'And you didn't have any better offers for the evening?'

'No.' He picked up a slice of beef, and his straight white teeth bit neatly into the pink meat. 'Not until you turned up.'

Kat set the plate down on the coffee table and slowly wiped her fingers on the napkin. 'You can flatter me all you want,' she said. 'It's not going to change things. I still have a job to do. Questions to be answered.'

'And suspects to be suspicious of.'

'Yes.'

'It doesn't bother me, being a suspect. Because I'm not guilty of anything. Neither is my company.'

'Still, the name Cygnus does keep popping up in all sorts of places.'

'What do you want me to say? Confess that I'm manufacturing some secret drug in the basement? Selling it on the streets for a profit? Or maybe we can come up with a truly diabolical scheme, say, I'm single-handedly trying to solve Albion's crime problem by killing off the junkies. The ultimate drug rehab! And *that's* why I was at the mayor's benefit. Because Sampson's in on it too!' He leaned forward and smiled. 'Come now, Kat,' he said. 'Doesn't that sound the slightest bit ridiculous?'

He did make it sound ridiculous, but she refused to back down. 'I don't discount any possibilities,' she said.

'Even wild and crazy ones?'

'Is it so wild and crazy?'

He was moving closer, but she was too stubborn to give up an inch of territory on the couch. She sat perfectly still, even as his hand reached up to touch her face, even as he stroked her cheek. Even as he leaned forward and pressed his lips against hers.

'Don't,' she said, as the sudden heat of desire flooded her face and roared through her veins. She said again, louder, '*Don't*,' and pressed her hands against his chest.

He pulled away, his gaze searching her face. 'What's wrong?'

'You. Me.' She pushed off the couch and rose to her feet. 'This won't work, Adam.'

'I thought it was working just fine.'

'*You* thought. Did you ask me how I feel about it? Do you even care?'

He gave a sheepish laugh. 'Man, I guess I misjudged *that*.'

'Why are you doing this?'

'I need an excuse for kissing an attractive woman?'

'You're trying to distract me with flattery, aren't you?'

'If you knew me, you wouldn't ask these questions.'

'That's just it. I *don't* know you. Except as a phone

number in the hand of a corpse, and that doesn't exactly inspire confidence.'

The phone rang. Reluctantly he broke off eye contact and rose to pick up the receiver. 'Hello, Grace,' he said. A pause, then: 'We're on our way.' He turned to Kat. 'The results are back.'

They found Grace sitting in front of the computer terminal. A readout was just rolling out of the printer. She tore off the page and handed it to Adam. 'There you have it, Mr. Q. A little booze. Traces of decongestant. And that.' She pointed to a band on the chromatographic printout.

'Did you analyze this band?' asked Adam.

'I ran it against mass and UV spectrophotometry. I'm not a hundred percent sure of its structure. It'll take some more noodling around. But I can tell you it's a morphine analogue. Something new. Levo-N-cyclobutylmethyl-6, 10 beta-dihydroxy class.'

Kat looked sharply at Adam. He was staring at the printout in shock.

'Zestron-L,' said Kat.

Grace glanced at her in puzzlement. 'Zestron-L? What's that?'

'Check with the research wing,' said Kat. 'They'll help you run the immunoassay. That should identify it once and for all.'

'You mean *our* research wing?' Grace looked at Adam. 'Then it's . . .'

Adam nodded. 'The drug is one of ours.'

# 8

Lou Sykes looked blearily across his desk at Kat. He hadn't slept much last night – domestic homicide at 2:00 A.M. – and his normally smooth face was sprouting the bristly beginnings of a new beard.

'It's gone beyond a simple trio of ODs, Lou,' Kat said. 'We're talking corporate theft. An untested drug, out on the streets. And maybe more deaths on the way.'

Ratchet shuffled in, looking just as shaggy as Sykes. He carried with him the definite odor of McDonald's – a sausage and biscuit, which he eagerly unwrapped as he sat down at his desk.

'Hey, Vince,' said Sykes. 'Hear the latest? You'll be just *thrilled*.'

Ratchet took a bite of his breakfast. 'What's new?'

'Novak's got a tox ID on two of our overdoses.'

'So what is it?' asked Ratchet, obviously more interested in his sausage.

'Something called Zestron-L.'

'Never heard of it.'

'Of course you haven't. It's something new they're cooking up at Cygnus. Shouldn't be on the street at all.'

'Somehow,' said Kat, 'it got out of Cygnus. Which means they've had a theft.'

Ratchet shrugged. 'We're Homicide.'

'This *is* homicide. Three dead people, Vince. Now, you don't really want any more bodies, do you? Or are you that desperate for overtime?'

Ratchet looked balefully at Sykes. 'Are we chasing this?'

Sykes leaned back and groaned. 'If only it was nice and neat, you know? A bullet hole, a stab wound.'

'That's neat?'

'At least it's cut and dried. Homicide with a capital H. But this is spinning our wheels. Folks who OD, it's a risk they take, sticking a needle in their veins. I don't really care where they get the stuff.'

'Would you care if it was strychnine they were shooting up?'

'That's different.'

'No, it isn't. In large doses, Zestron-L is every bit as deadly. How do you know we haven't got some right-wing fanatic out there, some nut trying to clear the junkies off the streets? And by the way, he's doing a good job.'

Sykes sighed. 'I hate that about you, Novak.'

'What?'

'Your unassailable logic. It isn't feminine.' He hauled himself out of his chair. 'Okay. Let me arrange for us to duck out a couple of hours. We'll head over to Cygnus.'

'Man, oh, man,' grumbled Ratchet, after Sykes had left the room. 'I should've stayed home in bed.'

The smell of Ratchet's sandwich was making Kat's stomach turn. She shifted in her chair and glanced down at Sykes' desk. A reed-thin black woman and two kids smiled at her from a framed photo. Lou's family? She forgot sometimes that cops *had* families and homes and mortgage payments. Another photo stood beside it: Sykes and another man, grinning like two hucksters on the steps of the Albion PD.

'Was this Lou's partner?' asked Kat. 'The one who got hit in South Lexington?'

Ratchet nodded. 'Sitting in a marked car, can you believe it? Some guy drives by and just starts shooting. From what I hear, he and Lou, they were like *this*.' He pressed two fingers together. 'We lost two down there, the same corner. Bad luck spot. Got a lot of bad luck spots in this town. Bolton and Swarthmore, that's another one. That's where my partner went down. Drug bust went sour, and he got boxed in a blind alley.' He put the sandwich down, as though he'd suddenly lost his appetite. 'And we lost one down on Dorchester, just last month. One of our girls, a five-year vet. Perp got hold of her gun, turned it on her . . .' He shook his head mournfully and began to gather up all the sandwich wrappings.

That must be how every cop sees this town, Kat realized. An Albion policeman looks at a map of the city and he sees more than just street names and addresses. He sees the corner where a partner got shot, the alley where a drug deal went bad, the street where an ambulance crew knelt in the rain trying to save a child. For a cop, a city map is a grid of bad memories.

Sykes came back into the room. 'Okay, Vince,' he said. 'Things are quiet for the moment. Might as well do it now.'

Kat rose. 'I'll meet you there.'

Ratchet fished his cell phone out of the drawer and clipped it to his belt. 'We going to Cygnus?' he asked.

'No choice,' said Sykes. 'Seeing as Novak here isn't going to let it drop.'

'I'm just asking you to do your job, Lou,' she said.

'Job, hell. I'm doing you a favor.'

'You're doing the city a favor.'

'Albion?' Sykes laughed and pulled on his jacket. 'The junkies are killing themselves off. Far as I'm concerned, the biggest favor I could do Albion is to look the other way.'

'It's a secured area,' said Adam. 'Only our cleared personnel are allowed in this wing.' He punched a keypad by the door, and the words *passcode accepted* flashed onto the screen. Adam swung the door open and motioned for his visitors to enter.

Ratchet and Sykes went in first, then Kat. As she passed Adam, he reached out and gave her arm a squeeze. The unexpected intimacy of that contact and the whiff of his after-shave made her stomach dance a jig of excitement. He had seemed all business when he'd greeted them, so sober in his gray suit. Now, seeing that look in his eye, she knew the spell was still alive between them.

'I'm glad you came,' he murmured. 'How did you manage?'

'Wheelock's covering for me. I took the day off. Told him I had to buy a new car.'

'Why not the truth?'

'He'd prefer I dropped this case. So would they.' She nodded toward Sykes and Ratchet, who were peering curiously at a blinking computer screen. 'I think I'm being conscientious. They think I'm a pain in the ass.'

They all moved to a door marked *Area 8*.

'This is where Zestron-L's being developed,' said Adam, leading them inside.

Kat's first impression was that she'd stepped through a time portal into a future world of black and white and chrome. Even the man who hurried to greet them did not violate that color scheme. His coat was a pristine white, his hair jet black. 'Dr. Herbert Esterhaus, project supervisor,' he said, reaching out to shake their hands. 'I'm in charge of Zestron-L development.'

'And this is the area you manage?' asked Sykes, glancing about the lab where half a dozen workers manned the various stations.

'Yes. The project's confined to this section – the room you see here and the adjoining three rooms. The only access is through that door you entered, plus an emergency exit, through the animal lab. And that's wired to an alarm.'

'Only authorized personnel are allowed in?'

'That's right. Just our staff. I really don't see how any Zestron could have gotten out.'

'Obviously it walked out,' said Sykes. 'In someone's pocket.'

Dr. Esterhaus glanced at Adam. There was a lot said in that glance, Kat thought. An unspoken question. Only now did she realize how skittery Esterhaus seemed, his bony fingers rubbing together, his rodent eyes noting Sykes' and Ratchet's every move.

'How well do you people screen your personnel?' asked Ratchet.

'When we hire someone,' said Adam, 'we're interested in scientific credentials. And talent. We don't do polygraphs or credit checks. We like to assume our people are honest.'

'Maybe you assumed wrong,' said Sykes.

'Everyone in this project is a long-term employee,' said Adam. 'Isn't that right, Herb?'

Esterhaus nodded. 'I've been here six years. Most of the employees' – he gestured to the workers in white coats – 'have been with Cygnus even longer.'

'Any exceptions?' asked Ratchet.

Esterhaus paused and glanced at Adam. Again, that nervous look, that silent question.

'There was my stepdaughter, Maeve,' Adam finished for him.

Sykes and Ratchet exchanged looks. 'She worked in *this* department?' asked Sykes.

'Just cleanup,' said Esterhaus quickly. 'I mean, Maeve wasn't really qualified to do anything else. But she did an acceptable job.'

'Why did she leave?'

'We had some . . . disagreements,' said Esterhaus.

'What disagreements?' pressed Sykes.

'She . . . started coming in late. And she didn't always dress appropriately. I mean, I didn't mind the green hair and all, but all the dangly jewelry, it's not really safe around this equipment.'

Kat looked around at the two-tone room and tried to imagine what a splash of color Maeve Quantrell would have made. All these white-coated scientists must have thought her some wild and exotic creature, to be tolerated only because she was the boss's daughter.

'So what?' said Sykes. 'You fired her?'

'Yes,' said Esterhaus, looking very unhappy. 'I discussed it with Mr. Quantrell and he agreed that I should do whatever was necessary.'

'Why was she coming in late?' asked Kat.

They all looked at her in puzzlement. 'What?' asked Esterhaus.

'That bothers me. The *why*. She was doing her job, and then she wasn't. When did it start?'

'Six months ago,' said Esterhaus.

'So six months ago, she starts coming in late, or not at all. What changed?' She looked at Adam.

He shook his head. 'She was living on her own. I don't know what was going on with her.'

'Strung out?' asked Sykes.

'Not that I was aware of,' said Esterhaus.

'She was angry, that's what it was,' said a voice. It was one of the researchers, a woman sitting at a nearby computer terminal. 'I was here the day you two had that fight, remember, Herb? Maeve was angry. Furious, really. Said she wasn't going to take your . . . bullshit any longer, and then she stomped out.' The woman shook her head. 'No control, that girl. Very impulsive.'

'Thank you, Rose, for the information,' Esterhaus said tightly. He motioned them towards the next room. 'I'll show you the rest of the lab.'

The tour continued, into the animal lab with its cages of barking dogs. The emergency exit was at the rear, and on the door was the sign: *Alarm will sound if opened.*

'So you see,' said Esterhaus, 'there's no way someone can just walk in and steal anything.'

'But somehow the drug got out,' said Sykes.

'There's one other possibility,' said Esterhaus. 'There could have been simultaneous development. Another lab somewhere, working on the same thing. For someone to steal *our* drug, they'd have to break into Cygnus, through a secured door. They'd have to know our access codes.'

'Which all your employees know,' said Sykes.

'Well, yes.'

'One question,' said Ratchet, who'd been jotting things in his notebook. 'Have you changed the access code lately?'

'Not in the last year.'

'So anyone employed here during the last year – say, Maeve, for instance – would know the code,' said Sykes.

Esterhaus shook his head. 'She wouldn't do it! She was difficult, yes, and maybe a little out of control. But she wasn't a thief. For heaven's sake, it's her father's company!'

'It was only an example,' said Sykes calmly.

Again, Esterhaus glanced at Adam. Suddenly Kat understood the looks that had flown between the two. They were both trying to cover for Maeve.

'Come on,' said Adam, smoothly redirecting their attention. 'We'll show you where the drug's stored.'

Esterhaus led them into a side room. One wall was taken up by a refrigeration unit. 'It's not really necessary to store it in here,' he said, opening the refrigerator door. 'The crystals are stable at room temperature. But we keep it in here as a precaution.' He pulled out a tray; glass vials tinkled together like crystal. Gingerly he removed a vial and handed it to Kat. 'That's it,' he said. 'Zestron-L.'

She raised the vial and studied it in wonder. Rose-pink crystals sparkled like tiny gemstones in the light. She turned the vial on its side and watched the contents tumble about, glittering. 'It's beautiful,' she murmured.

'That's just the crystalline form, of course, for storage,' said Esterhaus. 'What you're looking at is almost pure. It's injected in solution form. The crystals are dissolved in an alcohol and water solvent over heat. A little goes a long way.'

'How far *does* it go?'

'One of those crystals, just one, is enough to make, say, fifty therapeutic doses.'

'*Fifty?*' said Sykes.

'That's right. One crystal diluted in 50cc of solvent will make fifty doses.'

Ratchet was busy studying the catch on the refrigerator door. 'This thing isn't locked,' he said.

'No. Nothing here's locked. I told you, we trust our employees.'

'What about inventory control?' said Sykes. 'You keep track of all those vials?'

'They're numbered, see? So we'd know if any vials were missing.'

'But is there some way the drug could still get out? Without you knowing?'

Esterhaus paused. 'I suppose, if someone were smart about it . . .'

'Yeah?' prompted Sykes.

'One could take a crystal or two. From each vial. And we might not notice the difference.'

There was a pause as they all considered the implications. In that silence, the sudden ringing of a cell phone seemed all the more startling. Both cops automatically glanced down at their belts.

'It's mine. Excuse me,' said Sykes, and he retreated a few paces away to take the call.

'Well,' said Ratchet. 'I'm not sure there's much more we can do here. I mean, if two different labs can come up with the same stuff . . .'

'The odds are against simultaneous development,' said Adam. 'Zestron-L isn't something you just cook up in your basement. It took us years to get this far, and it's still not ready for the market.'

'But Dr. Esterhaus says another lab *could* do it.'

'Cygnus is the only lab around here with the facilities.'

'You'd be surprised,' said Ratchet, 'what the mob can

finance.' He closed his notebook. 'Let me be honest. We're not gonna have much luck here.'

'You could polygraph the staff,' said Kat. 'That would be a start.'

'It would also be an insult,' said Esterhaus. 'To every single one of them.'

'I don't see that you have a choice,' said Kat.

Adam shook his head. 'I hate to do it.'

'It'd probably be inconclusive, anyway,' said Ratchet. 'They'll all be nervous, upset. Chances are, you won't be able to pinpoint a leak, not this late in the game.'

'What about South Lexington?' said Kat. 'Check out the receiving end, Vince. Find out who's distributing it on the outside. Question the victims' families and friends. They might know the source.'

'Yeah. We could do that.' He turned as Sykes came back.

'Let's go, Vince,' said Sykes. 'We're done here.'

'Aren't you going to question anyone?' asked Kat.

'Later.' Sykes shook hands with Adam and Esterhaus, then he and Ratchet headed for the exit.

'Something's going on,' muttered Kat, watching them leave. 'Excuse me.'

She followed the two cops outside, into the parking lot. 'Hey! Lou!' she called.

Sykes turned to her with a look of weariness. 'What, Novak?'

'Why the abrupt exit?'

'Because I've got my ass to protect, okay? I also got a chief who's bitching about my wasting departmental time on this case.'

134

'That was a call from your chief?'

'Yeah. He wanted to know why I'm out saving the world's junkies when we've got murderers cruising the suburbs. And you know what? I couldn't think of a single good answer.' Sykes yanked open his car door. 'Let's go, Vince.'

'Wait. Who told the chief about it?'

'I didn't ask,' he snapped.

'But *someone* must have told him.'

Sykes got into the car and slammed the door. 'All I know is, I got orders from above. And we're out of here.' He looked at Ratchet and barked, '*Drive.*'

The car took off, leaving Kat standing alone in the parking lot.

*I got orders.* Whose orders? she wondered. Who had called the chief and told him to pull Sykes and Ratchet away? The mayor's office? Ed?

Suddenly she turned and gazed up at the letters CYGNUS mounted on the building. It was a possibility she didn't want to consider, but it was staring her in the face.

If anyone had a reason to halt the investigation, it was him. The man whose company would suffer. The man whose name would be dragged through the mud. The man she'd seen dining and shmoozing at the mayor's benefit.

*Where on earth did you park your brains, Novak?*

She turned from the building and headed to her car.

It was hard for Kat to give up the Mercedes, but she had her principles to uphold. She didn't want to owe Adam Quantrell a thing, not a single damn thing.

She turned in the Mercedes at Regis Rentals and paid the bill herself. Then she walked around the corner to Lester's Used Cars.

She drove out in a Ford – five years old, with a few rust spots on the fender. It smelled a little stale, and there was a rip in the back seat, but the engine ran fine and the price was right.

And she didn't feel guilty driving it.

From there, she headed straight to City Hall.

She tried getting in to see Mayor Sampson, but there was no chance they'd let her in – not after that scene in his office a day earlier. So she went instead to the DA's office. She found her ex-husband at his desk. He kept his workspace neat, every paper in its place, every pen and paper clip relegated to the proper slot. Ed himself looked immaculate as always, not a crease in his hundred-percent-cotton shirt. She wondered how she'd stood being married to the man for two years.

He looked up in surprise as she came in. 'Kat! Is this a social visit?'

'Who whispered in the police chief's ear?' she asked.

'Ah. Not a social visit.'

'Was it Sampson?'

'What are you referring to?'

'You know *what*.' She leaned across his desk. 'Lieutenant Sykes was told to lay off Cygnus. Who gave the order? Sampson? You?'

He sat back and smiled innocently. 'Wasn't me. Cross my heart.'

'Sampson?'

'No comment. But you know the pressure he's under. The police start digging around, it turns into a media event. We don't need that kind of publicity, not now.'

'Did Quantrell have anything to do with it?'

'What?'

'Did he ask Sampson to call off the cops?'

Ed looked perplexed. 'Why would he? Look, I don't know why you're getting worked up about this. Or are you back with the old underdog crusade?'

'I was never on any crusade.'

'Sure you were. Hell, you think it was easy for me, living with you? Putting up with that attitude of yours? I don't recall taking a vow of poverty when I married you. But I'd buy a BMW or . . . or join a racquetball club, and you'd wince.'

She looked at him in mock horror. 'I *didn't*.'

'You did. And here you are, still at it. Kat, no one *gives* a damn about junkies. We have *tourists* getting mugged out there! Nice tourists, from nice places. *Those* are the people we should be protecting. Not the trash out on South Lexington.'

'Oh, Ed.' She shook her head and laughed. 'Ed, I have to say that, until this very minute, I *never* realized.'

'What didn't you realize?'

'What a kind and sensitive bastard you are.'

'There's that attitude problem again.'

'Not an attitude, Ed. A principle.' She turned for the door. 'Maybe you'd recognize it. If you had one of your own.'

\*

Seconds after his ex-wife left the room, Ed Novak picked up the telephone and dialed the mayor's office. 'She was just here,' he said. 'And I don't think she's too happy.'

'You don't think she'll go to the newspapers, do you?' asked Sampson.

'If she does, we'll just have to stonewall them with *no comments.* Or deny there's a crisis.'

'That's the strategy we take. Make her look like a loose cannon. In the meantime, *do* something about her, will you? She's getting to be a pain in the ass.'

'I'll be honest, Mayor,' said Ed with a tired sigh. 'She always was.'

All afternoon, Adam waited for Kat to call. A nice meal to hash things out between them – that's what they needed. He was optimistic enough to make dinner reservations for two at Yen King. There he could make it clear that he was on her side, and that he intended to see more of her. But as the day wore on toward five o'clock, there was still no phone call.

When finally a call *did* come in, it wasn't from Kat. It was from his butler, Thomas.

'Dr. Novak returned the Mercedes,' said Thomas. 'I've just spoken with Regis Motors.'

'Yes, she said she was going to buy a car today.'

'The reason I'm calling, Mr. Q., is to tell you she paid for the Mercedes rental. The entire bill.'

'But the bill was supposed to be sent to me.'

'Precisely. And they explained it to her. But she insisted on paying it herself.'

'They should have refused her payment.'

'The staff at Regis tell me it was quite impossible to change her mind.'

What was going on with that woman? Adam wondered as he hung up. Just last night, she'd seemed pleased about the car. There had been no question that the rental was his gift. Why her sudden insistence on paying the bill?

At five-thirty, he left Cygnus and drove north. The Bellemeade turnoff was right on his way home; he decided to pass by Kat's house, on the off-chance he could catch her.

There was no car in the driveway, no answer to his knock on the door. He got back into his car and decided to wait.

Twenty minutes later he was about to give up and go home when he spotted a gray Ford coming around the corner. Kat was behind the wheel. She pulled into the driveway.

At once he was out of his car and moving toward her. She stepped out, holding a bag with *Hop Sing Take-out* printed on the side.

'Kat!' he said. 'I tried calling you—'

'I've been out all day.' Her tone was matter-of-fact and none too warm. She started toward her front door with Adam right behind her.

'Why don't we go out for some *good* Chinese food?'

'I happen to *like* Hop Sing,' she snapped, stepping through the door.

Determined not to be shut out, he followed her inside, into the kitchen. 'I don't understand what's happened—'

'I understand perfectly, Adam. If Cygnus were my company, I'd block the investigation, too.'

He shook his head. 'I didn't block any investigation.'

'I mean, think of the PR disaster. The headlines. *Cygnus manufactures killer drug.*'

'You think I'd go that far to protect Cygnus?'

'Haven't you?' She set the take-out bag on the counter and began to unload the contents. 'Look, I'm starving. I'd like to eat this before it gets – oh, *damn.*'

'What?'

'I left the fried rice in the car.' She spun around and headed back out the front door.

He was right on her heels, following her across the lawn. 'Come on, let's go out.'

'No, thanks.' She reached into the car and retrieved the second take-out bag. 'Tonight, I'm a solo act. Dinner. A hot bath. And absolutely *no* excitement of any kind.' She turned away from the car.

A deafening blast shook the house. She felt the sting of flying glass as she was hurled backward by the violent pulse of the explosion. She landed on her back, in the grass. Chunks of wood, flakes of asphalt tile rained down on her.

Then, like a gentle snowfall, a cloud of dust settled slowly from the sky.

# 9

Kat was too stunned to make sense of what had happened; she could only lie on her back in the grass and stare dazedly at the sky. Then, gradually, she became aware that someone was calling her name, that someone was brushing the hair from her eyes, stroking her face.

'Kat. Look at me. I'm right here. *Look at me.*'

Slowly, she focused on Adam. He was gazing down at her, undisguised panic in his eyes. He was afraid, she thought in wonder. Why?

'Kat!' he yelled. 'Come on, *say something.*'

She tried to speak and found all she could manage was a whisper. 'Adam?'

Through her confusion, she heard the sounds of running footsteps, shouting voices, calls of 'Is she okay?'

'What happened?' she asked.

'Don't move. There's an ambulance coming—'

'*What happened?*' She struggled to sit up. The sudden

movement made the world lurch around her. She caught a spinning view of bystanders' faces, of debris littering the lawn. Then she saw what was left of her house. With that glimpse, everything froze into terrible focus.

The front wall had been ripped away entirely, and the inner walls stood exposed, like an open dollhouse. Shreds of fabric, couch batting, splintered furniture had been tossed as far as the driveway. Just overhead, an empty picture frame swung forlornly from a tree branch.

'Jesus, lady,' murmured someone in the crowd. 'Did you leave your gas on or something?'

'My house,' whispered Kat. In rising fury she staggered to her feet. 'What did they do to *my house*?'

Then, as if there hadn't been enough destruction, the first flicker of fire appeared. Flames were spreading from what used to be the kitchen.

'Back!' shouted Adam. 'Everyone back!'

'*No!*' Kat struggled forward. If she could turn on the garden hose, if the pipes were still intact, she could save what little she had left. 'Let me go!' she yelled, shoving at Adam. 'It's going to burn!'

She managed only two steps before he grabbed her and hauled her back. Enraged, she struggled against him, but he trapped her arms and swung her up and away from the house.

'It's going to burn!' she cried.

'You can't save it, Kat! There's a gas leak!'

The flames suddenly shot higher, licking at the collapsing roof. Already the fire had spread to the living room, had ignited the remains of her furniture. Smoke swirled, thick and black, driving the crowd back across the street.

'My house,' Kat sobbed, swaying against Adam.

He pulled her against him and wrapped his arms tightly around her as though to shield her from the sight and sounds of destruction. As the first fire trucks pulled up with sirens screaming, she was still clinging to him, her face pressed against his shirt. The roar of the flames, the shouts of firemen, seemed to recede into some other, distant dimension. Her reality, the only one that mattered, was the steady thump of Adam's heart.

Only when he gently released her and murmured something in her ear was she wrenched unwillingly back into the real world. She found two uniformed men gazing at her. One was a cop, the other had an Albion Fire Department patch on his jacket.

'What happened?' asked the cop.

She shook her head. 'I don't know.'

'She'd just gotten home,' said Adam. 'We went inside, came back out again for a minute. That's when the house blew up. She caught the worst of it. I was standing behind her—'

'Did you smell gas?'

'No.' Adam shook his head firmly. 'No gas.'

'You're sure?'

'Absolutely. The fire started after the explosion.'

The cop and fireman looked at each other, a glance that Kat found terrifying in its significance.

She said, 'It was a bomb. Wasn't it?'

They didn't say a word. They didn't have to. Their silence was answer enough.

\*

143

It was after midnight when they finally pulled into Adam's driveway. They'd spent two hours in the ER getting their cuts and bruises tended to, two more hours in the Bellemeade police station, answering questions. Now they were both on the far side of exhausted. They barely managed to stumble out of the car and up the front steps.

Thomas was waiting at the door to greet them. 'Mr. Q.!' he gasped, staring in horror at Adam's torn suit. 'Not *another* brawl?'

'No. Just a bomb this time.' He raised his hand to cut off Thomas's questions. 'I'll tell you all about it in the morning. In the meantime, let's get Dr. Novak to bed. She's staying the night.'

Thomas nodded, utterly unruffled. 'I'll prepare the guest room,' he said, and went up ahead of them.

Slowly Adam guided Kat up the stairs. Her body felt so small, so fragile, as he helped her up the last step, and down the corridor. By the time they reached the south guest room, Thomas had already turned down the covers, placed fresh towels on the dresser, and closed the drapes. 'I'll see to your room now, Mr. Q.,' he said, and discreetly withdrew.

'Come. Into bed with you,' said Adam. He sat her on the covers, knelt down to take off her shoes.

'I'm such a mess,' she murmured, staring down at her clothes.

'We'll clean these in the morning. Right now, you need some sleep. Can I help you off with your clothes?'

She looked up at him with a faint expression of amusement.

He smiled. 'Believe me, my intentions are purely honorable.'

'Nevertheless,' she said, 'I think I'll manage on my own.'

Adam sat down beside her on the bed. 'It's gone too far,' he said. 'Doing your job is one thing, Kat. And I admire your persistence, I really do. But now it's turned ugly. This time you were fortunate. But next time . . .' He stopped, unwilling to finish the thought.

But it didn't matter. Kat had already fallen asleep.

She was still asleep when Adam looked in the next morning.

Quietly he sat down in the chair beside her. Sunlight winked through the curtains, the beams dancing around the walls and the polished furniture. He'd forgotten how charming this guest room could be, how lovely it looked in the morning light. Or perhaps it never *had* been this lovely before; perhaps, with this woman sleeping beside him, he was seeing the room's charm for the very first time.

There was a knock on the door. He turned to see Thomas poke his head in.

'I thought perhaps she would like some breakfast,' whispered Thomas, nodding at the tray of food he was carrying.

'I think what she'd really like,' said Adam, rising to his feet, 'is to be allowed to sleep.' He followed Thomas into the hall and softly closed the door behind him. 'Did you collect her clothes?'

'I'm afraid they're quite beyond repair,' Thomas said with a sigh.

'Then would you arrange to have some things sent up

to the house? She'll probably need her entire wardrobe replaced. I doubt anything survived the fire.'

Thomas nodded. 'I'll put a call in to Neiman-Marcus. A size six, don't you think?'

With sudden clarity, Adam remembered how slender she'd felt against him last night, climbing the steps to the guest room. 'Yes,' he said. 'A six sounds about right.'

Downstairs, Adam lounged about the dining room, sipping coffee, picking at his breakfast without much appetite. He listened with amusement as Thomas made phone calls in the next room. A complete wardrobe, Thomas said. Yes, undergarments as well. What cup size? Well, how should *he* know? Thomas hung up, and came into the dining room, looking distressed. 'I'm having a problem with, er . . . dimensions.'

Adam laughed. 'I think we're both out of our depth, Thomas. Why don't we wait until Dr. Novak wakes up?'

Thomas looked relieved. 'An excellent idea.'

They heard the sound of tires rolling over gravel. Adam glanced through the window and saw a blue Chevy pull up in the driveway. 'Must be Lieutenant Sykes,' he said. 'I'll let him in.'

He was surprised to find both Sykes and Ratchet waiting at the front door. Apparently they came as a matched set, even on Saturdays. They were even similarly dressed in strictly nonregulation golf shirts and sneakers.

'Morning, Mr. Q.,' said Sykes, pulling off his sunglasses. He held up a briefcase. 'I got what you wanted.'

'Come in, please. There's coffee and breakfast, if you'd like.'

Ratchet grinned. 'Sounds great.'

The three men sat down at the dining table. Thomas brought out cups, saucers, a fresh pot of coffee. Ratchet tucked a napkin in his shirt and began to adorn a bagel with cream cheese. Not just a dab here and there, but giant slabs of it, topped with multiple layers of lox. Sykes took only coffee, heavily sugared – a favorite energy source, he said, from his patrolman days.

'So what do you have?' asked Adam.

Sykes took several files from the briefcase and laid them on the table. 'The files you asked for. Oh, and about the explosion last night—'

'Not a gas leak?'

'Definitely not a gas leak. Demolitions went over what was left of the house,' said Sykes. 'It appears there was a pull-friction fuse igniter, set off when the front door opened. The igniter gets pulled through a flash compound, lighting a sixty-second length of fuse. That in turn leads to a blasting cap. And a rather impressive amount of TNT.'

Adam frowned. 'A sixty-second fuse? Then that explains why it didn't go off right away.'

Sykes nodded. 'A delay detonator. Designed to blow up *after* the victim is in the house.'

'They aren't fooling around. Whoever they are,' Ratchet added, around a mouthful of bagel.

Adam sat back, stunned by this new information. Until now he'd hoped for some simple explanation. A faulty furnace, perhaps; a natural gas leak whose odor he hadn't detected. But here was incontrovertible evidence:

Someone wanted Kat dead. And they were going to extra-ordinary lengths to achieve that goal.

He was so shocked by the revelation that he didn't realize Kat had come down into the dining room. Then he looked up and saw her. She seemed swallowed up in one of his old bathrobes, the flaps cinched together at the waist. She glanced around the table at Sykes and Ratchet.

'You heard what Lou said?' asked Adam.

She nodded. Then she took a deep breath. 'So I guess it's time to face the facts. Someone's really trying to kill me.'

After a silence, Adam said, 'It does appear that way.'

Hugging her arms to her chest, Kat began to move slowly around the room, thinking as she paced. She stopped by the window and gazed out at the sunwashed lawn and trees.

'Believe me, Kat,' said Sykes. 'Bellemeade Precinct's got all cylinders going on this. I've spoken with the detectives. They're checking all the possibilities—'

'Are they really?' she asked softly.

'There are a lot of angles to consider. Maybe it's some-one you gave expert testimony against in court. Or an ex-boyfriend. Hell, they're even questioning Ed.'

'Ed?' She laughed, a wild, desperate sound. 'Ed can't even program a VCR. Much less wire a bomb.'

'Okay, so it's probably not Ed. Not him personally, any-way. But he has been questioned.'

She turned to look at Sykes. 'Then everyone agrees. It's a bona fide murder attempt.'

'No doubt about it. It only takes one look at your house. Or what used to be your house.'

She looked out again, at the trees. 'It's because of them.'

'Who?'

'Nicos Biagi. Jane Doe. It's because of what's happening in the Projects.'

'You could have other enemies,' said Sykes. 'And you lost your purse, remember? One of those punks could've gotten into your house—'

'And set a sixty-second delay detonator?' She shook her head. 'I suppose they picked up a case of TNT at the corner grocery store. Lou, they were *kids*. I grew up with kids just like them! They wouldn't mess around with flash compounds or blasting caps. And what's their motive?'

'I don't know.' Sykes sighed in exasperation. 'They did rough you up—'

'But they didn't kill us! They had the chance, but they didn't.'

Adam looked at Sykes. 'She's right, Lieutenant. Those kids wouldn't know about fuse igniters. This bomb sounds like a sophisticated device. Built by someone who knew what he was doing.'

'A professional,' said Ratchet.

The word was enough to make Kat blanch. Adam saw her chin jerk up, saw the tightening of her lips. She was frightened, all right. She should be. In silence she moved to the table and sat down across from him. The bathrobe gaped open a little; only then did he realize she was naked beneath that terrycloth. How defenseless she looked, he thought. Stripped of everything. Even her clothes.

And at that moment, defenseless was exactly how Kat felt.

She sat hugging the robe to her breasts, her gaze fixed on the tabletop. She heard Sykes and Ratchet rise to leave; dimly she registered their goodbyes, their departing footsteps. Then there came the thud of the front door closing behind them. Closed doors. That's what she saw when she tried to look into the future. Closed doors, hidden dangers.

Once, life had seemed comfortably predictable. Drive to work every morning, drive home every night. A vacation twice a year, a date once in a blue moon. A steady move up the ranks until she'd assume Davis Wheelock's title of Chief ME. A sure thing, he'd told her once.

Now she was reminded that there were no sure things. Not her future. Not even her life.

'You're not alone, Kat,' said Adam.

She looked up and met his gaze across the tabletop.

'Anything you need,' he said. 'Anything at all—'

'Thanks,' she said with a smile. 'But I'm not big on accepting charity.'

'That's not what I meant. I don't think of you as some charity case.'

'But that's exactly what I am at the moment.' She rose and began to pace. 'Some sort of – of homeless person! Camping out in your guest bedroom.'

To her surprise, he suddenly laughed. 'To be perfectly honest,' he admitted, 'you *do* look a little threadbare this morning. Where did you find that bathrobe, by the way?'

She glanced down at the frayed terrycloth and suddenly she had to laugh as well. 'Your linen closet. I had to wear something, and I figured it was either this or a towel. Where are my clothes, by the way?'

'A lost cause. Thomas had to throw them out.'

'He threw out my clothes?'

'Some new things are being delivered.'

She caught his amused downward glance, and realized the robe had sagged open again. Irritably she yanked the edges back together.

She sat down and noticed the stack of papers on the table. 'What's all this?'

'Lieutenant Sykes dropped it off. They're police files. Or, rather, photocopies of files.'

'He *gave* them to you? That's highly irregular.'

'It's also just between us. He and I have what you might call a mutual back-scratching arrangement.'

'Oh. So what's in the files?'

Adam picked up the top folder. 'I have here Nicos Biagi. And Xenia Vargas. And Jane Doe.' He looked up at her, almost apologetically. 'I'll be honest with you, Kat. I didn't ask for these files on your behalf, but on mine. For Cygnus. I can't argue away the facts. That *is* my drug out there, killing people. I want to know how they got it.'

She focused on the top file. 'Let's see what's in there.'

He opened Nicos Biagi's folder. 'Names and addresses. His family might know where he bought the drug.'

'They won't talk. Even Sykes couldn't get it out of them.'

'Does that surprise you? They probably smelled *cop* a mile away. So I'm going to ask them.'

'I wonder what odor they'll pin on *you*.'

'The smell of money? It's very persuasive.'

'Adam, you can't walk into the Projects with a bulging wallet!'

'Can you think of a better incentive?'

'You go in there without protection, and they'll have you for an appetizer.'

'Then how am I supposed to *reach* these people?' he asked, pointing to the folders. 'I went through a half-dozen private detectives, trying to trace Maeve. So I don't have a lot of confidence in so-called professionals. I know that some friend of Nicos, or of Xenia Vargas, has to know the answers. You're the one who said it, Kat. If we can't pinpoint how the drug's getting out of Cygnus, perhaps we can figure out whom it's going to. And how he's getting it.'

'Are you sure you really want to find out?' she asked. 'What if the answer turns out to be a nasty surprise?'

'You're referring to Maeve?'

'Her name did cross my mind.'

He sighed. 'It's something I'll . . . have to face.'

'That's why you're doing this yourself, isn't it? Why you don't just hire a PI to do the legwork. You're afraid of what some outsider will find out about your daughter.'

He looked away. 'You know, I used to think I could protect her. Pull her off the streets and put her in some sort of program. But it's not going to happen. She refuses to be helped. And in the meantime, people are dying, and I don't know if she's the one responsible . . .'

'You can't protect her, Adam. One of these days, she'll have to face the music.'

'Don't you think I know that?' He shook his head in frustration. 'All these years, that's exactly what I've been doing! Protecting her, bailing her out. Paying her bills when she bounced her checks. Booking her appointments with therapists. I kept thinking, if she just had enough attention, if I could just do the right thing – whatever that was – that somehow she'd pull out of it. She wouldn't end up like Georgina.'

*Georgina*. She thought of the name she'd seen, inscribed on the plaque in Hancock General. *The Georgina Quantrell Wing*.

She asked, gently, 'How did your wife die?'

He was silent for so long, she thought perhaps he hadn't heard the question. 'She died of a lot of things,' he said at last. 'The official diagnosis was liver cirrhosis. But the illness really went back to her childhood. A father addicted to martinis and work. A mother addicted to pills and cigarettes. Georgina looked for comfort wherever she could find it. By the time we met, she'd already been through two husbands and Lord knows how many bottles of gin. I was twenty-four at the time. All I saw was this – this absolutely stunning woman with an adorable daughter. Georgina was adept at covering up. If she had to, she could go off the bottle for weeks at a time, and that's what she did before the wedding. But after we got back from the honeymoon, I noticed she was having a few too many highballs, a few too many glasses of wine. Then Thomas found the stash of bottles in the closet. And that's when I realized how far it had gone . . .' He shook his head and sighed. 'Fourteen years later, she was dead. And I'm still trying to deal with the aftermath. Namely, Maeve.'

'You stayed married to her through all that?'

'I felt I didn't have a choice. But then, neither did she. Self-destruction was in her genes, and she didn't have the will to fight. She just wasn't strong enough.' He paused, and added quietly, 'Unlike you.'

He looked at her then, and she found her gaze trapped in the blue-gray spell of his eyes. They reached out to each other across the table and their fingers touched, twined together. They held on, even through the ringing of the doorbell and the sound of Thomas's footsteps crossing the foyer to answer it.

Only the polite clearing of a throat made them finally look up. Thomas was standing in the doorway. 'Mr. Q.?' he said. 'The wardrobe consultant is here from Neiman-Marcus. I thought perhaps Dr. Novak would like to look over the selections.'

'*Wardrobe* consultant?' said Kat in surprise. 'But all I really need right now is a pair of jeans and a change of underwear.'

'You needn't take the consultant's advice,' said Thomas. 'Although . . .' He glanced at her bathrobe. 'I'm certain she'll have a number of, er, *helpful* suggestions.'

Kat laughed and pushed back from the table. 'Bring her on, then. I guess I need to wear something.'

'When you've made your selections, Dr. Novak,' said Thomas, 'just leave the bathrobe with me. I'll see that it's properly taken care of.'

'Whatever you say,' said Kat.

'Very good,' said Thomas and he turned to leave. As he walked out of the room, he muttered with undisguised glee, 'Because I'm going to burn it.'

Protection was what they needed in South Lexington. And when it came to hostile territory, Kat decided, the best to be had was from the natives. So it was to Papa Earl's apartment they went first, to have a talk with his grandson, Anthony. The boy might not hold any real power in the Projects, but he'd know how to reach those who did.

They found him slouched in his undershirt, watching *Days of Our Lives* in the living room.

'Anthony,' said Papa Earl. 'Katrina wants to talk to you.'

Anthony raised the remote control and changed the channel to *Jeopardy*.

'You listening, boy?' barked Papa Earl.

'*What?*'

'Katrina and her friend, they come to see *you*.'

Kat moved in front of the TV, deliberately blocking Anthony's view. He looked up at her with sullen dark eyes. It was heartbreaking to see how little was left of the child she used to babysit. In his place was a tinderbox of rage.

'We want to ask the big man a favor,' said Kat.

'What big man you talking about?'

'We're willing to pay up front. Safe passage, that's all we ask. And maybe a friend or two to watch our backs. No cops involved, we swear it.'

'What you want safe passage for?'

'Just to talk to some people. About Nicos and Xenia.' She paused and added, 'And you can tell Maeve we're not after her.'

Anthony twitched and looked away. So he was the one who had warned her, she decided. 'How much?' he asked.

'A hundred.'

'And how much does the big man get?'

The kid was sharp. 'Another hundred.'

Anthony thought about it a moment. Then he said, 'Move outta the way.' Kat stepped aside. He pointed the remote control and switched off the TV. 'Wait here,' he said. He stood up and walked out of the apartment.

'What do you think?' asked Adam.

'He's either going to come back with our bodyguards,' said Kat, 'or a hit squad.'

'Don't know what I'm gonna do 'bout that boy,' said Papa Earl. 'I just don't know.'

Ten minutes passed. They all sat in the kitchen, where Bella banged pots and pans on the stove. The smell of old cooking grease, of frying sausages and simmering pinto beans, was almost enough to drive them out. Those smells brought back too many memories for Kat, of stifling summer evenings when the smells from her mother's stove would kill whatever appetite she had, when the heat from the kitchen seemed to suck the air out of every room. Now, as she watched young Bella, she saw the ghost of her own mother, squinting into the haze of hot oil.

A door banged shut. Adam and Kat turned to see Anthony come into the kitchen. With him were two other boys, both about sixteen, both with the cold, flat expressions of foot soldiers.

'You got it,' said Anthony. 'Just this one day. You want to come back again, you pay again. They'll watch your backs.' He collected his two hundred dollars from Adam. 'So where do you want to go first?'

'The Biagi flat,' said Kat.

Anthony looked at the boys. 'Okay. Take 'em there.'

# 10

Nicos was a good boy, insisted Mr. and Mrs. Biagi. It seemed to be a universal mantra of parents in South Lexington – *he was a good boy*. A kid could pick up a gun and commit mass murder, and that refrain would still pop out of his parents' mouths.

The Biagis had no idea what Nicos had been doing with that needle and tourniquet. He had not been a drug addict. He had been a student at Louis French Junior College and had worked nights as a stockboy in the Big E supermarket in Bellemeade. He had bought a new car, paid for his own clothes.

*And his own drugs*, Kat thought.

After an hour, she and Adam gave up trying to break through that wall of parental denial. Yes, Nicos must truly have been a saint, they agreed, and left the apartment.

Their two bodyguards were lolling on the front steps, watching a little girl skip rope.

'. . . Mama called the doctor and the doctor said,

'Feel the rhythm of the heart, ding dong,

'Feel the rhythm of the heart . . .'

As Kat and Adam came outside, the girl stopped her chant and looked up at them.

'We're through here,' said Kat. 'Didn't learn a damn thing.'

The two boys glanced at each other with a wry look of *We could've told you that.*

The girl was still staring at them.

'Okay, let's try Xenia Vargas,' said Adam. 'Do you know where she lived?'

'Two blocks over,' piped up the girl with the jump rope. 'But she's dead.'

For the first time, Kat focused on the child. She was about eight years old, small and wiry, with a tangled bird's nest of hair. Her smock dress had been patched so many times it was hard to make out the pattern of the original fabric.

'Get outta here, Celeste,' said one of the boys. 'Your mama's callin' you.'

'I don't hear nothing.'

'Well, she's callin'.'

'Can't be. She's workin' till seven. So there.'

Kat crouched down beside the girl. 'Did you know Xenia?' she asked.

The girl swiped at her runny nose and looked at her. 'Sure. I seen her around all the time.'

'Where?'

'All over. She'd hang out at the laundromat.'

'Anyone else hang out with her?'

'Sometimes. The boys, they liked talkin' to Xenia.'

'Ain't all they liked doin' to Xenia,' one of the body-guards said with a snicker.

Celeste fixed him with a dirty look. 'Yeah, I seen those boys 'round *your* sister too, Leland.'

Leland's snicker died. He gave Celeste an equally dirty look. The girl smiled back.

'She ever hang out with Nicos Biagi?' asked Adam.

'Sometimes.'

'What about this lady?' Kat asked. She took out the morgue photo of Jane Doe. For a second, she hesitated to show it to the child, then decided she had to.

Celeste glanced at the picture with a clinical eye. 'Dead, huh?' Kat nodded. 'Yeah,' said Celeste. 'I don't know her name, 'xactly, but I seen her with Xenia. She's not a regular.'

'A regular?' inquired Adam.

'She doesn't live here. She just visits.'

'Oh. A tourist.'

'Yeah, like you.'

'Celeste,' said Leland. '*Scram.*'

The girl didn't move.

They started up the street. A block away, Kat glanced back and saw the little figure still watching them, the jump rope trailing from her hand.

'She's all by herself,' said Kat. 'Doesn't anyone look after her?'

'Everyone here knows her,' said Leland. 'Hell, they can't get *rid* of the brat.'

Celeste was skipping rope again, her quick steps bringing her along the sidewalk in undisguised pursuit.

They ignored her and walked two blocks to Building Three. Leland directed them to the sixth floor. Kat knocked at the door.

A woman answered – a girl, really – with makeup thick as putty and plucked eyebrows reduced to two unevenly drawn black slashes. Heavy earrings jangled as she looked first at Kat, then – much longer – at Adam. 'Yeah?'

'I'm from the medical examiner's office,' explained Kat. 'We think your roommate—'

'I'm not talkin' to no one from the Health Department.'

'I'm not from the Health Department. I'm from—'

'I went in for my shots. I'm cured, okay? So leave me alone.' She started to close the door, but Leland stuck his hand out to block it.

'They wanna know 'bout Xenia. I brought 'em here.'

'Why?'

''Cause this where she lived.'

'No, stupid. Why they askin'?'

'She died of a drug OD,' said Kat. 'Did you know that?'

The girl glanced nervously at Leland. 'Yeah. Maybe I did.'

'Were you aware she was shooting up?'

A cautious shrug. 'Maybe.'

Adam moved forward to interject himself into the dialogue. 'Could we, perhaps, come inside for a moment?' he asked. 'Just to talk?' He smiled at her, a brilliant smile that showed off all those perfect white teeth of his.

A smile, Kat suspected, that few females could resist.

The girl seemed suitably impressed. Her gaze took in his clothes – shirt without a tie, casual slacks, all of it displayed on a superb frame.

'You from the Health Department too?' she asked.

'Not exactly . . .'

'You a cop?'

'No.'

That seemed good enough for her. With a coquettish jangle of earrings, she indicated they could come in.

The place was like a Bedouin tent. Heavy drapes hung over the windows, casting the room in a purple gloom. Instead of chairs there were cushions on the floor and a single low-slung couch, its pillows embroidered with silk elephants and mirror chips. A familiar odor permeated the room – *pot*, thought Kat, with maybe the side-scent of patchouli. She settled on the couch next to Adam. Leland and his buddy stood off to the side, as though trying to blend into the Oriental wall hanging.

The girl – she told them her name was Fran – plopped down on a cushion and said, 'Xenia and I, we didn't talk a lot, you know? So don't go thinking I can answer a whole lot of questions.'

'Did you know she was a junkie?' asked Kat.

'She liked her stuff, I guess.'

'Where'd she get it from?'

'Lots of places.' Fran's gaze flicked sideways, toward Leland. She licked her lips. 'Mostly out of the neighborhood.'

'Where?'

'I don't know. I guess she had people she'd go to, up-town. I'd have nothin' to do with it, see. I'm into *natural* stuff. Stuff you get off plants.'

'Did she know Nicos Biagi?'

Fran laughed. 'Hell. Nicos was *everybody's* friend.'

Kat took out the morgue photo of Jane Doe. 'What about this girl? Recognize her?'

Fran paled as she realized it was a corpse she was looking at. She swallowed. 'Yeah. That's one of Nicos's friends. Eliza.'

'She's dead, too,' said Kat. 'Shot up the same stuff as Nicos and Xenia. Killed all three of them.'

Fran handed back the photo and looked away.

'She was your roommate, Fran,' said Adam. 'She must have told you something.'

'Look, she just lived here, okay? We weren't like best friends or somethin'. She had her room, I had mine.'

'What about her room? Are her things still there?'

'Naw, they already come and searched it.'

'Who did?'

'Cops, who else?'

Kat frowned at her. 'What?'

'You know, those creeps with the badges and billy clubs? They come and picked it all apart for evidence.'

'Did you get a name? A precinct?'

'You think I'm gonna argue when some guy's shovin' his badge in my face?'

Kat glanced at Adam, saw his look of puzzlement. Why had the police shown up, and what had they been searching for?

That question troubled her all the way back down the six flights of stairs. She and Adam stepped out into the pale sunshine and blinked up at the Project towers. *Those prison towers again*, she thought. A constant reminder that this was a world not easily escaped.

Or easily penetrated. They'd spent half the day in South Lexington, and had no information to show for it, except the knowledge that the three victims had indeed been acquainted.

Perhaps that was the best they could hope for.

They sent Leland and his buddy off with twenty bucks apiece extra, and walked back to Adam's car. It was still there, courtesy of Anthony's hired guards – an additional service, they were informed, requiring an additional fee. Once they had dispensed with those boys they got into the car and sat there, silently regarding the barren strip of South Lexington.

Adam let out a breath, heavy with disappointment. 'That wasn't very productive. Expensive, yes. But not productive.'

'Well, it's clear they all knew each other. Which means any one of them could've been the source, passed the drug on to the others. I'd bet on Nicos.'

'Why Nicos?'

'You heard what his parents said. He worked evenings at the Super E. Think about it. Since when can a part-time stockboy afford a new car?' She shook her head. 'He was dealing on the side. I'm sure of it. And somehow, he managed to get his hands on a supply of Zestron-L.'

They were quiet for a moment. Then Adam said, 'It could still be Maeve.'

She looked at him. He was staring ahead, his eyes focused on some faraway point. 'What if she *is* the source, Adam? What then?'

'I don't know.' He shook his head. 'I suppose there's no way around it. She'll have to be charged. Sale of a dangerous drug. Theft. Whatever the law requires. It's not in my hands any longer. Not with three people dead.'

Again, they fell silent. *He knows it now*, she thought. *Maeve is beyond salvation.* The time to set her right had long passed. All those missed opportunities, the months, the years when he might have made a difference, would haunt him, as they did every parent of a wayward child.

The sound of skipping feet and rope snapping rhythmically against the pavement penetrated the silence of the car. Kat looked out and saw Celeste jumping rope, her bird's-nest hair bouncing with each skip. The girl drew even with the car window and she jumped in place, all the time nonchalantly ignoring the occupants of the car.

'Hello there,' called Kat.

The girl glanced sideways. 'Hi.'

'You seem to be everywhere today.'

'Gotta keep myself busy.' The girl panted. 'That's what my mama tells me.' She stopped jumping and sidled up to Kat's window. Curiously she peered inside. 'Like your car.'

'Thank you.'

'Didn't tell ya nothin', did she?'

Kat frowned at her. 'What do you mean?'

'No way Fran's gonna talk, y'know. Not with that Leland hangin' around.'

'Is she afraid of Leland?'

'Everyone is. He's Jonah's man.'

'Jonah?'

'You know. The main man. Can't take a step round here, 'less Jonah lets you.'

'We asked for Jonah's help. He sent us Leland.'

''Course he sent Leland. Wasn't gonna let you talk to no one without a set of his ears around.' Celeste suddenly glanced over her shoulder and spotted a boy watching her from a doorway. At once she began to skip rope again, moving away up the sidewalk. Kat thought the girl would continue on her way, but when Celeste reached the front of the car, she circled left, onto the street, and back along the other side of the car, toward Adam's window.

'Jonah, he's worried, you know,' said Celeste, all the time skipping lightly on the blacktop.

'Why?' asked Adam.

'He thinks you're one of them. But that's stupid. I can tell you aren't. 'Cause you're too *obvious*.'

'What do you mean by—' Adam didn't finish the question, as Celeste was already skipping away, toward the rear of the car. He and Kat glanced at each other. 'This kid ought to be on police payroll,' he muttered.

Celeste had rounded the rear bumper and was moving on the sidewalk again, coming alongside Kat's window.

'Who's he afraid of?' Kat asked the bouncing child.

'The folks who killed Nicos.'

'And Xenia?'

166

'Same ones.'

'Who are you talking about, Celeste? *Which* people?'

The girl stopped jumping and looked at them as if they were idiots. 'The police, of course!' she said. Then, with a snap of the rope, she was off and bouncing again.

Adam and Kat stared at the girl. 'That's crazy,' muttered Adam. 'It's just the mentality around here. People are afraid of authority. Naturally they'd blame the police for everything.'

'Fran was clearly afraid of *something*,' said Kat.

'Of that fellow Jonah, no doubt.'

By now Celeste was moving up the sidewalk, to make her second circle of the car. When she came around to Adam's side, he was ready to pose the next question through his window.

'Why does Jonah think the police killed Nicos?' he asked.

'Gotta ask *him*.'

'How do I reach him?'

'Can't.' She skipped rope in place. 'He don't talk to outsiders.'

'Well,' sighed Adam. 'That's that.'

'Show her Maeve's picture,' said Kat. 'See if she knows her.'

Adam took out the photograph and flashed it at Celeste. 'Have you seen this woman?' he asked.

Celeste glanced at the photo and did a double take. She stopped jumping for a moment and bent forward for a closer look. 'Sure looks like her.'

'Like who?'

'Jonah's lady.' With that, Celeste bounced off, away from the window.

Adam looked at Kat in shock. 'Dear God, *Maeve?*'

'Ask her to take another look.'

They glanced back to see where Celeste was in her jump rope circuit around the car. To their dismay, the girl was halfway down the block, skipping swiftly away.

Instead of Celeste, it was Leland approaching their car. He bent to speak into Kat's window. 'Time you got movin',' he said. 'Like, right *now*.'

'I want to talk to Jonah,' said Kat.

'He don't talk to nobody.'

'Tell him I'm on his side. That I only want to—'

'You want I should give your car a shove or what?'

There was a silence, heavy with the threat of violence.

'We hear you,' Adam said, and started the engine. Swiftly he pulled into the street and made a U-turn. Leland was still glowering at them as they drove away.

'Not taking any chances, is he?' said Adam, glancing in the rearview mirror.

'Jonah's orders.'

Just ahead, Celeste was jumping rope along the sidewalk. As they drove past, she stopped and raised her hand in farewell. Then, aware that she too was being watched, she grabbed both ends of the rope and continued her bouncing progress along South Lexington.

For two days, Dr. Herbert Esterhaus had avoided going home. Instead, he'd holed up under an assumed name at the St. Francis Arms and ordered all his meals delivered.

It was a no-frills establishment, the sort of place frequented by traveling salesmen on tight budgets. The sheets were slightly frayed, the carpet well worn, and the water spewing from the faucet had a distinctly rusty tinge, but the room served his purpose; it was a place to hide while he considered his next move.

Unfortunately, he had few options to choose from.

That he'd soon be arrested, he had no doubt. The investigation into the Zestron-L theft had just begun; soon they'd be running background checks and polygraphing everyone in the lab, and he would fail the test. Miserably. Because he was guilty.

He could run. He could change his name, his identity. The way he had before. After all, it was a vast country, with countless little towns in which to hide. But he was weary of hiding, of answering to an assumed name. It had taken him ten years to feel comfortable with 'Herbert Esterhaus.' He loved his job. His work was valued and respected at Cygnus, and most important, *he* was valued and respected. Even by Mr. Q. himself.

Would they respect him when they learned what he had done?

He went to the window and stared down at the street. It was a blustery day, and bits of paper tumbled in the wind. Downtown Albion. All right, so it wasn't the city of his dreams, but it was home to him now. He had a house, a good paycheck, a job that kept him on the cutting edge of research. On Saturday nights he had his folk dancing club, on Sunday nights his watercolor classes. He didn't have the woman he loved, but there was always the chance Maeve would come back to him. 'This is my home now,' he said to himself. The sound of his own voice speaking aloud was startling. 'I live here. And I'm not going to leave.'

Which led to his second option: confession.

It carried consequences, of course. He would probably lose his job. But once they understood the circumstances, understood he was forced into the act, they wouldn't be so hard. Not when he could name names, point fingers.

*This time, by God, I'm not going to run.*

He reached for the telephone and dialed Adam Quantrell's house. Confession was good for the soul, they said.

But Quantrell wasn't home, the man at the other end told him. Would he care to leave a message?

'Tell him – tell him I have to talk to him,' said Esterhaus. 'But I can't do it over the phone.'

'What is this concerning, may I ask?'

'It's . . . personal.'

'I'll let him know. Where can you be reached, Dr. Esterhaus?'

'I'll be . . .' He paused. This slightly seedy hotel? It would be proof he'd fled, proof of his guilty conscience. 'I'll be at home,' he said. He hung up, at once feeling better. Now that he had decided on a course of action, all the energy that had been sucked into the useless machinery of uncertainty could be redirected to pure motion. He packed the few things he'd brought – a tooth-brush, a razor, a change of underwear. Then he checked out and drove home.

He parked in his carport and entered through the side

door, into the kitchen. Familiar smells at once enveloped him, the scent of the Cloroxed sink, the fresh paint from the newly redone hallway. Here, in his house, he felt safe.

The phone rang in the living room. Quantrell? The thought set his heart pounding. Fully prepared to blurt out the truth, he picked up the receiver, only to hear a child's voice ask, 'Is Debbie there?' He didn't hear the footsteps on the porch, or the wriggling of the doorknob.

But he did hear the knock.

He hung up on the kid and went to open the front door. 'Oh,' he said. 'It's you—'

'Everything's fixed.'

'It is?'

'I told you it would be.' The visitor stepped inside, shut the door.

'Look, I can't deal with this! I never thought it'd go this far—'

'But Herb, I'm telling you, you don't have a thing to worry about.'

'Quantrell's going to find out! It's only a matter of—' Esterhaus paused, staring at his visitor. At the gun. He shook his head in disbelief.

The gun fired twice, two clean shots.

The impact of the bullets sent Esterhaus jerking backwards. He sprawled against the couch, his blood sliding in rivulets across the fabric. Through fading vision, he stared up at his murderer. 'Why?' he whispered.

'I told you, Herb. You don't have a thing to worry about. And now, neither do I.'

*

Thomas, as usual, was waiting at the front door to greet them. By now he seemed a built-in part of the house, as affixed to it as the mantelpiece or the wainscotting, and just as permanent. The difference was, Thomas actually *wanted* to be there. Kat saw it now, in his smile of welcome, in the fatherly affection with which he helped Adam remove his coat. It was apparent they went back a long way, these two; she could almost see them as they must have been thirty years ago, the young man reaching down to assist the boy struggling out of his winter coat.

Thomas hung their jackets in the closet. 'There were two calls while you were out, Mr. Q.,' he said.

'Anything important?'

'Miss Calderwood phoned to ask if you were still on for the afternoon with the Wyatts. And if so, where were you?'

Adam groaned. 'Good Lord, I forgot all about Isabel!' He reached for the hall telephone. 'She's going to be furious.'

'She did seem rather put out.'

Adam dialed Isabel's number and stood waiting while it rang. 'Who else called?'

'A Dr. Herbert Esterhaus. About two hours ago.'

'Esterhaus?' Adam glanced up sharply. 'Why?'

'He wouldn't say. Something about the laboratory, I assume. He did imply it was somewhat urgent.'

'Where is he?'

'That's his number there, on the notepad.'

Adam hung up and dialed the number Thomas had written down. It kept ringing.

'He said he'd be home all day,' said Thomas. 'Perhaps he stepped out for a moment.'

Adam glanced at Kat. It was a look, nothing more, but she saw in his eyes a flicker of apprehension. *Something's happened. He feels it too.*

Adam hung up. 'Let's drive by his house.'

'But you've only just arrived,' said Thomas.

'It doesn't feel right. Herb wouldn't call me at home unless it was important.'

Resignedly, Thomas reached back into the closet for their jackets. 'Really, Mr. Q. All this rushing around.'

Adam smiled and patted him on the shoulder. 'At least you won't have us underfoot, hm?'

Thomas merely sighed and walked them to the door.

Just as they climbed into Adam's car, a Mercedes pulled into the driveway, its tires spitting gravel. Isabel stuck her head out the window. 'Adam!' she called. 'Have you forgotten about the Wyatts?'

'Give them my regrets!'

'I thought we were on for this afternoon—'

'Something's come up. I can't make it. Look, I'll call you later, Isabel, all right?'

'But Adam, you—'

Her words were cut off by the roar of the Volvo as Adam and Kat drove off. She was left behind in the driveway, staring in disbelief.

Adam glanced in his mirror at the receding Mercedes. 'Damn. How am I going to explain this away?'

'Just tell her what happened,' said Kat. 'She already knows what's going on, doesn't she?'

'Isabel?' He snorted. 'First, Isabel is not equipped to deal with unpleasantness of any sort. It's not in her sphere of knowledge. Second, she's not good at keeping secrets. By the time the gossip got down the street and back again, I'd be a major drug dealer and Maeve would have three heads and be practicing voodoo.'

'You mean . . . she doesn't know about Maeve?'

'She knows I have a stepdaughter. But she never asks about her. And I don't fill her in on the gory details.'

'Isn't a problem kid something you'd want to sort of *mention* to your girlfriend?'

'Girlfriend?' He laughed.

'Well, what *do* you call her then?'

'A social companion. Suitable for all occasions.'

'Oh.' She looked out the window. 'I guess that covers everything.'

To her surprise, he reached over and squeezed her thigh. 'Not quite everything.'

She frowned at his laughing eyes. 'What does it leave out?'

'Oh, street fights, exploding houses, the sort of occasions she wouldn't appreciate.'

'I'm not sure *I* appreciate them.'

He turned his gaze back to the road. 'I've never slept with her, you know,' he said.

That statement was so unexpected, Kat was struck silent for a moment. She stared at his unruffled profile. 'Why did you tell me that?'

'I thought you should know.'

'Well, thank you for satisfying my *burning* curiosity.'

'You're very welcome.'

'And what am I supposed to do with this knowledge?'

He winked. 'File it away in that amazing brain of yours.'

She shook her head and laughed. 'I don't know what to make of you, Quantrell. Sometimes I think you're flirting with me. Other times, I think it's all in my head.'

'Why wouldn't I? You know I'm attracted to you.'

'Why?'

He sighed. 'You're not supposed to say, "Why?" You're supposed to say, "And I'm attracted to *you*."'

'Nevertheless, *why*?'

He glanced at her in surprise. 'Is it so difficult to believe? That I'd find you attractive?'

'I think it's because I'm a novelty,' she said. 'Because I'm not like your other . . . companions.'

'True.'

'Which means it'd never work.'

'Such a pessimist,' he sighed. He gave her thigh another squeeze, flashed her another grin, and looked back at the road.


Rockbrook was one of those anonymous suburbs that lie on the outskirts of any large city. It was a white-bread world of trim lawns, two cars in every garage, yards strewn with kids' bicycles. The house where Herbert Esterhaus lived had no bicycles in the yard, and only one vehicle in the carport, but in every other way it was typical of the neighborhood – a tract home, neatly kept, with a brick walkway in front and azaleas huddled on either side of the door.

No one seemed to be home. They rang the bell, knocked, but there was no answer, and the front door was locked.

'Now what?' said Kat. She glanced up the street. A block away, two boys tossed a basketball against their garage door. The buzz of a lawnmower echoed from some unseen backyard.

They circled around to the carport. 'His car's here,' Adam noted. 'And that looks like today's paper on the front seat. So he's driven it today.'

'Then where is he?' said Kat.

Adam went to the side door of the house. It was un-locked. He poked his head inside and called out: 'Herb? Are you home?'

There was no answer.

'Maybe we should check inside,' suggested Kat.

They stepped into the kitchen. Again, Adam called out: 'Herb?' A silence seemed to hang over the house. And the sense of dead air, as though no window, no door, had been opened for a very long time.

Kat spotted a set of keys on the kitchen counter. That struck her as odd, that a man would leave the house with-out his keys.

'Maybe you should call Thomas,' she said. 'Esterhaus might have left you another message.'

'It's a thought, but first let's check the living room.' He headed out of the kitchen.

Seconds later, Kat heard him say, 'Oh, God.'

'Adam?' she called. She left the kitchen and crossed the dining room. Through the living room doorway, she spotted Adam, standing by the couch. He seemed frozen in place, unable to move a muscle. 'Adam?'

Slowly he turned to look at her. 'It's . . . him.'

'What?' She moved across the living room. Only as she rounded the couch did she see the crimson stain soaking the carpet, like some psychiatrist's nightmare inkblot. Stretched across the blood was an arm, its hand white and clawed.

The hand of Herbert Esterhaus.

# 11

The flash of the photographer's strobe made Kat wince. He was a crime lab veteran, and he strode casually around the body, choosing his shots with an almost bored detachment. The repeated camera flashes, the babble of too many people talking at the same time, the whine of yet another siren closing in, left Kat feeling disoriented. She'd been to crime scenes before, had been part of other, equally chaotic gatherings, but this scene was different, this victim was different. He was someone she knew, someone who, just a few short days ago, had met her handshake with one of warm flesh. His death was far too close to her, and she felt herself withdrawing into some safe, numb place where she floated on a sea of fatigue.

Only when a familiar voice called to her did her brain snap back into focus. She saw Lieutenant Sykes moving toward them.

'What the hell happened?' he asked.

'It's Esterhaus,' said Adam. 'He phoned me this afternoon. Said he wanted to talk. We came by and . . .'

Sykes glanced at the dead body sprawled on the couch. 'When?'

'We got here around five.'

'He's been dead awhile,' murmured Kat. 'Probably early afternoon.'

'How do you know?' asked Sykes.

She looked away. 'Experience,' she muttered.

The Rockbrook detective approached and greeted Sykes. 'Sorry you got dragged over, Lou. I know this one's technically ours, but they insisted I call you.'

'So what've you got?'

'Two bullet wounds in the chest. Took him down fast. No signs of forced entry. No witnesses. ME'll have to do a look-see, give us an approximate time.'

'Dr. Novak says early afternoon.'

'Yeah, well . . .' the detective shifted uneasily. 'They're sending over Davis Wheelock.'

*Because they're not about to trust me on this one,* thought Kat. The Rockbrook detective was a cautious cop. He couldn't be sure of Kat's role in all this. Her status had changed from ME to . . . what? Witness? Suspect? She could see it in the way he watched her eyes, weighed her every statement.

Now Sykes began to ask questions, the same ones they'd already answered. No, they hadn't touched anything except the phone. And, briefly, the body – to check vital signs. Events were dissected, over and over. By the time Sykes had finished, Kat was having trouble concentrating. Too many voices were talking in the room, and there were the sounds of the crowd outside, the neighbors, all pressing up against the yellow police line.

Esterhaus's body, cocooned in a zip-up bag, was wheeled through the front door and out of the house, into a night blazing with the flash of reporters' cameras.

Adam and Kat followed the EMTs out of the house. It was bedlam outside, cops shouting for everyone to stand back, radios crackling from a half-dozen patrol cars. Two TV vans were parked nearby, klieg lights glaring. A reporter thrust a microphone in front of Kat's face and asked, 'Were you the people who found the body?'

'Leave us alone,' said Adam, shoving the microphone away.

'Sir, can you tell us what condition—'

'I said, *leave us alone.*'

'Hey!' another reporter yelled. 'Aren't you Adam Quantrell? Mr. Quantrell?'

Suddenly, the lights were redirected into their eyes. Adam grabbed Kat's hand and pulled her along in a mad dash for the car.

The instant they were inside, they slammed and locked the doors. Hands knocked at the windows.

Adam started the engine. 'Let's get the hell out of here,' he growled, and hit the gas pedal.

Even as they roared away, they could hear the questions being shouted at them.

Kat collapsed back in exhaustion. 'I thought they were going to keep us there all night.'

He shot her a worried look. 'Are you all right?'

She shivered. 'Just cold. And scared. Mostly scared . . .' She looked at him. 'Why did they kill Esterhaus? What is going on, Adam?'

He stared ahead, his gaze locked on the road, his profile hard and white in the darkness. 'I wish to God I knew.'

They arrived home to find Thomas waiting for them.

'Mr. Q., the reporters have been calling—'

'Tell them to go to hell,' said Adam, guiding Kat toward the stairs.

'But—'

'You heard what I said.'

'Is that a . . . literal request?'

'Word for word.'

'Goodness,' said Thomas, sounding uncomfortable. 'I don't know . . .' He watched them climb up to the second floor landing. 'Is there anything you'll require, Mr. Q.?' he called.

'A bottle of brandy. And answer the phone, will you?'

Thomas glanced at the telephone, which had begun to ring again. Reluctantly he picked up the receiver. 'Quantrell residence.' He listened for a few seconds. Then, drawing himself to his full and dignified height, he said: 'Mr. Quantrell wishes to convey the following message: Go to hell.' He hung up, looking strangely satisfied.

'The brandy, Thomas!' called Adam.

'Right away,' said Thomas, and went off toward the library.

Adam turned Kat gently toward the bedroom. 'Come on,' he whispered. 'You look ready to collapse.'

He brought her into his room and sat her down on the bed. He took her hands in his. Her touch was like ice.

Thomas came into the room, bearing a tray with the brandy and two glasses.

'Leave it,' said Adam.

Thomas, ever discreet, nodded and withdrew.

Adam poured a glass and handed it to Kat. She looked blankly at it.

'Just brandy,' he said. 'A Quantrell family tradition.'

She took a sip. Closing her eyes tightly, she whispered, 'You Quantrells keep fine traditions.'

He reached up and gently brushed a lock of hair off her face. Her skin felt as cool as marble, but the woman beneath was alive and trembling and in need.

'If only I knew,' she said. 'If I just knew what I was fighting against. Then I wouldn't be so afraid.' She looked at him. 'That's what scares me. Not knowing. It makes the whole world seem evil.'

'Not the whole world. There's me. And I'll take care of you—'

'Don't make promises, Adam.'

'I'm not promising. I'm telling you. As long as you need me—'

She pressed her fingers to his lips. 'Don't. Please. You'll back yourself into a corner. And then you'll feel guilty when you can't keep your word.'

He grasped her hand, firmly, fiercely. 'Kat—'

'No promises.'

'All right. If that's what you want, no promises.'

'From either of us. It's more honest that way.'

'You'll stay here, though? As long as you need to. Unless . . . there's some other place you'd rather go?'

She shook her head.

He felt an intoxicating rush of happiness, of relief, that here was where she wanted to be. *With me.*

'There's no other place,' she said softly.

He had not planned to kiss her, but at that moment she looked so badly in need of a kiss that he drew her closer, and cupped her face in his hands.

It was only a brushing of lips, a taste of her brandied warmth. No passion, no lust, merely kindness.

And then, like a spark striking dry tinder, something else flared to instant brightness. He saw it in her eyes, and she in his. They stared at each other for a moment in shared wonder. And uncertainty. He wanted badly to kiss her again, but she was so vulnerable, and he knew that if he pressed her, she would yield. She might hate him in the morning, and she would have good reason. That, most of all, was what he didn't want.

He took a much-needed lungful of fortifying air and pulled away from her. 'You can stay here, in my room. It will feel safer.' He rose to leave. 'I'll sleep in yours.'

'Adam?'

'In the morning, we'll have to talk about what happens next. But tonight—'

'I want you to stay here,' she said. 'In this room. With me.'

The last two words came out in barely a whisper. Slowly

he settled back down beside her and tried to look beyond the glaze of fear in her eyes. 'Are you sure?' he asked softly.

Her answer left no doubt. She reached out to him, wrapped her arms around his neck, and pulled him against her. Their lips met. Hers were desperate, seeking, and he responded instantly to that unexpected assault with a hunger just as fierce.

He reached out to bury his fingers in her hair. It felt like the mane of a wild animal, crackling and alive. Suddenly *she* came alive, and all of her fear and exhaustion broke before a swelling tide of desire. Her hair brushed his face, and he inhaled the warm and feral scent of a woman. Such delicious sounds she was making, little whimpers and sighs, as her mouth eagerly met his, again and again.

They tumbled back onto the bed and rolled across the covers. First she was on top, her hair spilling like sheets of silk over his face. Then he was on top, covering her body with his. No passive participant was she; already, he felt her pressing up against him, her back arching, her body starved for more intimate contact. Fear had made her desperate; he could sense it in her kisses.

He forced himself to pull back. 'Kat,' he said. 'Look at me.'

She opened her eyes. They had the brief, bright glow of tears.

He took her face in his hands, cradled her cheeks so she could not turn away from him. 'What's wrong?'

'I want you,' was all she said.

'But you're crying.'

'No, I just want you . . .'

'And you're afraid.'

There it was – the briefest of nods, as though she didn't want to say it. 'I'm afraid of everything,' she said. 'Everyone. The whole world.'

'Even me?'

She swallowed back another flash of tears. 'Especially you,' she whispered.

Long after he'd fallen asleep, Kat lay awake in his arms. They might both be exhausted, but only he was able to sleep untroubled and unafraid.

*He* wasn't the one falling in love.

She burrowed closer, wondering about the man who lay beside her. The man who had everything.

*Now he has me, as well.*

She felt helpless, trapped not only by her own heart, but by circumstances. Rule number one for the independent woman: Never let a man become indispensable. It was the rule she tried to live by, and already she'd violated it.

She looked at Adam and felt yet again that stirring of hunger. And something else, having nothing to do with desire. Tenderness. Joy. She felt pushed and pulled between wanting to believe in love and knowing better.

When she finally did sleep, it was like falling into some small, dreamless space. A prison without windows.

She was the first to awaken. Sunlight was shining through the curtains. Adam slept on, his golden hair tousled

185

beyond help of any mere combing. She left him and went into the bathroom to shower. It was only when she came out again, bundled in his robe, that he stirred awake and gazed at her with amusement.

'Good morning,' he murmured. 'Are you an early riser or am I just lazy?'

She smiled. 'Since it's already eight-thirty, I guess that makes you lazy.'

'Come here.' He patted the bed. 'Sit down with me.'

Reluctantly she complied and was reminded yet again of how susceptible she was to his attractions. Already, those hormones were doing their work; she could feel them flooding her face with heat.

'I dreamt about you last night,' he said, his fingers lightly tracing the length of her spine.

'Adam,' she said. 'What happened last night—' She felt a shudder of pleasure as his hand moved upward, crept under the flap of the robe to graze her breast. At once she stood up and moved away from the bed. She shook her head. 'It's not going to work.'

He didn't say a thing. He just watched her, his gaze too searching for comfort.

She began to move around the room, anything to avoid that look of his. 'I walk into your bathroom,' she said. 'And everything's marble and – and gold. The soap's French. And the towels all match.' She stopped and laughed. 'Adam, in all my life, I've *never* had towels that matched.'

'You're saying it won't work because of my towels?'

'No, I'm saying I can't see myself . . . fitting in here. I

can't see your friends accepting me. Or *you* accepting me. Right now, maybe, I'm exciting for you—'

'Without a doubt.'

'But it doesn't last, the novelty of a girlfriend from South Lexington. Look, you're a nice guy. I know you don't mean to hurt me. Maybe you'll even feel guilty about it when it falls apart. But I'm not the kind of woman who gets hurt, okay? I *refuse* to be hurt. And that's why I'd much rather stay your friend.'

'Because you think our relationship is doomed?'

'Well, yes. I guess.'

For a moment he considered that statement without apparent emotion. Then he said, quite calmly, 'I suppose it *is* better for you. We both know how it is with these rich bastards. Love 'em and leave 'em – that's what you say, isn't it?'

'Oh, Adam.' She sighed. 'Please.'

He rose from the bed, snatching up his clothes. 'I'm insulted. I'm really insulted. We make love – what I *thought* was love – and then you hand me the script to the rest of the affair!'

'Because I've played this part before. With Ed. With other men—'

'Also rich bastards?'

The knock on the door startled them both.

'What is it?' snapped Adam.

Thomas entered, looking quite taken aback at his employer's tone of voice. 'I . . . thought perhaps you should know. The police are downstairs.'

'What?'

187

'Lieutenant Sykes and that chubby sergeant. Shall I set breakfast?'

Adam sighed. 'Go ahead. Lay on the bagels for Ratchet.'

'And some extra cream cheese,' Thomas added and withdrew.

Adam and Kat looked at each other. The tension was still there, crackling between them. So was the desire.

Push and pull. Attraction and fear. That was what she felt when she looked at him.

She picked up her clothes. 'I'll see you downstairs,' she said. Then she left to get dressed in the other room.

The two cops were sitting at the dining table, Sykes nursing a cup of black coffee, Ratchet wolfing down scrambled eggs and sausages. Both men seemed quiet, maybe a little cautious, this morning. As though they had to be careful about what they said.

*Something has changed*, thought Kat, studying them.

She and Adam sat across the table from them. Though Adam was right beside her, he didn't touch her, didn't glance at her. She felt the distance between them widen with every minute that passed.

Sykes said, 'It's about the Esterhaus murder. Rockwood Precinct's handed the case to us.'

'Why?' asked Adam.

'Because of what's come to light.' Sykes put a large envelope on the table and slid it across to Adam. 'I'm sorry to be the one to show these to you. But I need you to confirm the identity.'

Puzzled, Adam pulled out a dozen photographs. At

his first glimpse of the woman in the pictures, he paled. They were nude shots, in grainy black and white, amateurish and obviously home-processed. In one, the woman was sprawled suggestively across a bed, her hair fanned out, her hands cupping her breasts. In another, she pouted seductively from a bar stool, a whiskey glass raised to the camera. More photos, some taken with an apparent effort at artistic shading, others blatantly prurient. Adam stared at the thin and girlish face gazing back at him from an array of poses. Then he looked away and dropped his head in his hands.

Sykes asked: 'Is it her?'

'Yes,' murmured Adam. 'It's Maeve.'

Sykes nodded. 'I thought so. I recognized her face from the photos you gave me earlier.'

Adam looked up. 'Where did you find these?'

'In Herbert Esterhaus's bedroom.'

'*What?*'

'They were in a bureau drawer. Along with a lot of other . . . interesting things.'

Adam stared at him, shocked by the revelation. 'Esterhaus and Maeve . . .'

'We're trying to find her, bring her in for questioning. But we can't seem to get near her. That's a tight group she hangs out with in South Lexington. It's only routine questions, of course. Ex-girlfriends are always on the list—'

'You don't think *Maeve* had anything to do with it?'

'As I said, it's routine. Just a drill we go through—'

Adam pointed to the photos. 'I'd say Maeve is the victim here, Lieutenant!' he shot back.

'I know exactly how you feel, Mr. Q.,' said Sykes. 'I've got a little girl of my own, and I'd want to wring the neck of any bastard who used her like this. But a man's been killed. And now we have to go through the paces.'

'I know Maeve! She wouldn't—'

'Did you know about her and Esterhaus?'

Adam paused. 'No,' he admitted at last. 'I didn't.'

Sykes shook his head. 'There's a lot you never know about people. Even your own family. I'm not saying you should get panicked or anything. You're probably right, she had nothing to do with it. With the evidence we found, I'm ninety-nine percent sure she didn't. Still—'

'What evidence?' asked Kat.

'Things we found. In the victim's house.'

'Aside from nude photos of ex-girlfriends?'

'Yes.' Sykes looked at Adam. 'What did you know about Esterhaus when you hired him?'

'Just what was in his résumé. As I recall, he came well-qualified. Excellent references. Had a research position somewhere out in California.'

'That should've tipped you off right there,' said Ratchet, spearing another sausage. 'Who in his right mind leaves sunny California and moves to Albion?'

'You mean his references were falsified?' asked Kat.

Sykes nodded. 'Courtesy of the U.S. government.'

'*What?*'

'See, the name Herbert Esterhaus was an alias. We found his old IDs in his house. His real name was Dr.

Lawrence Hebron. Oh, he was a biochemist, all right, but he didn't work for a company in California. He worked in Miami. A designer drug lab owned by the mob. A real genius, so I hear. Then he got busted and turned state's evidence. They put him in the Witness Protection Program, gave him a new name, a new résumé. And a new job, with Cygnus. Where, I take it, he was working out just fine.'

Adam nodded. 'He was one of our best.'

'And you think that's why he was killed?' asked Kat. 'Old mob connections?'

'There are folks in Miami who aren't happy with him. If they traced him to Albion, then he was a dead man.'

'We figure,' said Ratchet, wiping sausage grease from his mouth, 'Esterhaus is the key to it all. Maybe he needed some extra cash, so he rips off a few grains of Zestron-L from the lab, sells it on the street. A few junkies die as a result. Then his old buddies from Miami get wind of his whereabouts, come up, and perform a little thirty-eight caliber justice.'

There was a silence as Kat and Adam considered the theory. 'So we're supposed to believe that Miami boys drove up and did your job for you?' said Kat. She shook her head. 'Too neat. And who blew up my house?'

'Esterhaus was a biochemist,' said Ratchet. 'He could put together a respectable bomb.'

'Why? Just to shut me up?'

Sykes laughed. 'There are times, Novak, when I would *love* to shut you up. Consider what the man was faced with, if you kept pushing your investigation. Charges of theft. Manslaughter, for those junkies. Plus, you'd blow his cover identity, so his life was at stake as well.'

'And Maeve?' said Kat, glancing at the nude photos. 'How does she figure in?'

'We don't know,' said Sykes. 'We thought maybe Mr. Q. could shed some light.'

Adam shook his head, troubled by what he'd heard. 'Maeve never said a word to me about any of this.'

'You had no idea she was seeing Esterhaus?'

'She had her own life, her own apartment. I suspected there was a man, but I didn't know his name. And she wouldn't bother telling *me*.' In disgust, he swept up the photos and stuffed them back in the envelope. 'I'd strangle him myself, if he weren't already dead.'

Kat caught the glance that flew between Sykes and Ratchet. *Careful, Adam*, she thought. *They're looking for suspects. Don't provide them with one.*

She said, quickly, 'Do you think Maeve knew about his real identity? We know she and Esterhaus weren't getting along – those arguments at the lab, remember? Maybe it had nothing to do with the job. Maybe it was personal. Maybe she learned the truth about him. And she walked out. Not on the job, but on *him*.'

'She could have told me,' said Adam. 'But she didn't. Lord, what a disaster I've been as a father.'

Kat touched his arm. It wasn't enough to close the gap yawning between them; perhaps nothing could close that gap. But it let him know she cared. 'Maybe she couldn't tell you. Maybe she was ashamed she had fallen for the guy in the first place. Or scared.'

'Of what?'

'The man she was sleeping with had a price on his head. And he was pushing poison on the street. That would scare a lot of people.'

'Then why didn't she come to *me*?' said Adam. 'I would have kicked him out of Cygnus so fast, he wouldn't know what hit him.'

'You may have answered your own question,' said Kat. 'If she had any feelings at all for Esterhaus, she wouldn't expose him. So she just walked away. Went some place he couldn't find her.'

'South Lexington?' Ratchet snorted. 'I can think of better neighborhoods to hide in.'

Sykes scooped up the envelope of photos and rose to leave. 'We'll keep trying to find her,' he said. 'But I'm afraid it's turned into a game of hide-and-seek. And Maeve's pretty damn good at it.' He glanced at Adam. 'As you already know.'

Adam shook his head, a weary gesture of acceptance. Defeat. 'You won't find her,' he said. 'No one will. Not unless she wants to be found.'

They spotted Celeste a block away, her curlicued hair bouncing up and down as she skipped rope. She didn't break stride as they drove closer and pulled up next to her. She was counting to herself in a soft, flat drone: 'One twenty-eight, one twenty-nine, one thirty . . .'

'Are you sure this is a good idea?' Adam whispered to Kat. 'Maybe we should try Anthony again.'

'And lose another two hundred dollars?' Kat shook her

head. 'This kid knows her way around. Let's see if she'll help us out.'

'One thirty-eight, one thirty-nine . . .'

'Hello, Celeste,' Kat called through the open car window. 'Can we talk to you?'

'One forty-four, one forty-five.'

'We need a little help.'

'One forty-eight . . .' The rope suddenly fell limp, snagged by Celeste's shoe. She stamped her foot in annoyance. 'I was goin' for a record, too.' Resignedly she turned to Kat. 'So what do you need?'

'We want to talk to Jonah,' said Kat. 'The big man.'

'What for?'

'Just talk. About what's coming down.'

'Jonah doesn't talk to outsiders.'

'Maybe he'll talk to us. A new jump rope says he will.'

'I'd rather have a watch. Y'know, with all those fancy dials and things.'

'And you thought Anthony was steep,' muttered Adam.

'Okay,' said Kat. 'A watch. But only if he talks to us.'

Celeste grinned. 'Wait here,' she said, and trotted off down the street. She turned left, into an alley, and vanished.

'Is this going to work?' said Adam.

'We can't get to Maeve any other way. So we have to try going to the top. If she's Jonah's lady, that's where she'll be. With him.'

'Maeve won't talk to us. She won't let us anywhere near her.'

'But things have changed. Esterhaus is dead. She's a

suspect. So she'd better talk to us. Before the police *make* her talk.' She looked at Adam. 'Besides, this is your chance to call off the feud, or whatever it is between you two. It's gone on long enough. Don't you think it's time for you and Maeve to be a family again?'

He gazed down the street, at the alley where Celeste had vanished. 'You're right,' he said softly. 'It's time . . .'

They waited. Ten minutes, fifteen.

Instead of Celeste, it was their old escort Leland who emerged from the alley. He sauntered over to their car and peered inside.

'You two again,' he said.

'We want to see Jonah,' said Kat.

'What for?' demanded Leland.

'This place is gonna be thick with cops. I thought the big man might want to know what's coming down.'

Leland looked skeptical. 'You doin' him a favor? Sure.'

'I got one to ask in return.'

An exchange of favors – that concept, Leland could grasp. He opened Kat's door. 'Okay, you're on. Just you, not the dude.'

'Now wait a minute,' said Adam, climbing out of the car as she did.

'It's the chick or nobody.'

'She's not going in there without me.'

'Then she ain't goin' in at all.'

'If those are the terms, then we're not—'

'Adam, can I speak to you?' Kat grabbed his arm and pulled him aside. 'Don't ruin it.'

'You don't know anything about this Jonah character!'

'And I never will, if I don't go in.'

Adam glanced at Leland, who was standing by the rear bumper. 'He's twice your size. No, he's twice *my* size. If he wanted to, he could—'

'Do you want to contact Maeve or not?'

'Not if it means sending you off with him.'

Her eyes narrowed. 'I'm not afraid of him, you know.'

'Which says something about your sanity.'

'There's a code of honor here, Adam. You may not believe it, but people do play by the big man's rules. Jonah says I'm in, then I'm in. And no one touches me.'

'What if the rules have changed?'

'I'm gambling they haven't.'

'There's the word for it. Gambling.'

'Are you comin' or what?' said Leland.

'I'm coming,' said Kat, and turned to follow him.

Adam caught her arm. 'One question, Kat. Why are you doing this?'

'Because you need your daughter. And I think she needs you.' With that she pulled away and followed Leland up the street.

They turned left, into the alley, then right, up another alley. There Leland halted. He pulled out a bandanna and tossed it to her. 'Put it over your eyes,' he said.

'You boys got a secret hideout?'

'We wanna keep it that way.'

*Stupid kid stuff,* she thought as she wrapped the bandanna over her eyes and tied it at the back. The cloth stank of cheap after-shave. 'Okay. I'm blind as a bat. Now don't screw up and let me trip on anything.'

'You, lady, I'll be happy to throw out a window. Come on.' She felt his paw take hold of her arm – not gently, either.

They moved forward. She felt glass skitter away before her blindly shuffling feet. Leland's grip remained firm, her only link to the world. She tried counting paces, then gave up after awhile, knowing only that they'd traveled a long way – maybe in circles. She stumbled over a threshold, was dragged back to her feet. They were in a building, she realized, listening to their footsteps echo across the floor. Too many turns to keep track of now. Up some stairs, then back down. Cold air on her face – outside? A walkway, perhaps? Back inside – those echoing footsteps again.

The echoes elongated, bounced off widely spaced walls. There were others here; she could hear footsteps and a murmur of voices.

Leland halted.

'Where are we?' she asked.

'My castle,' said a voice – one she didn't recognize. It boomed forth, like an actor's from the stage.

'Are you Jonah?' asked Kat.

'Why don't you see for yourself?' said the man. 'Take off your blindfold.'

Kat hesitated. Then, slowly, she reached up and pulled off the bandanna.

# 12

She was standing in a dark room – a warehouse. On her right was a window, covered over by fabric. Only the faintest light managed to seep through the weave, offering her a dim view of scattered crates, sagging posts. *I have an audience*, she thought with a sudden flash of nervousness as she realized shadows were moving around her.

A light sprang on, a single bare lightbulb swaying from a wire.

She squinted against the glare, trying to make out the faces surrounding her. There were at least a dozen of them, all with eyes trained on her, watching her, waiting for signs of fear or vulnerability. She tried not to show either.

'So,' she said, 'which one of you is Jonah?'

'That depends,' someone said.

'On what?'

'On who *you* are.'

'The name's Kat Novak. And this used to be my neighborhood.'

'She's a cop,' said Leland. 'Goes around askin' questions like one, anyway.'

'Not a cop,' said Kat. 'I work for the medical examiner's office. People die, my job's to find out why. And you've had folks dying around here.'

'Hell,' someone said with a laugh. 'Folks dyin' all the time. Nothin' special.'

'Nicos Biagi wasn't special? Or Xenia? Or Eliza?'

There was a silence.

'So why do *you* care, Kat Novak?'

Even before she turned to face the speaker, she knew it was Jonah. The tone of command in his voice was unmistakable. She found herself gazing at a magnificent man, towering, with unnaturally pale eyes and a lion's mane of brown hair. The others remained silent, as he moved forward to confront her in the circle of light.

'Is it so hard to believe, Jonah, that I *would* care?' she asked.

'Yeah. Because no one else does.'

'You forget. This was my neighborhood. I used to hang out on the same streets you hang out on now. I knew your mothers. I grew up with them.'

'But *you* left.'

'No one ever really leaves this place. You can try all your lives, but it stays with you. Follows you wherever you go.'

'Is that why you're here? To help the lost souls you left behind?'

'To do my job. To find out why people are dying.'

'To do your job? Is that all?'

'And—' She paused. 'To warn your lady, Maeve.'

Jonah stood stock-still. No one moved.

Then the steady click-click of boot heels across the floor cut through the silence. A shadow, sleek as a cat's, came out of the darkness. Casually the woman strolled into the circle of light where she stood with arms crossed, gazing speculatively at Kat. She was dressed all in black, but in various textures of black: leather skirt, knit turtleneck, a quilted jacket with patches of shimmery satin. Her hair looked like broomstraw – stiff and ragged, the blond strands tipped with a startling shade of purple. She was thin – too thin, her eyes dark hollows in a porcelain face.

The woman walked a slow, deliberate circle around Kat, studying her from the side, from behind. She came around to the front, and the two women stood face to face.

'I don't know you,' said Maeve. Then, with that declaration, she turned and started to walk away, back into the shadows.

'But I know your father,' said Kat.

'Congratulations,' said Maeve over her shoulder.

'And I knew Herb Esterhaus. Before he was shot to death.'

Maeve froze. She turned to face her.

'You're a suspect,' said Kat. 'The police'll be coming around, asking questions.'

'No, they won't.'

'Why not?'

'Because they already know the answers.'

Kat frowned. 'What do you mean?'

Maeve glanced at Jonah. 'This is between me and her.'

After a pause, Jonah nodded and snapped his fingers. 'Out,' he said.

Like magic, the circle of people melted into the shadows. Maeve waited for the last footsteps to fade away, then she reached for a crate and shoved it toward Kat. 'Sit,' she said.

'I'll stand, thank you,' said Kat, unwilling to yield the advantage of height.

Maeve, unruffled, propped one black boot on the crate and regarded her adversary with new interest. 'Where did you meet my father?'

'The city morgue.'

Maeve laughed. 'That's a new one.'

'He came in to look at a body. We thought it might be yours.'

'He must've been disappointed when it wasn't.'

'No, as a matter of fact, he was terrified by the prospect. As it turned out, it was someone you probably knew.'

'Eliza?' Maeve shrugged. 'Everyone knew her. You couldn't avoid it. She'd empty your pockets one way or another.'

'And your last matchbook?'

'What?'

'She had a matchbook. L'Etoile Restaurant. Had your father's phone number written in it.'

Again, Maeve shrugged. 'She needed the matches. I didn't.'

'What about Nicos and Xenia? Did you know them too?'

'Look,' said Maeve. 'They were stupid, that's all. Took some bad medicine.'

'Who passed it to them?'

Maeve didn't answer.

'You know, don't you?'

'Look, it was a mistake—'

'On whose part?'

'Everyone's. Nicos's. Xenia's—'

'Yours?'

Maeve paused. 'I didn't know. The bastard never bothered to tell me. He just said he wanted to make a delivery, needed a runner out to Bellemeade.'

'And you told him Nicos was available.'

'I didn't know Nicos was dumb enough to snitch a sample for himself. Pass it to his girlfriends.'

'So you arranged it all,' said Kat, not bothering to keep the disgust out of her voice. 'You do this sort of thing all the time?'

'No! It was a favor, that's all! Old times' sake. I didn't know—'

'That it was poison?'

'He said it was a one-time thing! All he wanted was a delivery boy.'

'All *who* wanted?'

Maeve let out a breath and looked away. 'Herb. Esterhaus. He and I, we used to be . . .'

'I know, Maeve. We saw the photos.'

'Photos?'

202

'You know. All that X-rated posing you did for your good friend Herb.'

There was a flash of regret in Maeve's eyes. 'Dad saw them too?'

'Yes. He wasn't pleased. Would've strangled Esterhaus if the man wasn't already dead.'

Maeve snorted. 'I'd like to strangle him myself. For using me.'

'Did he use you often? For these deliveries?'

'I told you, it was just a one-time thing.' She shook her head. 'And I thought he was clean, you know? After he got busted last year, he was real careful to—'

'Wait. Esterhaus was arrested? When?'

'About a year ago. It was small time, a few pot plants in his backyard. I don't know how he squirmed out of the charges, but he did. I figure, the feds stepped in and helped him out. They look after their witnesses.'

'You knew he was in the Witness Protection Program?'

'He told me about Miami. When he got busted, that really scared him. He didn't want Miami to find out. And he didn't want to lose his job. Hell, he *liked* being cooped up in that lab! Me, I hated it. After a while I couldn't take *him* either.'

'So you left him.'

'I wasn't mad at him or anything. I just got bored.'

'The police say you're a suspect in his murder.'

'They'd say anything.'

'You have a better suspect?'

Maeve moved away from the crate and began to pace, weaving in and out of the shadows. 'Herb was just your average guy, trying to make a living. And trying to stay clean.'

'Then why was he stealing Zestron-L? Moving it out onto the streets?'

'He was being squeezed.'

'By whom?'

Maeve turned to look at her. 'Try the people at the top. The ones who'd like to wipe South Lexington off the map.'

'Who, City Hall? The cops?'

'The list goes on and on. People at the top, they look down at us like we're rats, crawling around in the sewers. And what do people do with rats? They exterminate them.'

Kat shook her head. 'Wild accusations won't earn you any points, Maeve.'

'No. People like you never listen to people like us.'

'Hey, you're not exactly scraping bottom, okay? You're a *Quantrell*.'

'Don't remind me,' snapped Maeve. She turned and started to walk away.

'Your father's waiting out on the street,' Kat called after her. 'He wants to talk with you.'

Maeve turned around. 'Why? He never bothered to talk with me before. It was always *at* me, not with me. Ordering me around. Telling me to clean up my act, toss out my cigarettes. He's not even my real father.'

'He wanted to be.'

'But he isn't, okay?'

'So where *is* your real father? Tell me that.'

Maeve glared at her, but said nothing.

'He isn't here, is he?' said Kat.

'He's living in Italy.'

'Right. In Italy. But Adam's *here*.'

'He's *not* my father.'

'No, he just acts like one. And hurts like one.'

Maeve shoved away a crate and sent it toppling.

'Oh, great,' said Kat. 'Now we're going to have a tantrum.'

'You're a bitch.'

'Maybe. But you know what I'm not? Your mother. And I don't have to take this crap.' With that, Kat turned and walked away. She heard, off in the shadows, a scrambling of footsteps, then Maeve's command: 'Forget it. Let the bitch go.'

Kat managed to navigate her own way out of the building. It took her a few wrong turns, a half-dozen rickety flights of stairs, but she finally found her way outside. Looking back, she realized she'd been in the abandoned mill building. Boarded-up windows and graffiti-splashed brick was all one saw from the street. She wondered how many pairs of eyes were watching her from behind that wall.

She walked on, heading briskly back to South Lexington Avenue, back to Adam.

She saw him pacing by the car, his fair hair tumbled by the wind, his hands deep in his pockets. The instant he spotted her, he started toward her.

'I was about to call the police,' he said. 'What happened?'

'I'll tell you all about it.' She opened the car door and got inside. 'Let's get out of here.'

He slid in beside her. 'Did you see Jonah?'

'Yes.'

'And?'

'It was an unforgettable experience.'

He started the engine and muttered, 'So was waiting for you.'

They pulled onto South Lexington and headed north.

'I saw Maeve,' said Kat.

Adam almost slammed on the brakes. 'She was *there*?'

'Celeste got it right. She's Jonah's lady.' She glanced back at the line of cars honking behind them. 'Keep moving, you're holding up traffic.'

Adam, still rattled, turned his attention back to the road. 'Did she seem . . . happy?' he asked.

'To be honest?' Kat shook her head. 'I don't think that kid was ever happy.'

'Will she talk to me?'

Kat heard it in his voice and saw it in his face: a father's fear, a father's despair. All at once she wondered about her own father, that nameless man with the green eyes. She wondered where he was, if he knew or cared he had a daughter. *Of course he doesn't*, she thought. *Not the way this man does*.

She looked ahead, at the line of traffic. 'She isn't ready to see you,' she said.

'If I tried to—'

'It isn't the time, Adam.'

'When *will* it be the time?'

'When she grows up. If she ever does.'

He gripped the steering wheel, staring ahead in frustration. 'If I only knew what I did wrong . . .'

'Some kids are just born angry. In Maeve's case, my guess is she's angry at her real father. But he's not around to scream at, so she takes it out on you. Nothing you do is right. You exert a little control, and you're a tyrant. You try to set limits, she smashes them.' Kat reached over and touched his knee. 'You did the best you could.'

'It wasn't enough.'

'Adam,' she said gently, 'it never is.'

He drove in silence, his troubled gaze focused on the road. How quickly he accepted the blame, she thought. As if Maeve had no responsibility for her own life, her own mess.

'She did clear up a few things,' said Kat. 'In fact, she cleared up a lot. Esterhaus *was* the source. He stole the Zestron and passed the drug to Nicos for a delivery. Nicos must have kept some for his own use. That's how it got into the Projects.'

'A delivery? To whom?'

'Maeve didn't say. But you know who she says is behind it all?' Kat laughed. 'The city elite, unspecified. Meaning all the creeps in power. She figures they're distributing the drug in order to clean the trash off the streets.'

'I hate to admit it, but she's got the city elite pegged just about right.'

Kat glanced at him with a raised eyebrow. 'But systematically pushing poison? To clean the riffraff from Albion? That's a big leap.' She gazed out at the numbing landscape of abandoned buildings, shattered windows. 'Still, I admit the same thought did cross my mind a few days back. But that's paranoia for you. Conspiracies are seductive . . .' She paused. 'By the way. Did you know Esterhaus was arrested a year ago? Possession of marijuana plants.'

'No, I was never informed.'

'Somehow it stayed off his record, and he walked. Maybe the feds stepped in to protect their old witness. Had him released.'

There was silence. Quietly Adam said, 'What if it wasn't the feds?'

'Come again?'

'What if he made, say, other arrangements to avoid the charges?'

'You mean . . . bribery?'

'He had access to an inexhaustible supply of narcotics. At Cygnus. That's a pretty persuasive bribe.'

'So he cuts a deal. With a judge. Or . . .'

'The police,' Adam finished for her.

They were back on the old conspiracy kick, but it was hard to let it go. Esterhaus's death had been an apparent execution. She thought of what Maeve said – that Esterhaus was being pressured to steal the Zestron and deliver it somewhere. The bombing of her house had been a professional job. She thought about all the doors that had slammed in her face when she'd tried to publicize the overdose victims. The powers that be in Albion had systematically shrugged off the deaths of those three junkies in South Lexington.

*Shrugged off? Or covered up?*

'Head downtown,' she suddenly said.

'Why?'

'We're going to City Hall. I want to see Ed.'

Adam turned onto the downtown exit. 'Why?'

'Force of habit – I like to torment him. Plus, he might get us the information we need. Namely, which cop arrested Esterhaus – and then let him go. And what else the said cop has been involved in.'

'Would Ed know that?'

'He has a direct pipeline into Police Internal Affairs. If there's a crooked cop involved, they might have a file on him.'

'Unless they're all crooked.'

'Please,' she groaned. 'Don't even mention the possibility.'

City Hall had been turned into a media circus. Banners were everywhere: *Mayor Sampson Presents the Albion Bicentennial, 200 Years of Vision, Albion: looking toward the third century.* In the hall was posted a map of Friday's two-mile parade route. Anyone who bothered to study that map would see that the parade didn't even go anywhere near Albion's center, but skirted around it, along the northern city limits, thereby avoiding the South Lexington district entirely.

Ed was in his office, barricaded by a fortress of papers. Campaign posters were plastered across the wall behind him. A picture of a kid serenely skipping rope caught Kat's eye: *Albion. Safe, and getting safer. For whom?* she felt like asking.

Ed, as usual, did not look happy to see her. 'I haven't got a lot of time, okay?' he grumbled as Kat and Adam settled into chairs. 'This bicentennial thing is turning into a disaster. The weatherman says rain. Three high school bands have dropped out because of sniper rumors. And now the cops say they can't guarantee crowd control.'

'Yep, that's our town,' said Kat sweetly. 'Safe, and getting safer.'

'What do you want?' snapped Ed.

'Some service for my tax dollars, Mr. DA.'

He sighed. 'This isn't about the drug ODs again, is it?'

'Peripherally. By now, you've heard about my exploding house. And the dead Cygnus researcher.'

'That was a paid hit, Miami mob. At least, that's what the cops tell me.'

'The cops also say Esterhaus stole the drug from Cygnus and bombed my house to stop me from asking too many questions.'

Ed laughed. 'I can think of a lot of reasons to bomb your house.'

'But that theory strikes us as too simple,' said Adam. 'Blame all those acts on a dead man. Esterhaus kept his nose clean for years. He had only one arrest – a year ago, for growing marijuana.'

'I didn't hear about that,' said Ed.

'He wasn't charged. It appears he was rather quickly released. We want to know who made the arrest.'

'Why?'

'Pot growing's an open-and-shut case,' said Kat. 'Find the plants, you've got your conviction. Now, why go to the trouble of arresting someone, and then let him walk without charges?'

'The decision could've been made on a number of levels.'

'We want to know the street level,' said Kat. 'The name of the cop.'

'Yeah? What else do you want?'

'We want to know if Esterhaus might have offered this cop a bribe. Whether this particular cop suddenly found some new . . . prosperity. Check with Internal Affairs, see if there's a file.'

'There may not be.'

'Then just the name, Ed. Get me that.'

Ed shook his head. 'You're just fishing, Kat. You've got nothing.'

'I've got an empty lot where my house used to be.'

'And I've got a dead researcher,' said Adam.

Ed leaned back. 'So you're *both* fishing, huh?'

'You should be too,' said Adam. 'It's part of your job, Mr. DA.'

'And he's a terrific one, too,' said a voice from the doorway. They turned to see Mayor Sampson, looking dapper in a three-piece suit. He strolled into the office and, like any good politician, reached out to pump Adam's hand. 'Mr. Quantrell, good to see you again. Coming to the bicentennial ball, aren't you?'

'I hadn't made plans.'

'But I thought Isabel reserved two inner-circle tickets.'

'She didn't mention them to me.'

Sampson glanced at Kat and she saw the look of dislike

on his face, quickly smothered by a smile. 'Keeping busy, Dr. Novak?' he asked.

'Too busy,' grumbled Ed.

'Oh, Lord. Not those junkies again?' Sampson gave Kat an indulgent pat on the shoulder, the sort of gesture she resented. 'You are taking this case entirely too personally.'

'Yeah. It got *real* personal when my house blew up.'

'But Ed is right on top of things,' said Sampson. 'Aren't you?'

'Absolutely.'

'Now, isn't it time we got moving?' asked Sampson.

'Huh?' Ed glanced at his watch. 'Oh, yeah. Gotta go, Kat. Parade committee.'

They all walked out of the office together. In the hall, Ed raised an arm, a gesture that could've meant either goodbye or good riddance, and headed off with the mayor. Kat watched the two men disappear around the corner and then snorted in disgust. 'Our tax dollars, hard at work. I'll be glad when this damn bicentennial is over.'

They got into the elevator, joining a City Hall clerk, her arms loaded down with a pile of gaudy flyers. 'Take one!' she said in a cheery voice.

Kat snatched one up and read it: *Mayor Sampson's Bicentennial Ball. General Tickets: $500. Contributor: $2,500. Inner Circle: $10,000.*

'Do you think Ed will help us out?' asked Adam.

'I'll hound him to the grave if he doesn't.'

Adam laughed. 'I'd say that's a pretty potent threat, coming from you.'

They stepped off the elevator. 'Hardly,' said Kat, still gazing down at the flyer.

Inner circle tickets were $10,000 each and Isabel had two of them.

'I'm not a threat to anyone,' she muttered. Then she tossed the flyer into a trash can.

The cook had laid out a lovely dinner for them: Cornish hens glazed with raspberry sauce, wild rice, a bottle of wine chilling in the bucket. And candlelight, naturally. Everything, thought Adam, was perfect. Or *should* have been perfect.

But it wasn't.

Kat was chasing a sliver of carrot around her plate now. Where *was* her appetite? With a sigh, she put down her fork and looked at him.

'Thinking about Esterhaus again?' he asked.

'And . . . everything, I guess.'

'Including us?'

After a pause, she nodded.

He picked up his wineglass and took a sip. She watched him, waiting for him to say something. It was unlike her to hold back words. *Are we so uncomfortable with each other?* he wondered.

'It's not healthy for me,' she said. 'Staying here.'

He glanced at her scarcely touched meal. 'At least you'd eat properly.'

'I mean, emotionally. I'm not used to counting on a man. It makes me feel like I'm up on stilts, tottering around. Waiting to fall. I mean, *look* at this.' She waved at the elegant table setting, the flickering candles. 'It's just not *real* to me.'

'Am I?'

She looked directly at him. 'I don't know.'

He pinched his own arm and said with a smile, 'I seem real enough to myself.'

She didn't appreciate his humor. In fact, he couldn't get even the glimmer of a smile out of her. He leaned forward. 'Kat,' he said. 'If you always expect to be hurt, then that's what will happen.'

'No, it's the other way around. If you're ready for it, then you can't be hurt.'

Resignedly he sat back. 'Well, that pretty much wraps up the future.'

She laughed – a sad, hollow sound. 'See, Adam, I take one day at a time. Enjoy things while I can. I can enjoy this, being with you. But I'm going to ask you to promise something: When it's over, tell me. No BS, just the straight scoop. If I'm not what you want, if it's not working, tell me. I'm not crystal. I don't break.'

'Don't you?'

'No.' She picked up her wine and took a nonchalant sip. The truth was, he thought, that she had a heart as fragile as that wineglass, and she wouldn't let it show. It was beneath her dignity to be weak. To be human. She was convinced that one of these days he would hurt her.

*And maybe she's right.*

He pushed his chair back and rose to his feet. 'Come on,' he said.

'Where?'

'Upstairs. If this is a doomed affair, then we should make the most of it. While we can.'

She gave him a careless laugh and stood up. 'While the sun shines,' she said.

'And if it doesn't work—'

'We'll both be fine,' she finished for him.

They headed up the stairs, to his bedroom, and closed the door, shutting out the rest of the world. *One day at a time*, he thought as he watched her unbutton her clothes, watched the garments slide to the floor, *one moment at a time*.

*And what comes after is for tomorrow to decide.*

He took her in his arms, kissed her. He wanted to be gentle; she wanted to be fierce. As though, in making love, she was battling some inner demon, struggling against it and him, against even herself. Love and war, delight and despair, it was what he felt that night, making love to her.

When it was over, when she'd fallen asleep in pure exhaustion, he lay awake beside her. He gazed around his darkened bedroom, saw the gleam of antique furniture, the vaulted ceiling. *It comes between us*, he thought. *My wealth. My name. It scares her.*

Clark was back from vacation, sporting a red sunburn and even redder mosquito bites. While the mosquitoes had found the pickings good, Clark, it seemed, had not.

'One lousy fish,' he said. 'The poorest excuse for a trout I ever saw. I didn't know whether to cook it or put it in a bag of water for my kid's goldfish bowl. A whole damn week, and that's what I had to show for it. Lost three of my best lures, too. I tell you, the rivers up there are fished out. Totally fished out.'

'So how many did Beth catch?' asked Kat.

'Beth?'

'You know. Your wife.'

Clark coughed. 'Six,' he mumbled. 'Maybe seven.'

'Only seven?'

'Okay, maybe it was more like eight. A statistical fluke.'

'Yeah, she's good at those flukes, isn't she?'

Clark yanked his lab coat off the door hook and thrust his arms into the sleeves. 'So how's it been here? Anything exciting happen?'

'Not a thing.'

'Why do I bother asking?' Clark muttered. He went over to the in-box and fished out a pile of papers. 'Look at all this stuff.'

'All yours,' said Kat. 'We left 'em for you.'

'Gee, thanks.'

'And you've got two dozen files on your desk, waiting for signatures.'

'Okay, okay. It's enough to keep a guy from ever going on vacation.' He sighed and headed down the hall to his office.

Kat sat at her desk, listening to the familiar squeak of his tennis shoes moving down the hall. It was back to business as usual, she thought. The same old routine she had had for years. So why was she so depressed?

She rose and poured another cup of coffee – her third this morning. She was turning into a caffeine junkie, a sugar junkie. A love junkie. Hopeless relationships – that was her specialty. She dropped back into her chair. If she could just stop thinking about Adam for a day, an hour, maybe she'd regain some control over her life. But he had become an obsession for her. Even now, she wondered what he was doing, whether he was sitting at *his* desk, missing *her*.

She grabbed a file from the stack on her desk, signed her name, and slapped the file shut again. She almost groaned when she heard those tennis shoes come squeaking back down the hall toward her office.

Clark reappeared in her doorway. 'Hey, Kat,' he said.

'What?'

'What the hell's this supposed to mean?' He read aloud from a lab slip. ' " Results of mass and UV spectrophotometry show following, nonquantitative: Narcotic present, levo-N-cyclobutylmethyl-6, 10-betadihydroxy class. Full identification pending." ' He looked up at her. 'What's all this?'

'You must have one of my slips. The drug's Zestron-L.'

'Never heard of it.'

'Here, I'll take care of the report.'

'But it's got my name on it.'

A frightening thought suddenly occurred to Kat. 'Who's the subject?'

'Jane Doe.'

'Oh.' Kat sighed with relief. 'Then that's mine.'

'No, it's *my* Jane Doe.' He held the slip out to her. 'See? There's my name.'

Frowning, Kat took it. On the line next to *authorizing physician* was typed the name Bernard Clark, M.D. She scanned the Subject ID data. Name: unknown. Sex: female. Race: White. ID #: 372-3-27-B. Processing date: 3/27.

A full week before *her* Jane Doe had rolled in the morgue doors.

'Get me this file,' she said.

'Huh?'

*'Get me the file.'*

'Whatever you say, mein Führer.' Clark stalked away and returned a moment later to slap a folder on her desk. 'There it is.'

Kat opened the file. It was, indeed, one of Clark's cases. She had seen this file before; she remembered it now. This was the Jane Doe of the glorious red hair, the marble skin. The page from the central ID lab was clipped to the inside front flap, with a notice of a fingerprint match. As Kat now remembered, the corpse's name was Mandy Barnett. She had a police record: shoplifting, prostitution, public drunkenness. She was twenty-three years old.

'Do we still have the body?' asked Kat.

'No. There's the release authorization.'

Kat glanced at the form. It was signed by Wheelock the day before, releasing the body to Greenwood Mortuary.

'I called it a probable barbiturate OD,' said Clark. 'I mean, it seemed reasonable. There was a bottle of Fiorinal next to her.'

'Were barbs found in her tox screen?'

'Just a trace.'

'No needles found on site? No tourniquet?'

'Just the pills, according to the police report. That's why I assumed it was barbs. I guess I was wrong.'

'So was I,' she said quietly.

'What?'

She reached for the telephone and dialed the police. It rang five times, then a voice answered, 'Sykes, Homicide.'

'Lou? Kat Novak. We've got another one here.'

'Another what?'

'Zestron OD. But this one's different.'

She heard Sykes sigh. Or was that a yawn? 'I'm *real* interested.'

'The victim's name is Mandy Barnett. She was found in Bellemeade – a week before the others. And get this – she was set up to look like a barbiturate OD.'

'Are you going to tell me what is going *on*?' whined Clark.

Kat ignored him. 'Lou,' she said. 'I'm going to stick my neck out on this one.' She paused. 'I'm calling it murder.'

# 13

Sykes tossed the police file down on his desk and looked across at Kat. 'Dead end, Novak. No motive. No witnesses. No signs of violence. Mandy Barnett was a loner. We can't locate even a single relative or friend.'

'Someone must have known her.'

'No one who'll come forward.' Sykes leaned back in his chair. 'We're stuck. If it's murder, then someone's committed the perfect crime.'

'And chosen the perfect victim,' said Kat. She looked at Ratchet, who was hunched at his desk, making a ham sandwich disappear. 'Vince? You talk to Greenwood Mortuary?'

'They've had no calls, and the burial's tomorrow. But someone *did* pay the expenses.'

'Who?'

'Anonymous. Envelope stuffed with cash.'

Kat shook her head in disbelief. 'And you guys aren't chasing that?'

'Why? Not a crime to pay for a woman's burial.'

'It shows that *someone* knew her. And cared about her. Don't you guys have anything?'

'We know she lived out in Bellemeade,' said Sykes. 'Had an apartment on Flashner and Grove. We asked around the building, and you know what? No one even knew her name. They'd seen her come and go, but that was it. So much for witnesses.'

'How did she get the drug?'

Sykes shrugged. 'Maybe she bought it off Esterhaus. Or got a free sample in exchange for, uh, services.'

'Prostitution?'

'She'd been busted for it before. It's hard to teach an old dog new tricks, pardon the double entendre.'

'So we're back to blaming Herb Esterhaus?'

'I don't know who else to blame. It's a dead end for us.'

*For Mandy Barnett as well*, thought Kat. She remembered the woman's flame-colored hair, her porcelain beauty, shrouded in the cold mist of the morgue drawer. Not the sort of looks that went unnoticed in this world. Surely there'd been friends, lovers? Men who'd known the pleasures of her company, if only for a night. Where were they now?

*A woman dies, and no one seems to notice.* She thought about this as she walked through the police station. She thought about herself, wondered how many would notice *her* death, would come to *her* funeral. Clark, of course. Wheelock, out of duty. But there'd be no husband, no family, no giant mounds of flowers on the grave. *We're alike, Mandy and I. Whether by choice or by circumstance, we've made our way alone through life.*

She stopped at the elevators and punched the Down button. Just as the floor bell rang, she heard a voice say behind her, 'Well, speak of the devil.'

Turning, she saw her ex-husband emerge from the chief's office. *You wouldn't come to my funeral, either*, she thought with a sudden dart of hostility.

'My, what a nice scowl you're wearing today,' said Ed.

They both stepped into the elevator and the doors slapped shut. He was looking dapper as usual, not a scuff on his shiny Italian shoes. What had she ever seen in him? she wondered. Then she thought morosely, what had he ever seen in her?

'I got what you asked for,' he said.

'What?'

'The name of the cop who arrested Esterhaus last year. You still want it, don't you?'

'Who was it?'

'The name was Ben Fuller, Narcotics detail. A sergeant with eighteen years on the force. He filed the arrest report. Possession of three live marijuana plants.'

'Did Fuller also arrange the release?'

'Nope. Feds did. They stepped in and pulled their ex-witness out of the fire. So you can drop the conspiracy angle. Fuller had nothing to do with it.'

'Can I see his Internal Affairs file?'

'Won't do you any good.'

'Why not?'

The elevator doors slid open. 'Because Ben Fuller's dead,' he said, and walked out.

Kat dashed after him into the first floor lobby. 'Dead? How?'

'Shot to death in the line of duty. He was a good cop, Kat. I've talked to his buddies. He had a wife, three kids, and a whole drawer full of commendations. So lay off the guy, okay? He was a hero. He doesn't deserve anyone mucking up his memory.' With that, Ed went out the front door.

Kat watched her ex-husband stride away down the sidewalk. Then she stalked off to her car.

Traffic was heavy on Dillingham, and she didn't have the patience to deal with it. Every red light, every idiot making a left turn, seemed to jog her irritation up another notch. By the time she got back to the morgue, she felt like a menace to the public.

In her office two dozen long-stemmed roses sat in a vase on her desk. 'What the hell's *this*?'

Clark stuck his head out of his office and called out sweetly: 'So who's the new lover boy, Novak?'

She slammed the door on his laughter. Then she sank into her chair and sat staring at the roses. They were gorgeous. They were blood red, the symbol of love, of passion.

Once, Ed had sent her roses, that very same color. Just before he'd asked for a divorce.

She dropped her head in her hands and wondered morbidly what sort of flowers Adam Quantrell would send to her funeral.

Her dark mood lasted all afternoon, through the processing of a hit-in-the-crosswalk old lady, through hours of paper catch-up and court depositions. By the time she drove through Adam's stone gate that evening, she was good and ready for a warm hug and some pampering. Or at the very least, a stiff drink.

What she found instead was Isabel's Mercedes parked in the driveway.

Kat got out of her car and stood for a moment by the Mercedes, gazing in at the leather upholstery, the kidskin gloves lying on the front seat. Then, in an even blacker mood, she went to the front door and rang the bell.

Thomas opened the door and regarded her with surprise. 'Oh dear! Did Mr. Q. neglect to give you a key, Dr. Novak?'

Kat cleared her throat. It had never occurred to her to simply walk in the door. After all, she was a guest and would always feel like one. 'Well, yeah,' she said. 'I guess he did give me a key.'

Thomas stepped aside to usher her in.

'I thought I should ring first,' she added as he took her jacket.

'Of course,' he said. He reached into the closet for a hanger. 'Mr. Q. hasn't arrived yet. But Miss Calderwood dropped by for a visit. She's in the parlor, if you'd care to join her for tea.'

Joining Isabel was the last thing she felt like doing, but she couldn't think of a graceful way to avoid it. So, hoisting a socially acceptable smile onto her lips, she entered the parlor.

Isabel was seated on the striped couch. Her sweater, a fluffy cashmere, hung fetchingly off the shoulder. She seemed unsurprised to see Kat; in fact, she appeared to have expected her.

'Hope you haven't been waiting long,' said Kat. 'I don't know when Adam's expected home.'

'He gets home at six o'clock,' said Isabel.

'Did he call?'

'No. That's when he always gets home.'

'Oh.' Kat sat down in the Queen Anne chair and wondered what else Isabel knew about Adam's habits. *Probably more than I ever will.* She glanced at the end table and saw the empty teacup, the plate of biscuits. The book Isabel had been reading lay beside her on the couch – the title was in French. The very air held the scent of her perfume – something cool, something elegant; no drugstore florals for her.

'Six o'clock is his usual time,' Isabel went on, pouring more tea into her cup. 'Unless it's Wednesday, when he kicks off early and gets home around five. He occasionally has a drink before supper – Scotch, heavy on the soda – and perhaps a glass of wine with his meal, but only one glass. After supper, he reads. Scientific journals, the latest pharmaceuticals, that sort of thing. He takes his work seriously, you see.' She set the teapot back down. 'And then he makes time for fun. Which normally includes me.' She looked at Kat and smiled.

'Look, if you're telling me all this because you feel threatened, Isabel, don't bother. With me, what you see is what you get. No blue blood, no pedigree.' She laughed. 'Definitely no class.'

'I didn't mean to put you down,' said Isabel hastily.

'I simply thought I could clear up a few things about Adam.'

'Such as?'

'Oh, I don't know . . .' Isabel shrugged. 'Aspects of his life you may not be familiar with. It must seem quite disorienting. Being thrust into this huge old house. All these portraits of strangers hanging on the walls. And then there's a whole circle of his friends you've never met.'

'I guess you know them all.'

'We grew up in that same circle, Adam and I. I knew Georgina. I watched the whole sad affair. And I was there when he needed a friend.' She paused, and added significantly, 'I'm still here.' *And I'll be here long after you're gone*, was the unspoken message. Isabel took a sip of tea and set the cup and saucer back down on the end table. 'I just wanted you to think about this. So you know what to expect.'

Kat did think about it. She thought about it as Isabel walked out the front door, as the Mercedes drove down the driveway. She thought about the gap between Surry Heights and South Lexington – a distance measured not in miles but in universes. She thought about country clubs and back alleys, picket fences and barbed wire.

And she thought about her heart, recently healed, and how long it takes to put the pieces back together once it's broken.

She went upstairs, collected her toothbrush and underwear, and came back down again.

Thomas, carrying a tray of fresh tea and biscuits, met her in the hall. 'Dr. Novak,' he said. 'I was just bringing this in to you.'

'Thanks. But I'm on my way out.'

He frowned when he saw the car keys she'd already removed from her purse. 'When shall I tell Mr. Q. you'll be returning?'

'Tell him . . . tell him I'll be in touch,' she said, and walked out of the house.

'But, Dr. Novak—'

She got into her car and started the engine. 'You've been great, Thomas!' she called through the car window. 'Don't let Miss Calderwood push you around.' As she drove off, she could see him in her rearview mirror, still staring after her.

The stone pillars lay ahead. She was in such a hurry to get away, she almost crashed into Adam's Volvo, driving in through the gate. He skidded to a stop at the side of the road.

'Kat?' he yelled. 'Where are you going?'

'I'll call you!' she yelled back, and kept on driving.

A half mile later, she glanced in her mirror and saw, through a film of tears, that the road behind her was empty. He hadn't followed her. She blinked the tears away and, gripping the steering wheel more tightly, drove on, toward the city.

Away from Adam.


*I'll call you.* What the hell did that mean?

Adam watched Kat's taillights disappear into the dusk

and wondered when she'd be back. Had there been a call from the morgue? Some urgent reason for her to rush to work? An emergency autopsy?

He pulled in front of the house and parked. Even before he'd climbed the front steps, Thomas had appeared in the doorway.

'Evening, Thomas. What's up?'

'I was about to ask you. Dr. Novak just left.'

'Yes, I passed her at the gate.'

'No, I mean she's *left*. Taken her things with her.'

'What?' Adam turned and stared up the driveway. By now, she would be a good mile or more away, perhaps already turning onto the freeway. He'd never be able to catch up with her in time.

He looked back at Thomas. 'Did she say why she was leaving?'

Thomas shrugged. 'Not a word.'

'Did she say *anything*?'

'I never had the opportunity to speak with her. She and Miss Calderwood were taking tea, and—'

'*Isabel* was here?'

'Why, yes. She left a short time before Dr. Novak did.'

At once, Adam turned and headed to his car.

Isabel was home. He saw her Mercedes parked in the garage, the groundsman busy polishing the flanks to a gleaming finish. Adam took the front steps two at a time. He didn't bother to knock; he just walked in the door and yelled: 'Isabel!'

She appeared, smiling, at the top of the stairs. 'Why, Adam. How unexpected—'

'What did you say to her?'

Isabel shook her head innocently. 'To whom?'

'Kat.'

'Ah.' With new comprehension in her gaze, Isabel glided down the stairs. 'We spoke,' she admitted. 'But nothing of earth-shattering significance.'

'*What did you say?*'

She came to a stop on the bottom step. The crystal chandelier above spilled its pool of sparkling light onto her hair. 'I only told her that I understood the difficulties she must be having. The transition to a large house. A new circle of friends. She's not having an easy time of it, Adam.'

'Not with friends like you.'

Her chin jutted up. 'I was only offering her my advice. And sympathy.'

'Isabel.' He sighed. 'I've known you a long time. We've shared some . . . reasonably enjoyable moments together. But I've never known you to be, in any way, shape, or form, sympathetic to anyone. Except maybe yourself.'

'But Adam! Look at who she is, where she comes from! I'm telling you this as a friend. I don't want to see you make a mistake.'

'The only mistake I ever made,' he said, walking out of the house, 'was calling you a *friend*.' He slammed the door shut behind him, got back in his car, and drove home.

He spent all evening trying to locate Kat. He called her cell phone. It was switched off. He called the city morgue.

He called Lou Sykes. He even called Ed Novak. No one knew where she'd gone, where she was spending the night. Or, if they knew, they weren't telling him.

At well past midnight, he went up to bed in frustration. There, lying in the darkness, Isabel's words came back to assail him. *Look at who she is, where she comes from.* He asked himself over and over if it made a difference to him.

And the honest answer was: *no.*

He'd already had a 'proper' marriage, to a proper woman. Georgina was everything the social register required: blue-blooded, wealthy, well-glossed by finishing school. Together they were, by the standards of their social set, the perfect couple.

They had been miserable.

So much for proper partners.

Kat Novak's origins, her hardscrabble youth, were, if anything, an asset. She was a survivor, a woman who'd wrestled the challenges life had thrown at her and come out the stronger for it. Could any of his friends, with their money and their platinum exteriors, have done the same? he wondered.

And then, even more troubling, was the next thought: Could he have?

The phone was ringing when Kat walked into her office the next morning. She ignored it. Calmly she hung up her coat, slid her purse in the desk drawer, revved up the coffee machine for a six-cup pot. An IV infusion of caffeine was what she really needed this morning. It had been a sleepless night on a lumpy motel bed, and she was feeling as alert as a grizzly bear in January and just about as cheerful.

She found her desk littered with pink message slips, taped in a haphazard collage. Calls from her overwhelmed insurance agent, from the DA's, from defense attorneys, from a mortuary. And from Adam, of course – five calls, judging by the number of slips. On the last slip, the night tech had scrawled in frustration: '*Call* this guy!' Kat crumpled up all the message slips from Adam and tossed them in the trash can.

The phone rang. She frowned at it, watched it ring once, twice, three times. Wearily she picked it up. 'Kat Novak.'

'Kat! I've been trying to reach you—'

'Morning, Adam. How're things?'

There was a long pause. 'Obviously,' he said, 'we have to talk.'

'About what?'

'About why you left.'

'Simple.' She leaned back and propped her feet up on a chair. 'It was time to leave. You've been great to me, Adam. You really have. But I didn't want to wear out the welcome. And I had to find my own place eventually, so I—'

'So you ran.'

'No. I walked.'

'You *ran*.'

Her spine stiffened. 'And what, exactly, am I supposed to be running from?'

'From me. From the chance it might not work.'

'Look, I have things to do right now—'

'Is it so hard for you, Kat, to stick your neck out? It's not easy for me, either. I take a step toward you, you take a step back. I say the wrong thing, look at you the wrong way, and you're off like a shot. I don't know how to deal with it.'

'Then don't.'

'Is that what you really want?'

She sighed. 'I don't know. Honestly, I don't know what I want.'

'I think you do. But you're too scared to follow your heart.'

'How the hell do you know what's in my heart?'

'Wild guess?'

'It's not like Cinderella, okay?' she snapped. 'Girls from the Projects don't have fairy godmothers to spiff them up. And they don't find happily-ever-afters in Surry Heights. Isabel gave me the straight scoop and I appreciate that. I'd be out to sea with your country club set. Too many damn forks on the table. Too many cute French words. Face it, I can't ski, I can't ride a horse, and I can't tell the difference between Burgundy and Beaujolais. It's all red wine to me. I don't see any way of getting past that. No matter how much you may lust after my body, you'll find after a while that it isn't enough. You'll want a fancier package. And I'll just want to be *me*.'

'I never took you for a coward before.'

She laughed. 'Go ahead, insult me if it makes you feel better.'

'You'll risk your neck for an old car. You'll march into a

damn combat zone without blinking. But you're too scared to take a chance on *me*.'

She looked down at one of the message slips taped to her desk, and noticed it was from the Greenwood Mortuary, in response to a call she'd made to them yesterday.

'Kat?' Adam asked. 'Are you listening?'

'I can't talk now,' she said, and folded the slip in half. 'I have to go to a burial.'

Grim affairs, burials. Grimmer still is a pauper's burial. There are no gaudy sprays of gladioli, no wreaths, no sobbing family and friends. There is just a coffin and a muddy hole in the ground. And the burial crew, of course: in this case, two sallow-faced gravediggers, their hats dripping with rain, and a blacksuited official from the Greenwood Mortuary, huddled beneath an umbrella. Mandy Barnett was being laid to her everlasting rest in the company of total strangers.

Kat stood in the shelter of a nearby maple tree and sadly watched the proceedings. It was the starkest of ceremonies, words uttered tonelessly under gray skies, rain splattering the coffin. The official kept glancing around, as though to confirm that he was playing to an audience – any audience. *At least I'm here*, thought Kat. *Even if I am just another stranger at her graveside.* A short distance away, Vince Ratchet also stood watching the scene. Cemeteries were routine stops for the boys from Homicide. They knew that two types of people attended victims' funerals: those who came to mourn, and those who came to gloat.

In Mandy Barnett's case, no one at all appeared. Those who passed through the cemetery this afternoon seemed intent on their own business: a couple bearing flowers to a loved one; an elderly woman, picking dead leaves off a grave; a groundskeeper, rattling by in a golf cart filled with tools. They all glanced at the coffin, but their looks were only mildly curious.

The rain let up to a fine drizzle. In a still mist, the burial crew set to work, shoveling earth into the trench. Ratchet came over to Kat and muttered, 'This was a bust. Not a goddamn soul.' He fished a handkerchief out of his pocket and blew his nose. 'And I'll probably catch pneumonia for my trouble.'

'You'd think there'd be someone,' said Kat.

'Weather might have something to do with it.' Ratchet glanced up at the sky and pulled his raincoat closer. 'Or maybe she didn't have any friends.'

'Everyone has a connection. To someone.'

'Well, I think we got us a dead end.' Ratchet looked back at the grave. 'Real dead.'

'So there's nothing new?'

'Nada. Lou's ready to call it quits. Told me not to bother coming out here today.'

'But you came.'

'Hate to walk away from a case. Even if Lou thinks it's a waste of time.'

They watched as the last shovelful of dirt was tossed onto the grave. The crew patted it down, gave their handiwork one final inspection, and walked away.

After awhile, so did Ratchet.

Kat was left standing alone under the tree. Slowly she crossed the wet grass to the grave and stared down at the mound. There was no headstone yet, no marker. Nothing to identify the woman who lay beneath this bare pile of dirt. *Who were you, Mandy Barnett? Were you so alone in this world that no one even noticed when you left it?*

'It's not as if you can do anything about it,' said a voice behind her.

She turned and saw Adam. He was standing a few feet away, mist sheening his hair.

She looked back down at the grave. 'I know.'

'So why did you come?'

'I guess I feel sorry for her. For anyone who doesn't have a mourner to her name.'

Adam came to stand beside her. 'You don't know a thing about her, Kat. Maybe she didn't want any friends. Or deserve any friends. Maybe she was a monster.'

'Or just a victim.'

He took her arm. 'We'll never know. So let's just go inside somewhere. Get warm and dry.'

'I have to go back to work.' She paused as a flicker of movement drifted through her peripheral vision. She focused on two figures, a woman and a child, both dressed in black, standing beneath a distant tree. It was an eerie apparition, almost ghostly through the mist. They seemed to be gazing in her direction, their faces very still and solemn. Or was it Mandy Barnett's grave they were looking at?

Suddenly the woman noticed that Kat had spotted them. At once the woman grabbed the child's hand and began to lead her away, across the grass.

'Wait!' called Kat.

The woman was moving quickly now, almost dragging the child after her.

Kat started after them. 'I have to talk to you!'

The woman and child were already scurrying towards a parked car. Kat dashed across the last patch of lawn, reaching the blacktop just as the woman slammed her car door shut.

'Wait!' said Kat, rapping on the window. 'Did you know Mandy Barnett?'

She caught a glimpse of the woman's frightened face, staring at her through the glass, and then the car jerked away. Kat was flung backwards. The car made a sharp U-turn, spun around in the parking lot, and took off toward the cemetery gates.

Footsteps thudded toward her across the pavement. 'What's going on?' said Adam.

Without a word, Kat turned and made a dash for her car.

'Kat?' he yelled. 'What the hell—'

'Get in!' she snapped, sliding into the driver's seat.

'Why?'

'Okay, *don't* get in!'

He got in. At once, Kat turned the ignition and hit the gas pedal. They screeched across the slick blacktop and through the cemetery gates.

'We've got a choice,' said Kat as they approached the first intersection. 'East or west. Which way?'

'Uh . . . east is back to town. She'd probably go that way.'

'Then we go west.'

'What?'

'Just a hunch. Trust me.' Kat turned west.

The road took them past a shopping mall, past a Pizza Hut, an Exxon gas station, a Burger King – the institutional underpinnings of Anytown, U.S.A. At the first red light, Kat pulled to a stop behind a line of cars. The windshield filmed over with mist. She turned on the wipers.

A block ahead, a dark green Chevy pulled out of a Dunkin' Donuts parking lot.

'There they are,' said Kat.

Adam shook his head in amazement. 'You were right.'

'First rule of escape: Never move in a straight line. See? She's heading north. I bet she'll circle back towards town. The long way around.'

The light turned green. Kat turned north, in pursuit of the Chevy. She kept her distance, with two cars between them. A half mile along, the Chevy turned east. As she'd predicted, her quarry was moving in a wide circle, taking secondary roads back to town.

'Is this why you went to the burial?' asked Adam.

'The same reason the cops went. To see who'd turn up to pay their last respects. I figured someone would. The same anonymous person who slipped Greenwood Mortuary the cash for that coffin. It was just bottom-of-the-line plywood and veneer, but it was paid for. Our mystery lady in that Chevy must've been the one.'

'Did you get a look at her?'

'Just a glimpse. Late twenties, maybe. And a kid about six years old.'

They followed the Chevy to the Stanhope district, a bluecollar suburb of single family homes lined up on postage-stamp lots. From a block away, they saw the Chevy pull into a driveway. The woman got out and helped the child from the car, and together they climbed the porch steps into a house. It was a pink stucco box, irredeemably ugly, with cast-iron bars on the windows and a TV antenna the size of an oil rig on the roof.

Kat parked. For a moment they sat studying the house. 'What do you think?' she said.

'It's like approaching a trapped animal. She could be dangerous. Why don't we just call the police?'

'No, I think she's afraid of the police. Otherwise she'd have called *them*.'

After a pause, he nodded. 'All right, we can try talking to her. But the first sign of trouble and we're *out* of there. Is that clear?'

They got out of the car and she smiled across the roof at him. 'Absolutely.'

They could hear the sound of the TV as they approached the front door. Some kids' show – cartoon voices, twinkly music. Kat stood off to the side of the porch, and Adam knocked.

A little girl appeared at the screen door.

Adam flashed his million-dollar smile. 'Can I talk to your mommy?' he said.

'She's not here.'

'Can you call her, then?'

'She's not here.'

'Well, is she in another room or something?'

'No.' The voice wavered, dropped to a whisper. 'She went away to heaven.'

Adam stared at her pityingly. 'I'm sorry.'

There was a silence, then the girl said, 'You wanna talk to my Auntie Lila?'

'Missy? Who's out there?' called a voice.

'Just a man,' said the girl.

Bare feet slapped across the floor and a woman came to the screen door. She peered out blankly at Adam. Then her gaze shifted and she caught sight of Kat, standing off to the side. The woman froze in recognition.

'It's all right,' said Kat. 'My name's Dr. Novak. I'm with the medical examiner—'

'It was you. At the cemetery . . .'

'I've been trying to find someone who knew Mandy Barnett.'

'My mommy?' said the child.

The woman looked down at the girl. 'Go on, honey. Go watch TV.'

'But she's talking about my mommy.'

'Just grownup stuff. Listen! I think *Spongebob* is on! Go on, you watch it.'

The girl, faced with the choice of adult conversation or her favorite cartoon, chose the latter. She scampered off into the next room.

The woman looked back at Kat. 'Why're you asking about Mandy? You with the police?'

'I told you, I'm with the medical examiner's office.' She paused. 'I think Mandy Barnett was murdered.'

The woman was silent as she considered her next move. 'It's not like I know anything,' she said.

'Then why are you afraid?'

'Because people might think I know more than I do.'

'Tell us what you know,' said Adam. 'Then we'll all know it. And you won't have to be afraid.'

The woman glanced toward the sound of the TV, now blaring out a cereal commercial. She looked back at Kat. Then, slowly, she unlatched the screen door and motioned them to come in.

# 14

They sat in the dining room, in chairs upholstered in green and yellow plaid. There was a bowl of plastic fruit on the table and on the wall hung a picture of a soulful young Elvis, gazing like some patron saint from an oil and canvas eternity. Lila lit a cigarette, blew out tendrils of smoke that wreathed her close-cropped hair.

'I was just a friend of hers,' said Lila. 'I mean, a good friend, but that's all. We used to hang out together, cruise the bars. You know, girl stuff.' She flicked off her ash. 'Then I got married, and we sort of drifted apart. I knew she was having a hard time of it. Kept trying to borrow money from me till I just didn't have any to give her. See, Mandy, she liked to party, and she wasn't exactly responsible. Had this kid at home and she'd just go out and leave her.'

'Is that Mandy's child?' asked Kat, nodding toward the TV room.

'Yeah. That's Missy. Anyway, I got tired of Mandy coming around for cash, so we had this falling out. It was her fault. I mean, she was working and all, but she just couldn't manage her wallet.'

'She had a job?'

'She worked the phones in some boiler room. A company called Peabody or Peabrain, over on Radisson and Hobart. They do telemarketing. You know, sell Florida vacations to poor shmucks in Jersey. Easy work, sitting all day on your tush. It wasn't bad money, either. But Mandy, she liked nice stuff. She couldn't keep any money in the bank.'

'We never heard she had a job,' said Adam.

Lila's brown eyes focused admiringly on Adam. Married or not, the woman still had an appreciation for the masculine form. She exhaled a lungful of smoke. 'It was under the table. You know, no taxes, that kind of thing. Anyway, she quit about six months ago.'

'Then how did she support herself?'

'Hell if I know.' Lila laughed. 'Girls like Mandy, they survive. One way or another, they do okay. If they can't bum off friends, then they pick up cash somewhere else. Maybe she found herself a sugar daddy.'

'She mention any names?' asked Kat.

'No. But I figure there must've been someone, 'cause she suddenly had money to burn. All she'd say was, she got lucky, that she was set up for life. I'd babysit Missy once in a while, see, and Mandy'd drop her off here. God, she'd come back high as a kite.'

'You mean on drugs?'

'Oh, yeah. She liked a hit once in a while. Not all the time. She wasn't *that* irresponsible.'

'So this started when?' asked Kat. 'The money, the drugs?'

'About six months ago.'

'The same time she quit her job.'

'Yeah. About.'

'And then what happened?'

Lila shrugged. 'She started getting . . . weird.'

'How?'

'Looking over her shoulder. Closing all my curtains. I figured it was the drugs. You know, they make you a little crazy after a while. I tried talking to her about it, but all she'd say was, things were fine. Then, a couple of weeks ago, she dropped Missy off and told me to keep her for a while. Said she was gonna party seriously.'

'Meaning?'

'Get high. She was going to try out some new stuff she'd bought off a kid in the neighborhood.' Lila crushed out her cigarette butt. 'And that was the last time I saw her.'

'Why didn't you call the police?' asked Adam. 'Report her missing?'

Lila paused and looked away. 'I didn't want to get involved.'

*There's more to it than that*, thought Kat, watching the woman's eyes, noting how she looked everywhere but at *them*.

'Why are you afraid of the police?' asked Kat.

'Get busted a few times,' Lila muttered, 'and *you* wouldn't be a fan either.'

'No, you're actually *afraid* of them.'

Lila looked up at Kat. 'So was *she*. The last thing she says to me – the last time I saw her – she tells me, any cop comes around, it was real important I play stupid. Tell 'em the kid's mine and I don't know any Mandy. She says I could get hurt if I start blabbing. That's why you scared me, at the cemetery. I thought maybe you were one of *them*.'

In the next room, Missy was flipping channels. They could hear the clack-clack of the dial, the intermittent blasts of music.

'What about Missy?' Adam asked. 'What happens to her now?'

Lila thought about it for a moment. 'I guess she'll stay with me.' She sighed. 'I sort of like the kid. And my old man, he doesn't mind.' Lila gave a shrug and lit up another cigarette. 'After all,' she said, blowing out a cloud of smoke, 'where else is the kid gonna go?'

'So Mandy Barnett turns out to be a major screwball,' said Kat as she drove north on Sussex.

'You almost sound disappointed.'

'I don't know why. I guess I kept thinking of her as a victim. And I felt sorry for her. No one at the burial, no one even asking about her. A sort of . . . lost soul.' She sighed. 'Maybe I identified with her.'

'You're not a lost soul. You never were.'

She glanced at him, saw he was watching her with that penetrating gaze of his. Quickly she looked back at the road. 'Oh yeah, I'm tough,' she said with a laugh. 'No chinks in my armor.'

'I didn't say you were invulnerable.'

*One look at you, and I know just how vulnerable I am,* she thought. The old temptation was back, to give it a chance, to let this relationship take root. She was feeling brave and scared at the same time, one minute certain it would work, the next minute just as certain it would be a disaster. This was someone she could love far too much, and for that sin of recklessness, there was a special place reserved in hell. Or heaven.

She concentrated on her driving, navigating the stop-and-go traffic along Sussex.

'Where are we going?' he asked.

'Just a detour. To Bellemeade.'

'Why?'

'I have this hunch. Something that might pull together some loose ends.'

'And which of the dozen-plus loose ends are we talking about?'

'Nicos Biagi.'

She turned onto Flashner Boulevard. A half mile up, they came to the intersection of Flashner and Grove. On one corner stood La Roma Arms, a white stucco apartment building with wrought-iron verandas. From its name, Kat assumed it was designed to resemble an Italian villa; it looked more like a crumbling version of the Alamo. She pulled into the Roma driveway and parked next to the pool area. The pool itself was empty, and a sign was posted on the fence: *Temporarily closed for maintenance.* About two years' worth of dead leaves were rotting at the bottom.

'Mandy's apartment?' asked Adam.

'This is it. Flashner and Grove.'

'Why are we here?'

'I just wanted to take a look at the neighborhood.' She glanced up and down the street, her gaze tracing Grove Avenue. 'There it is.'

'There *what* is?'

'The Big E Supermarket.' She pointed up the street to the grocery store, looming at the next corner. 'Only a block away.'

'The Big E,' muttered Adam, frowning. 'Isn't that where Nicos Biagi worked? As a stockboy?'

'You got it. A convenient location, wouldn't you say? All Mandy had to do was walk down to the Big E, pick up her purchase, and she's ready to party. And Nicos goes home with a nice delivery fee. And his own private sample of the drug.'

'Which kills all of them.'

'But see, that's the part that doesn't add up,' she said. 'Business-wise, I mean. Here you've got a new drug that could make you millions on the street. What supplier would hand out a poisonously pure sample, thereby killing off his market?'

'A supplier who's out to kill one buyer in particular,' said Adam. 'Mandy Barnett.'

'But why Mandy?' Kat frowned, trying to pull the pieces together. She knew Mandy was a party girl, a flake. A loser on a permanent downhill slide. Then, six months ago, her fortunes had changed. Suddenly she had money to burn. She'd quit her job and embarked on a spree of spending and partying. *Was* there a sugar daddy, as Lila had suspected? Or some new job with high rewards – and high risks?

'We're missing something entirely,' said Adam. 'Where did all her money come from? She was getting a steady supply of cash from *somewhere*. And that was *after* she quit her job . . .'

Kat suddenly popped the car into gear. 'That's our next stop. Radisson and Hobart.'

'What, her old job?'

Kat grinned at him. 'Your synapses are finally catching up.'

'Whatever happened to solving crimes the old-fashioned way? Letting the police do it?'

'Under normal circumstances, yeah. I'd take the lazy gal's way out and dump this mess in their laps.'

'Under normal circumstances?'

'When alarm bells aren't going off in my head. But I'm hearing enough bells to give me a splitting headache. First, Maeve swears it's the city elite that's killing off junkies – meaning, the authorities. Then we hear Mandy was afraid of the cops. So afraid, in fact, that she hid her kid from them, and told the babysitter Lila to play dumb. And finally, there's Esterhaus. Okay, so maybe he *did* steal the Zestron and have it delivered to Mandy. But *why*? Who could've pushed him into it?'

'Someone who knew about his old connections with the mob. And could blackmail him.'

Kat nodded. 'The authorities.'

'Good Lord.' Adam sat back, shaken by the thought. 'A revolutionary method to mop up crime.'

'I'm not going to jump to conclusions here. Let's just say I'm not quite ready to take this to the cops.'

It was a good twenty-minute drive to the Watertown district. Along the way, they stopped at a phone booth to check the yellow pages. There was no listing for Peabody under Telemarketing. In fact, there were no *p*s listed at all. Directory Assistance likewise came up with a blank.

They drove on anyway, to Watertown.

It was a section of the city Kat seldom had reason to visit. Situated at the southeast corner of Albion, it had evolved over a half century from a thriving port to a malodorous district of fish processing plants, decaying piers, and ramshackle warehouses. At least there was still evidence of economic life in the neighborhood, mostly dockside bars and army surplus outlets. In fact, standing at the intersection of Radisson and Hobart, Kat could spot three surplus stores. Across the street, a sign hung in the window: *Guns and ammo – for the sake of those you love.* The Atlantic Ocean was only a block away, but the sea wind couldn't wash the smells of diesel and processed fish from the air.

The name of the company, it turned out, was Piedmont, not Peabody. They had to ask at a corner bar to find it, as the name itself appeared on none of the buildings. The company occupied a third-floor office in the Manzo Building on Hobart Street. The sign on the door said simply: *Piedmont.* From the room inside came the whine of a printer.

They knocked.

'Yeah, who is it?' a man called.

Kat hesitated and then said, 'We're friends of Mandy Barnett.'

An instant later the door opened and a man appeared, looking cross. 'Where the hell has she been?' he demanded.

'Maybe we can talk about it?' said Kat.

The man waved them inside, then shoved the door shut. It was a dismal office, if one could even call it that. Bare walls, a steel desk. In the corner sat a computer, its printer spewing out a list of names and telephone numbers. Another doorway led to an adjoining room, equally dismal.

'So what's going on?' said the man. 'She wanna come back to work or something? Well, you can tell her, forget it. And by the way, she still owes me.'

'For what?' asked Kat.

'Two weeks' salary. I give her an advance, and she skips out.'

'Excuse me, Mr. . . .'

'Rick. Just Rick.'

'Rick. I guess you haven't heard. Mandy Barnett's dead.'

He stared at her, looked at Adam, then back at her. 'Aw, Christ. Now I'll *never* get the three hundred back.' The phone rang. He went over to the desk, picked up the receiver, and slammed it down again. 'That's what I get for being Mr. Nice Guy.'

'You're not the least bit interested in how she died?' said Adam with undisguised disgust.

'Okay,' Rick sighed. 'How'd the bitch die?'

'A drug overdose.'

'I'm *real* surprised.' Rick dropped into a chair and looked at them with utter disinterest. 'So why're you here? She leave me something in her will?'

'Rick, my friend,' said Kat, pulling up a chair. 'We have to talk. I'm from the medical examiner's office, see, and I have to ask you some questions.'

'You and what cop?'

'Take your pick. There's my buddy in Homicide, Lieutenant Sykes. Or maybe you'd like to meet the guys in Fraud. They'd probably like to meet *you*.' She glanced around the office. 'What *is* it you sell here, by the way? Bargain vacations?'

Rick sank, glowering, into his chair.

'We're in the right mood now, are we?' said Kat.

'I don't know nothing.'

'Mandy quit her job six months ago. Is that right?'

Rick grunted, a sound Kat took to be a yes.

'Why did she quit?'

Another grunt, coupled with a sullen shrug. Communication worthy of a caveman.

'Was she mad about something?' asked Adam. 'Did she give you a reason?'

Maybe it was the fact a man was now asking the questions; Rick finally decided to answer. 'She didn't tell me anything. She just walked off the job. Called a few days later to say she wasn't coming back. She had something better going.'

'Another job?'

'Who knows? The bitch was flaky, you know? One

minute she's at her desk, working the phone. Then I get back from lunch and there's a note on the door sayin' she's out of here. No explanation, just – poof! Here I am, paying rent on two rooms, and I can't get anyone to man the other desk.'

'She had her own office?' said Adam.

'That room over there.' He pointed to a doorway. 'Her own private space. Didn't appreciate it none.'

'May we see the office?' asked Adam.

'Go ahead. Won't tell ya nothin'.'

The adjoining room was like the first, but without a computer. There was a window that looked down on a grim back-alley view of broken glass, trash cans.

Adam opened and closed a desk drawer. 'Not much in here,' he said.

'She took it all with her,' said Rick. 'Even the pencils. *My* pencils.'

'No papers, no notes.' Adam pulled out the last drawer. 'Nothing.' He shut it.

'See?' said Rick. 'I told ya there wasn't anything to look at. Just a desk and a telephone.' He glanced at Kat, who was gazing down at the alley. 'And a window,' Rick pointed out. 'I was generous. I let *her* have the view.'

'And a lovely view it is,' said Kat dryly.

'Okay, so it's not the seaside. But it faces south and you get some sun. And Bolton's a quiet street so you don't get blasted away by traffic noise.'

'Well,' said Adam. 'I guess there's not much more to see in here.'

'That's what I said. You satisfied now?'

Kat was still gazing out the window. In the alley below, a man appeared, lugging a trash bag. He dumped it in a can, slammed down the lid, and retreated back up the alley. Something was still bothering her. It had to do with this window, with Mandy Barnett and the reason she'd left her job so abruptly six months ago.

She turned to Rick. 'Did you say that was Bolton Street out there?'

'Yeah. Alley comes off it.'

'What are the nearest cross streets?'

'To Bolton?' Rick shrugged. 'Radisson's to the east. And west, that'd be, uh . . .'

'Swarthmore,' said Kat softly. It came to her like a lightning flash of memory: the name of the street. Its significance.

*Bolton and Swarthmore. That's where my partner went down. Drug bust went sour, got boxed in a blind alley . . .*

Kat swung around to look at Adam. 'My God, that's *it*. That has to be it!'

Adam shook his head. 'What are you talking about?'

'There was a cop killed there! In that alley!' She glanced at Rick. 'When did Mandy quit her job?'

'I told ya. Six months ago—'

'I need the exact date!'

Rick went into the front office, pulled out a ledger book. 'Let's see. Last call she logged was October second.'

'I have to make a call,' snapped Kat, pulling out her cell phone.

Adam was shaking his head, trying to catch up with her leaps of logic. 'A dead cop? How does that fit in?'

'It was blackmail,' she said, punching in the phone number. 'That's where Mandy's money was coming from. She saw a cop get killed in that alley. And she was squeezing the killer for cash . . .'

'Until he refused to be squeezed any longer,' Adam finished for her.

'Right. So he arranges to have a little poison slipped her way. Courtesy of the local drug dealer, Nicos . . . Hello? Ed?'

The voice on the other end of the line sounded harassed. 'Kat? I'll call you back, I'm already late—'

'Ed, one question. That cop, Ben Fuller. The one who arrested Esterhaus. Where was he killed?'

'Somewhere out in Watertown.'

'The date?'

'That's two questions.'

'The *date*, Ed!'

'I don't know. October sometime. Look, the parade starts in twenty minutes and I gotta get out to the limo—'

'Was it October second, Ed?'

A pause. 'Could've been.'

'I want you to find out one more thing.'

'*Now* what?'

'The name of Ben Fuller's partner.'

'I'd have to check—'

'Then *do* it.'

'Yes, *ma'am*!' growled Ed and hung up.

She looked at Adam. 'It *was* Ben Fuller who died in that alley. The police called it a drug bust gone sour. I think he was murdered. By another cop.'

They stared at each other, both of them shaken by their conclusions. By what they had to do next.

Adam took her arm. 'Let's go. We're taking this straight to the police commissioner.'

'He'll be in the parade. So will everyone else.'

'Then we head for City Hall. The sooner we unload this bomb, the sooner we can stop watching our backs.'

'You think he knows we're on to him?'

'Are you kidding? Ed's probably griping to everyone in earshot about his ex-wife and her wild theories. The word'll be out.'

'Hey!' called Rick, as they headed out the door. 'What's all this with the cops? Am I gonna have trouble?'

'Not to worry,' said Adam. 'You, Rick, are of absolutely *no* interest to anyone.'

'Oh. Well, that's good,' said Rick.

They left the office and headed down the stairs. Their descent had suddenly taken on the panic of flight. *We know too much*, Kat thought. *And it could get us killed.*

By the time they reached the ground floor, her hand was sweaty against the banister. They emerged from the building, into the gloom of an impending storm. From the Atlantic, black clouds were roiling in, and the very air smelled of brine and violence.

Adam glanced up and down Bolton Street, his gaze quickly surveying the shabby buildings, the windblown sidewalks. Across the street, a man emerged from a bar, hugged his coat, and trudged away. At the intersection, a car stood idling, music booming from its radio. So far there was no sign of danger. Still, she was glad when

Adam reached for her hand; the warmth of his grasp was enough to steady her nerves.

They started up the street. Her car was right around the corner, on Radisson. As they reached it, the first fat drops of rain were beginning to fall.

Kat pulled out her keys; Adam reached over and took them out of her hand. 'I'll drive,' he said. 'You look shaken up.'

She nodded. 'Thanks.'

He unlocked the passenger door and helped her in. Then he circled around and slid into the driver's seat, bringing in with him the comforting scents of damp wool, of skin-warmed after-shave. He pulled the door shut. 'We'll get this over with,' he said, 'and then I'm taking you home.'

She looked at him. 'I think I'd like that,' she said softly. 'I'd like that very much.'

They smiled at each other. He reached down to put the key in the ignition. Her gaze was still focused on his face. Only vaguely did she register the shadow moving alongside the car, closing in on her window. She glanced to her right just as the door was yanked open.

A blast of chilly air swept across her face; colder still was the icy gun barrel pressed against her temple.

Kat jerked taut. 'No! Vince—'

'Not a muscle,' growled Ratchet. 'Got that, Quantrell?'

Adam sat frozen behind the wheel, his gaze locked on Kat. 'Don't,' he said, panic seeping into his voice. 'Don't hurt her.'

'Into the back seat,' Ratchet ordered. '*Move it, Novak.*'

On wobbly legs, Kat stepped out of the car and climbed through the rear door into the back seat. Ratchet slid in beside her and slammed the door shut. The gun barrel was still pressed to her head.

'Okay,' said Ratchet. 'Drive.'

Adam turned to look at them. 'Leave her alone! There's no reason for this—'

'She knows. So do you.'

'So does the DA!'

'He doesn't know crap. Far as he's concerned, it's a nuisance case. And his ex-wife's a pain.' Ratchet clicked back the gun hammer. 'Which she is.'

'No!' cried Adam. 'Please—'

'Then *drive*.'

'Where?'

'Up Radisson.'

Adam threw Kat a desperate look. He had no choice. Then he turned and started the engine. As they pulled into traffic, she could see his knuckles were white on the steering wheel. There was nothing he could do; one false move and Ratchet would blow her away.

She said, 'They'll figure it out, Vince. Ed knows you were Ben Fuller's partner. He's already wondering what really happened to Fuller. How could you do it to your own partner?'

'He wasn't a good sport.'

'Meaning what? He wouldn't play along? Wouldn't take the payoffs?'

'Goddamn Boy Scout. God, honor, country. That stuff doesn't pay the bills. Ben and I, we just never came to an understanding. No common ground, see.'

'Not like you and Mandy Barnett,' said Adam.

'Hey, Mandy, I could sorta understand. Bitch saw an opportunity, she grabbed it. Trouble is, she started getting greedy. More money, always more.'

'So you had Esterhaus pass along some poison. Something you thought couldn't be identified,' said Adam.

Ratchet gave a grunt of surprise. 'He talked?'

'He didn't have to,' said Kat. 'We knew about his arrest. You were Fuller's partner at the time, weren't you? You would've heard all about Esterhaus. And his troubles.'

'Yeah. Those Miami boys.' Ratchet laughed. 'He was scared to death of them.'

'So you two cut a deal. He got you the drug. And you didn't call Miami.'

'Hey, it worked.'

'Except for one detail, Vince. Zestron-L killed a few too many victims. One body, the ME might overlook. But four? That was a trend.'

They pulled to a stop at a red light. Ratchet glanced at the street sign. 'Turn right,' he said.

'Where are we going?' asked Adam.

'The docks.'

Adam flashed Kat a backward glance. *Keep your cool*, it said. *I'll get us out of this somehow.*

He turned right.

Three blocks east took them to the wharf. The rain-swept docks were deserted. A series of piers jutted out, most of them long since abandoned to disuse. A single fishing trawler rocked in the gray water, straining at its moorings.

'That warehouse up ahead,' said Ratchet. 'Drive there.'

'The pier won't hold the weight,' said Adam.

'Yes it will. *Go.*'

Adam pulled off the pavement and slowly guided the car onto the pier. They could hear the wood creak under the weight, could feel the thump of the tires over the boards. At the warehouse entrance, they rolled to a stop.

'Okay,' said Ratchet. 'Out of the car.'

Kat stepped out. The wind whipped her hair and lashed her face with sea spray. She stood with the gun shoved against her back, her heart pounding.

'Quantrell! Open the warehouse door,' ordered Ratchet.

'Two more murders,' said Adam. 'What's it going to get you, Vince?'

'My freedom, maybe? Open the door.'

Adam reluctantly set his shoulder against the sliding panel. 'You killed Fuller,' he grunted, pushing against the door. 'And Esterhaus. And Mandy Barnett.' Slowly the panel slid open, revealing a seemingly impenetrable darkness. 'Where's it going to end?'

'With you two.' Ratchet waved the gun. 'Inside.'

There was no arguing with a bullet. They stepped out of the wind's assault, into the gloom. The darkness smelled of dust and sea rot.

'Sykes will figure it out,' said Adam. 'He'll find us—'

'Not for a while. See, this particular warehouse belongs to Vito Scalisi. And his sentence runs another eight years. By the time they open the building again, the rats'll have taken care of things. If you catch my drift.'

*Meaning our bodies*, thought Kat with a rush of nausea. Quickly she glanced around and saw, through the shadows, a jumble of old crates, wooden pallets. Overhead, ropes dangled from a catwalk. And high above, rainwater dripped steadily through a hole in the roof. There were no other exits, no way out.

Adam was still trying to buy time. 'People saw you at the burial, Vince—'

'I was there in the line of duty.'

'They saw us, too! They'll put it together – know you followed us—'

'Me? I went home to bed. This damn virus, you see.' He raised his gun. 'Both of you, against the wall. Don't want to have to drag you. Not with my bad back.'

Adam moved close to Kat and wrapped his arms around her. She felt his breath warm her hair, felt his lips brush the top of her head. 'Get ready,' he whispered. 'When I move, you *run*.'

In bewilderment she stared up at him, and saw the unbending command in his gaze: *Don't argue. Just do it.*

'Skip the tender farewells, okay?' barked Ratchet. 'Against the wall.'

With a nudge, Adam pushed her away, placing himself between her and Ratchet. Calmly, he turned to face the gun.

'You know, Vince,' said Adam. 'You've neglected a few vital details. The car, for instance.'

'Getting rid of the car's easy.'

'I'm talking about *my* car.' Adam took a step forward, so

small it was scarcely noticeable. 'An abandoned Volvo at the cemetery . . .' He took another step toward Ratchet. Toward the gun. 'It'll raise a lot of questions.'

'I can take care of that, too.'

'And then there's the matter of Mandy Barnett's boyfriend.'

'What?'

'You think she kept her little gold mine a secret?' Another step. 'You think he didn't ask where all her drugs, all her cash, was coming from?'

Ratchet was poised on the verge of finishing off the whole bloody business, but new doubts had been stirred. His hand wavered, the gun barrel dropping a fraction of an inch.

Adam was still ten feet away, too far to make his move. But he might not get a better chance.

Kat, standing behind Adam, could almost sense the tensing of his muscles, the last coiling up before the spring. *Dear God, he's going to do it.*

Adam's body would take the first bullet, and probably the second as well. By that time she could be on Ratchet. It was a last-chance gamble, one they were almost certain to lose, but the alternative was to go down like sheep in a slaughterhouse.

She leaned forward, poised like a sprinter on the balls of her feet, waiting for Adam's move. Any second now . . .

The ringing of Ratchet's cell phone suddenly seemed to trap them in an instant's freeze-frame. Pure force of habit made Ratchet glance down at the phone on his belt. In that split second of inattention, Adam sprang.

He was halfway to Ratchet when the first shot exploded. The thud of the bullet into his flesh scarcely slowed his momentum. Before Ratchet could even squeeze off a second shot, Adam hurtled against him. Both men toppled to the ground.

Kat scrambled forward to help, but the men were rolling over and over in a confusing tangle of limbs, grappling for the gun. Another shot went off, this one wild – the bullet whistled past Kat's cheek. Adam's hand shot out to grab Ratchet's wrist. He managed to grunt out: '*Run!*' before Ratchet, roaring like a bull, flung him aside.

Kat attacked, clawing for the gun, but Ratchet had too firm a grip. Enraged, he swung at her, his fist slamming into her jaw. The blow sent her flying. She tumbled across the floor to land in a pile of damp burlap. Through eyes half blinded by pain, she saw Ratchet turn and walk over to look at Adam, who now lay motionless.

*He's dead*, she thought. *He's dead*. Fueled by grief, by rage, she staggered to her feet. Even as blackness gathered before her eyes, she struggled desperately toward the warehouse door, toward the far-off rectangle of daylight.

Just as she reached the doorway, Ratchet turned to her, raised his gun, and fired.

The bullet splintered the frame, and fragments of wood stung her cheek. She flung herself through the doorway, into the driving wind.

With Ratchet right behind her, a few seconds' head start was all she had. Still dizzy from the blow, she was moving like a drunken woman. The car was parked a few feet ahead. Beyond it stretched the pier, barren of any cover. Running was futile. It would be a single shot, straight into her back.

*No escape*, she thought. *I can't even see straight.*

Just as Ratchet came tearing out of the warehouse, Kat ducked around the rear of the car. He fired; the bullet pinged off the rear fender. Kat scurried alongside the car and yanked the passenger door open. One glance told her the keys weren't in the ignition. No escape in there, either – the car would be a trap.

Ratchet was moving in for the kill.

She heard the creak of the planks as he moved along the other side of the car, circling to the rear. Ahead there was only the warehouse, another dead end.

She took a deep breath, pivoted away from the car, and leaped off the pier.

# 15

The stomach-wrenching plunge hurled her into icy water. She sank in over her head, into a frightening swirl of brine. She floundered to the surface, gasping, her eyes and throat stung by the salt. One breath was all she managed; the zing of a bullet through the water sent her diving once again into the depths.

Frantically she stroked her way under the pier and surfaced again to cling at the foundation post. Wind-blown waves churned and thrashed against her face. Her hands had already gone numb from cold and fear, but at least her head was now clear. She glanced toward land, saw that the only way to shore would mean a clamber across exposed rocks. In other words, suicide.

She looked up through the gaps in the planks, and she spied Ratchet at the other edge of the pier, scanning the water. He knew she wouldn't swim away from the cover of the pier. He also knew the water was frigid. Fifteen

minutes, a half hour – eventually she'd die of hypo-
thermia. For him it was a simple waiting game. One she
was sure to lose.

Numbness was creeping up her feet. She couldn't bob
in this icy bath forever. Neither could she risk climbing
those rocks. She had no choice – she had to do the
unexpected.

Treading water with her legs, she managed to pull off
her jacket. She tied the sleeves together, trapping air in
the body, and tossed the jacket away, towards the edge
of the pier where Ratchet was crouched. Then she dove
and began to swim frantically in the other direction, into
open water.

The sound of gunshots told her the ruse had worked.
Ratchet was too busy firing at her jacket to see that she
was swimming away from the cover of the pier. She
surfaced for another breath, dove, and kept swimming an
underwater course parallel to shore, surfacing, diving
again. She could hear Ratchet still shooting. Sooner or
later, though, he'd realize he was aiming at an empty
jacket and he'd turn to scan the open water; she had only
a few precious seconds to put as much distance as
possible between her and the warehouse pier.

She surfaced a fifth time and saw that she'd pulled even
with the next pier, where the trawler was moored. She
turned toward shore and began to stroke for all she was
worth, aiming for the trawler.

The gunshots had ceased. She came up for air and
glanced in Ratchet's direction. He was pacing the pier
now, his gaze scanning an ever-growing perimeter. She

ducked under the surface and kicked wildly. When she came up again, the stern of the trawler was only twenty feet away. From the gunwale hung a rusty chain ladder – she could pull herself aboard! With escape so near at hand, she began to swim with abandon across the surface, drawing closer and closer to the trawler. Finally she reached up; her fingers closed around the first steel rung.

A gunshot rang out, ricocheted off the trawler's hull. He had spotted her!

Soaked, exhausted, she could barely pull herself up onto the next rung. So little time – already, Ratchet was dashing back up the warehouse pier, toward shore. Another few seconds and he'd be on the next pier, cutting off her escape. She reached for the next rung, and the next. Water streamed off her clothes. The wind kept banging the ladder against the hull, bruising her fingers. She grabbed the edge of the gunwale and hauled herself up and over.

She tumbled, gasping, onto the deck. *No time, no time!* She struggled to her feet and dashed to the starboard side, ready to leap off onto the pier.

Too late. Ratchet was already running along the shore. He'd reach the head of the pier before she could. Her escape route was cut off.

She scrambled to the ship's pilot house, yanked at the door. It was locked. *What now? Back in the water?*

She ran back to the stern and gazed down at the roiling waves, preparing herself for another dive. But she knew she didn't have the strength to swim any longer. Her whole body was shaking from the cold. Another ten minutes in the sea would finish her.

She looked toward shore: Ratchet was on the pier now, and coming her way.

Her gaze shifted back to the stern, and two words stenciled in red on a deck locker caught her eye: *Emergency Supplies*.

She threw open the lid. Inside were life jackets, blankets, tools.

And a flare gun.

She reached for it. With trembling hands, she slipped a flare in the barrel, cocked the gun. One shot – that was the only chance she'd have.

Ratchet's footsteps thudded closer across the pier.

Kat swiveled, ducked around to the port side of the pilot house. There she crouched, waiting, listening. She heard his footsteps come to a stop on the pier somewhere along the starboard side. Then she heard the soft metallic thump as he stepped aboard.

Which way was he coming? Fore or aft?

She took a gamble – maybe the last she'd ever take – and moved toward the bow. There she crouched at the edge of the pilot house. Not a sound reached her. Not a footstep, nothing. There was only the roar of her own blood through her ears.

Then, suddenly, there he was. He stepped around the corner of the pilot house, right in front of her. There was no pity in his gaze, no expression at all. He raised the pistol.

She brought the flare gun up and fired.

His shriek was like a wild animal's, cutting through the roar of the wind. He staggered backward, his chest hissing with phosphorescent sparks. His gun clattered to the deck. Kat scrambled forward and grabbed it. Ratchet fell on his back and lay jerking in agony, screaming, tearing at his clothes. Kat clutched the pistol and stood over him, the barrel pointed at his head. *I could pull this trigger*, she thought. *I could blow you away. I want to blow you away.*

But she only stood there, watching him twitch. The terror, the exhaustion, had drained her of the ability to move. She was afraid to turn her back on him, even for an instant, afraid he'd suddenly rise up like a monster from the grave. So she kept the gun pointed at him, even as the sound of sirens wailed closer, even as the wind shrieked in her ears. She heard car doors slam, heard footsteps pounding up the pier. Only when they'd twice yelled the command: 'Drop it!' did she finally look up.

Two cops stood on the pier, their guns pointed at her.

'Drop it or we shoot!' one of them shouted.

She dropped the gun and kicked it away, where Ratchet wouldn't reach it, even if he could. Then, slowly, she turned to the cops and staggered toward them.

'Help me,' she said. She stretched her hands to them, and her voice dissolved into a moan of grief. *'Help me . . .'*

He still had a pulse. Crouching beside him in the darkness of the warehouse, Kat felt the faint throb of Adam's carotid artery. 'He's alive!' she cried.

The cop shone his flashlight, and the beam came down on Adam's blood-soaked shirt. 'Jesus,' he muttered, and turned to yell at his partner. 'Get the ambulance crew in here first!'

'Adam,' whispered Kat. She brushed back his hair, cradled his face in her lap. 'Adam, you have to live. Do you hear me? Damn you, *you have to live!*'

He didn't answer. All she heard was the sound of his breathing. It came in short, unsteady gasps, but at least his lungs were working.

She was still holding him in her arms when the EMTs arrived. They swept in with their stretcher, their IV bottles, their bag of tricks. As she stood by uselessly, they bundled him up and away, into the ambulance. She was left standing in the buffeting wind as the wail of sirens faded into the distance.

'You have to live,' she whispered. 'Because I love you.'

Footsteps creaked across the pier. Dazed, she turned to see Lou Sykes, holding out a blanket. 'Blue lips aren't very becoming,' he said, and slipped the blanket over her shoulders. 'You okay, Novak?'

'Just . . . cold.' She shuddered, and the tears suddenly flooded her eyes. 'He saved my life.'

'I know.'

'And I didn't believe in him. I was afraid to believe in him . . .'

'Maybe it's time you did.'

She looked up at Sykes's gleaming face. *Leave it to a homicide cop*, she thought. An old hand at death dishing out advice to the living.

She turned to his car. 'Take me to the hospital.'

'Right now?'

'Right now,' she said, and climbed into the car. 'When he wakes up, I want to be there.'

She was there when he came out of surgery. She stayed at his bedside as he slept all night. Other visitors came and went, but she remained. He slept most of the next morning as well, kept under by narcotics. The bullet had passed through his left lung, nicked his pericardium, and missed his ventricle by a fraction of an inch. He'd lost massive amounts of blood, his lung was collapsed, and he had plastic tubes gurgling out of his chest, but he was a lucky man.

At 10:00 A.M., Sykes appeared to fill her in on the latest. Ratchet had massive phosphorus burns on his chest, but he would be okay – certainly well enough to stand trial for murder times three. Ed Novak was telling the press he'd long had suspicions about Ben Fuller's death, and only his tireless efforts had broken the case. He was going to come out smelling like a rose, but Kat didn't care. She figured that if the voters of Albion chose to elect Ed Novak and Mayor Sampson, then mediocrity was exactly what they deserved.

At noon, another visitor showed up. There was a knock, and then Maeve appeared. She didn't come in at first; she just stood in the doorway, staring across the room at her sleeping father. She was stuffed tight as a sausage into a black leather dress, but her rainbow-tinted hair had been gathered almost demurely into a ponytail, and her face was white with fear.

'Is he gonna be all right?' she said.

'I think so,' said Kat. 'Why don't you come in?'

Maeve crept almost timidly to the bedside. She said, 'Dad?' Adam didn't stir.

'Sleeping meds,' said Kat. 'He's out cold.'

Maeve touched her father's face, then pulled away, as though embarrassed.

'He almost died,' said Kat.

For a moment Maeve didn't respond; she just stared at Adam. Softly she said, 'He drove me crazy, y'know? Telling me what to do, what not to do. But he was always there. I have to say that for the old man. He was always there . . .' She wiped her hand over her eyes. Then, abruptly, she turned and walked toward the door.

'Maeve?'

Maeve stopped, looked back. 'Yeah?'

'Come back. When he's awake.'

Maeve shrugged. 'Maybe,' she said, and left the room.

*You'll be back*, Kat thought with a smile.

It was late afternoon when Adam finally stirred and opened his eyes. The first face he saw was Kat's, gazing down at him.

'Hello, hero,' she said.

He groaned. 'Who are you talking to?'

'To you.' She leaned forward and kissed him. As she pulled back, his face blurred away through her tears. She shook her head and laughed. 'You are one crazy man. Do you know what you did?'

'What?'

'You saved my life.'

'If that's what it takes,' he whispered. 'To keep you around.'

She smiled. He smiled.

And they both knew that, this time, she would be staying.